Biopharmaceutics and Clinical Pharmacokinetics

AN INTRODUCTION

Third Edition, Revised and Expanded

Robert E. Notari

College of Pharmacy
The Ohio State University
Columbus, Ohio

MARCEL DEKKER, INC.,   New York and Basel

Library of Congress Cataloging in Publication Data

Notari, Robert E
    Biopharmaceutics and clinical pharmacokinetics.

    First-2d ed. published under title:
Biopharmaceutics and pharmacokinetics.
    Includes bibliographical references and indexes.
    1. Biopharmaceutics. 2. Pharmacokinetics.
I. Title. [DNLM: 1. Biopharmaceutics.
2. Kinetics. 3. Pharmacology. QV38 N899b]
RM301.4.N67   1980   615'.7   80-10676
ISBN 0-8247-6928-7

MARCEL DEKKER, INC.
270 Madison Avenue, New York, New York 10016

Current printing (last digit):
10 9 8 7 6 5 4 3 2

Printed in the United States of America

To my parents

CONTENTS

Preface to the First Edition   vii
Preface to the Second Edition   ix
Preface to the Third Edition   xi

1. Bioavailability   1
   References   4

2. Rate Processes in Biological Systems   5
   I. Introduction   6
   II. Transport of Drugs   6
   References   42

3. Principles of Pharmacokinetics   45
   I. Introduction   46
   II. Pharmacokinetic Parameters   48
   References   103

4. Biopharmaceutics: Clinical Applications
   of Pharmacokinetic Parameters   107
   I. Introduction   109
   II. Blood Level Curves   111
   III. Absorption of Drugs from the
   Gastrointestinal Tract   119
   IV. Continuous Blood and Tissue Levels
   in Therapy   149
   References   169

5. Dosage Regimens   173
   I. Introduction   174
   II. Accumulation During Repetitive Dosing   176
   III. Adjustment of Dosage Regimen
   in Renal Failure   202
   References   211

6. Pharmacokinetic Aspects of Structural
    Modifications in Drug Design and Therapy   213
    I.   Introduction   215
    II.   Antimicrobial Agents   223
    III. Oral Bioavailability   258
    IV.   Pharmacokinetics of Prodrugs   264
          References   278

7. An Overview of Pharmacokinetic Applications
    in Clinical Practice   290
    I.   Introduction   291
    II.   Pharmacokinetic Drug Interactions   294
    III. Clinical Pharmacokinetics   308
          References   333

    Appendix A: Fick's Law   338
    I.   Passive Transport Energetics: Fick's Law   338
    II.   Relationship of Fick's Law to A ⇌ B
          Reversible First-Order Kinetics   339

    Appendix B: Vd   341
    I.   Volume of Distribution in the
          One-Compartment Open Model   341
    II.   Volume of Distribution in the
          Two-Compartment Open Model   342

    Appendix C: Area Under I.V. Curves   346
    I.   One-Compartment Open Model   346
    II.   Two-Compartment Open Model   347

    Appendix D: Multiple-Dose Equations
          for the One-Compartment Model   348

    Appendix E: List of Symbols of General Occurrence   351

Natural Log Tables   355

Author Index   365
Subject Index   379

Preface to the First Edition

This book is designed as an introductory text for use in formal courses or for self-study. It is aimed at both biomedical researchers and practitioners. The book assumes no prior knowledge of either kinetics or calculus on the part of the reader. Derivations are provided for those who are mathematically inclined. Those who are not may simply make use of the final or "working" equations. None of the subjects is beyond the level of comprehension of an advanced undergraduate with no calculus background. However, one must approach this book "actively," with graph paper and pencil in hand and with desire to learn well in mind. The material is presented in "building-block" fashion, and it is imperative that the user solve the examples and practice problems to have all of the pieces necessary to build a solid foundation. Topics are covered in a cumulative manner, and skipping a principle will almost certainly result in an inability to understand a subsequent topic fully. Although it is not a programmed text, it must be approached in the same fashion—as a workbook. Casual reading will not suffice.

One problem that faces those who develop an interest in learning biopharmaceutics and pharmacokinetics for the first time is how to get started. Byron once wrote, "Nothing is more difficult than a beginning." This is certainly true for the present subject. Most current references are not written at the basic introductory level. They assume that the reader has some level of sophistication in either calculus or kinetics or both. In addition they do not provide for active participation in the form of problem solving. A teacher wishing to develop a course would have to do so from the literature. Yet it is difficult to read the literature without a fundamental knowledge of the field. This book is meant to provide that knowledge for teachers, students, biomedical practitioners, and research scientists in medicinal chemistry, pharmacology, pharmacy, and other biomedical disciplines. Chapters 2 and 3 comprise the basic introductory materials, and Chapter 4 illustrates some of the applications. An understanding of this text should provide sufficient introduction to the field to allow further reading of more complex applications in the literature.

During the past six years I have been teaching biopharmaceutics to senior students in the College of Pharmacy of The Ohio State University. The absence of a textbook for the course has presented a number of difficulties. Although assigned readings of review articles and selected chapters have proven helpful, they fail to provide the structural foundation that a textbook achieves. Students repeatedly failed to visualize the total structure of the subject material until the course was nearly complete in spite of the fact that detailed syllabi and other outlines were distributed each quarter. Students were generally accustomed to working with a required text which serves to define the course goals in much more detail and provides a means for reading ahead. Furthermore, when a student experienced difficulties in solving homework problems, there was no reference book to provide additional information over and above that found in the lecture notes. Problem sets had to be created, printed, and distributed in lieu of an available source such as a required text. There was no provision for additional practice problems for the student who felt the need for such experience.

As a result, the outlines, problem sets, graphic demonstrations, classroom handouts, short presentations of principles, etc., grew in both number and in size until some of the materials distributed to the class approached the size of a chapter or even a small book. Most of the contents of this text have evolved from the development of these undergraduate teaching aids. Some of the subject matter was added later to accommodate an intermediate level graduate course. All of the examples and practice problems have been worked many times over by undergraduate and graduate students alike. Over the past two years (and prior to its publication) the book has been successfully used as a required text in both undergraduate and graduate courses here at Ohio State.

It would be impossible to list the names of all those students whose comments and general interest served to stimulate the writing of this book as well as to influence its contents and mode of presentation. Certainly I must acknowledge the graduating classes of the College of Pharmacy of The Ohio State University from 1965 through 1971, who had the dubious honor of serving as "guinea pigs" for the development of this course. Sincere thanks for their patience and enthusiasm. It is with pleasure that I thank the graduate students and faculty who read the text and in some cases helped develop the problems and examples. Among them I wish especially to acknowledge the efforts of Miss Marilyn Lue Chin, Mrs. Joyce DeYoung, Imtiaz Chaudry, Raymond Anderson, and Dr. Richard H. Reuning. The physical appearance of the text is a testimonial to the fine art work of Mrs. Yvonne Holsinger and the excellent typing of Miss Carol J. Lusk.

Finally, any comments, criticisms, suggestions, errors or improvements would be most gratefully received by the author.

Robert E. Notari

Preface to the Second Edition

The objectives of this book are identical to those of the first edition. It is a place to begin your studies—an introduction. Hopefully, it is both simple and accurate. And the agreement between reader and author has also remained constant. This is a workbook. If you are willing to work the problems, the principles should become meaningful to you by the process of discovery.

To that end the second edition has been modified to make it more self-sufficient. As each new principle is introduced, two types of problems are presented. Sample problems are completely solved so that you can diagnose your error when your answer is not correct (and assuming that mine is!). Practice problems are designed to test your ability to apply what you have learned. They are generally slightly more difficult.

The constancy of objectives is not a reflection of a lack of progress in the field or a lack of change between the editions. Indeed, the second edition is largely a new book. In accomplishing the updating and improving of the book, the author gratefully acknowledges the indispensible contributions of co-authors Joyce L. DeYoung (Chapters 2 and 3) and Raymond C. Anderson (Chapter 5).

Those who are familiar with the first edition will find it helpful to know what changes have been made. Chapters 2 and 3 have been completely rewritten and restyled. While they cover the same subject matter, the order of presentation is different. Chapter 2 now contains pharmacokinetic models and the basic kinetics required to understand them. For example, a beaker is still used to teach two-compartment model kinetics, but it is immediately followed by the analogous situation in pharmacokinetics. The basic kinetics are therefore kept minimal and limited to models with pharmacokinetic counterparts. Chapter 3 contains methods and discussions for calculating pharmacokinetic parameters. Among the notable changes is the expansion of the section dealing with the apparent volume of distribution. This has been completely updated to include both discussion and equations regarding variation in calculated values obtained by different methods for multicompartmental drugs.

Chapter 4 has been expanded. It begins with a revised section on the interpretation of blood level curves and ends with a new addition covering dosage regimen calculations in patients with normal renal function or with renal failure. This latter area is one of the most widely recognized contributions of pharmacokinetic sciences to improved clinical therapy.

Chapter 5 is a new addition to the book. It is aimed at fostering both an understanding and an interest in the effects of molecular manipulation on pharmacokinetic parameters and the resultant pharmacologic impact. This is a field which is relatively undeveloped (as compared with studies on dosage-form effects) but which will be a key to future evaluation and development of new drugs.

The second edition is amply referenced. Each chapter provides sufficient citations for the interested reader to check on the validity or limitations of the subject matter presented or to become more familiar with a particular field.

Again, I would greatly appreciate receiving comments, criticisms, suggestions, opinions, or notifications of errors regarding any section of the book. A similar invitation in the preface to the first edition was accepted by several people, whose comments had a direct influence on the production of the second edition. While I cannot cite them all, I would particularly like to thank Dr. Adam Danek, Dr. Gerald E. Schumacher, Dr. Donald A. Zuck, and Dr. James W. Ayres for their helpful suggestions, encouraging comments, and poignant questions.

Robert E. Notari

Preface to the Third Edition

The first edition, written during the 1960s and published in 1971, noted that "The approaches discussed here may seem a bit too sophisticated and costly to the reader who has not previously come upon the concept of an individualized dosage regimen." This statement followed a discussion suggesting that "pharmacokinetics will make an ever increasing contribution to the rational clinical use of drugs . . ." The second edition (1975) contained "a new addition covering dosage regimen calculations in patients with normal renal function or with renal failure," together with an additional chapter on the pharmacokinetic aspects of molecular modification. The latter was described as "a field which is relatively undeveloped." These applications of pharmacokinetics were minor components in the second edition and absent from the first edition.

The immense progress in these two areas, clinical pharmacokinetics and pharmacokinetic drug design, has necessitated the writing of this third edition. They now occupy roughly one-half of this text. Chapters 5 and 7 are devoted to clinical pharmacokinetics. The application of pharmacokinetics to drug design and evaluation comprises Chapter 6, the longest in the text. Progress in the development of prodrugs represents a major portion of this expanded chapter.

I must reemphasize that the text is not intended as a review but rather an introduction. Development of concepts is the primary goal, and examples have been selected to illustrate them. Problem solving by the reader remains the *modus operandi* for comprehending the principles and their applications. As in previous editions, it is the author's hope that this text will provide a starting place for those who wish to pursue further study or who want only a simplified but quantitative appreciation of the field.

The many inquiries I have received over the years have proven invaluable in identifying areas for revision. I am most grateful to all those who have graciously given helpful comment or asked for clarification; both provide insight that an author cannot attain for himself. I particularly wish to acknowledge Dr. Adam Danek, Dr. Jacek Bojarski, and Dr. Halina Krasowska, who stimulated the publication of the second edition in Poland (1978) and who translated the English edition into Polish. This experience provided great encouragement to me, and the questions surrounding the translation called attention to several ambiguities that have led to rewording in the third edition. The continued beautiful art work of Yvonne Holsinger and the excellent typing of Sue Sheffield are most sincerely appreciated.

I would be grateful to receive any comments or questions from readers of the third edition as I truly regard both as a service to the author.

Robert E. Notari

Chapter 1

BIOAVAILABILITY

It is both an enlightening and astonishing experience to read the labels on
so-called cure-alls and tonics on display in museums and occasionally found
collecting dust in remote corners of storerooms in old established pharmacies.
Since we are no longer obliged to take these medicines when we become ill, we
may even see a great deal of humor in their claims. Therapeutic effectiveness
was generally certified on the basis of testimonials or anecdotal evidence.
Modesty was not a characteristic of promotional statements. *Hamlin's Wizard
Oil*, "The Great Medical Wonder," recognized no limitations in stating "There is
no sore it will not heal. No pain it will not subdue." *Dr. King's New Discovery*
was favorably compared with other recent inventions such as the steamship,
steam engine, automobile, telephone, telegraph, and radio. According to the
advertisement it rated well as "The Greatest of All." "*No-To-Bac* made a man of
me," another advertisement read, and picturing a young man embracing a young
woman it noted that by use of this product he had "thrown away his pipe and
tobacco and thereby won the love of this stunning girl." A delightful review of
that era can be found in the book, *One for a Man, Two for a Horse* [1]. That
title in itself shows that individualization of dosage regimens (discussed in
Chap. 5 of this text) is not as innovative as one might think. As a final example
of immodest claims and an unbelievable dosage regimen, consider the statement
regarding *Pond's Extract* and made by the popular fictional character, Buster
Brown: "From my own personal experiences, *Pond's Extract* is the best remedy
for all inflammations, hemorrhages, sprains, cuts, bruises, chill blains, burns,
scalds, frostbite." So much for the indications. Now for the clinical results: "It
has made a better and healthier boy of me and is my best friend." And finally
the dosage regimen: "Used externally, internally, and *eternally.*"
  How well did the products and claims of yesteryear measure up to the
standards of today? One might use the following criteria:

1. Contents
2. Percent strength

  3. Purity
  4. Safety
 *5. Clinical effectiveness
 *6. Bioavailability

   Not only did the contents of such products not appear on the label, but it is unlikely that the manufacturer himself knew the ingredients. If the contents are not known, the question of percent strength becomes meaningless. Plant sources sold for the production of drug products were often adulterated. Even if the plants used were pure, the active ingredients, if there were any, were not known. Chemical analyses were neither possible nor of great concern to a naive society. Some awareness of the danger in such a system probably evolved as a direct result of unfortunate experiences with products that not only failed to cure but also caused toxic effects that may have been worse than the malady. Initially, society responded with legislation aimed at ensuring that medicines were safe and free from adulterants. No doubt these seemingly simple goals presented tremendous problems, without adding concern for therapeutic effectiveness which was generally certified on the basis of testimonials or anecdotal evidence.

   The development of analytical chemistry brought about an acute awareness of the importance of controlling the contents of a product. That each drug should have an adequate purity rubric became the concern of those given the responsibility for setting standards for the protection of society. Tests for physical characteristics were introduced, and as analytical technology advanced the sophistication of product tests increased. Trace analysis made limitations on allowable contamination practical. Chemical content and product purity advanced to a scientific level commensurate with the analytical technology of the day.

   And so we can observe that since the turn of the century, product development has evolved from cure-all herb teas to stable, pure formations containing known amounts of chemicals that have been defined as drugs. It was quite natural that the scientific community and society at large had confidence in a product which adhered to its purity rubric. This philosophy dominated from 1938 (when the final drug safety amendments to the Federal Food, Drug, and Cosmetic Act were made) until relatively recent years. During that time it was widely assumed that all products containing equal doses of the same drug were equipotent when put to use by the clinician. The first four criteria in our list were regarded as sufficient. More recently, we have come to the sometimes surprising realization that percentage chemical strength is not the sole criterion for clinical effectiveness. In fact, formulations were produced and marketed which satisfied all of the required legal standards but were not therapeutically active. It became obvious that a dosage form must not only contain the correct amount of the labeled drug but must also release that drug upon administration to the patient. *Clinical effectiveness* and *bioavailability* were thus added to the criteria for effective drug product development. A drug should be not only safe, but beneficial as well, and its therapeutic claims must be based upon sound clinical evidence. Furthermore, a drug which has been proven effective can be rendered ineffective due to lack of bioavailability.

What is bioavailability? The simplest concept to consider is that of a *bioavailable dose*. This is the dose available to the patient, in contrast to the dose stated on the label. Only a drug that is completely absorbed into the bloodstream will have a bioavailable dose equal to that stated on the label. In the case of tablets or capsules administered orally, the bioavailable dose will generally be less than the administered dose. Bioavailability therefore deals with the transfer of drug from the site of administration into the body itself as evidenced by its appearance in the general circulation. Since a transfer process is involved, it may be characterized by both the rate of transfer and the total amount transferred. The bioavailable dose refers only to the total amount transferred. A complete description of the bioavailability of a drug from a dosage form must include both the rate and the amount. Methods for such characterizations are discussed in this book. Bioavailability has been defined in various ways [2-5]. Those which ignore the rate of transfer [2,3] are inadequate to explain cases where products show differences in blood levels and/or clinical response due in total or in part to rate of release of drug. A more acceptable definition for *bioavailability* is therefore [5]: "A term used to indicate the rate and relative amount of the administered drug which reaches the general circulation intact."

The measure of success in the use of any drug is the degree to which the results obtained agree with those expected. Therefore, the degree of success achieved by the use of a drug product may be altered by factors which affect bioavailability, such as certain foods, other drugs, the dosage regimen, the route of administration, a less than optimum formulation, or the inappropriate use of a suitable formulation. Biopharmaceutics deals with such problems. It is concerned with obtaining the expected therapeutic effect from a drug product when it is in use by the patient. One such definition has been offered as follows [5]: "*Biopharmaceutics* is the study of the factors influencing the bioavailability of a drug in man and animals and the use of this information to optimize pharmacologic or therapeutic activity of drug products in clinical application."

Since studies involving the rates of drug transfer employ kinetic methods, biopharmaceutics is closely linked to pharmacokinetics. Indeed, the terms have been interchanged often in the literature. In this book the following definition [5] will be used: "*Pharmacokinetics* is the study of the kinetics of absorption, distribution, metabolism, and excretion of drugs and their pharmacologic, therapeutic, or toxic response in animals and man."

Finally, consider the term *bioequivalency*. Like the others, it has been defined in various ways. We shall use the simplest interpretation. Two drug products containing equal doses of a drug will be said to be bioequivalent if they do not differ significantly in either their bioavailable dose or its rate of supply.

Thus, the time course for drug in the blood following administration of either product would be identical. Bioequivalency therefore includes not only the amount of active ingredient available but also the rate at which it is available.

A corollary to the more recent concerns for product quality and effectiveness is the challenge to physicians and pharmacists to consider the impact of these sciences on clinical practice. For example, the clinician must be informed when the co-administration of other drugs or foods may influence the bioavailability of an active ingredient. As research defines the critical factors influencing the absorption of drugs, the information must be put to clinical use so that practitioners are aware of those situations that should be avoided.

This concept can be further extended into all areas of biomedical drug research. Let us consider pharmacology as a case in point. In a broader sense the concept of bioavailability cannot be circumvented by choice of route of administration. Regardless of where the experiment begins, the final observations are a function of the bioavailability of the drug to the site of action, and the factors influencing its arrival there are many. Since the movement of drug from the site of administration to the site of action requires time, the overall process may best be analyzed by pharmacokinetics. Thus, the bioavailability time profile is again critical in the comparison of drugs or drug analogs. A pharmacological study is greatly enhanced by a knowledge of how much of the drug has reached the receptor as a function of time.

The concept of bioavailability in biomedical drug research, pharmaceutical product development, and rational clinical use of formulations is the subject of this book.

REFERENCES

1. G. Carson, *One for a Man, Two for a Horse,* Bramhall House, New York, 1961.
2. *National Formulary XVIII,* American Pharmaceutical Association, Washington, D.C., 1970.
3. Food and Drug Administration, *Federal Register 38,* No. 3, 885-887 (Jan. 5, 1973).
4. *Guidelines for Biopharmaceutical Studies in Man,* A.Ph.A. Academy of Pharmaceutical Sciences, Washington, D.C., Feb. 1972.
5. Pharmacokinetics and Biopharmaceutics: A Definition of Terms, *J. Pharmacokin. and Biopharm. 1,* 3 (1973)..

Chapter 2

RATE PROCESSES IN BIOLOGICAL SYSTEMS

I.   INTRODUCTION   6

II. TRANSPORT OF DRUGS   6
    A. Passive Diffusion   6
       1. Two-Compartment Closed Model   6
          a. Time Course for Concentration in A and B   7
          b. The Rate Constant: A Time-Independent Parameter   8
          c. The Determination of First-Order Rate Constants   9
            Sample Problem 1   10
            Practice Problem 1   11
          d. Nonequivalent Compartments   13
            Sample Problem 2   15
            Practice Problem 2   17
       2. Two-Compartment Open System   18
          a. Time Course for Concentration in B, T, and C   18
          b. Rate Constants   19
          c. Determination of Rate Constants   20
            Sample Problem 3   24
            Practice Problem 3   25
       3. Pre-Equilibrium or One-Compartment Open Model   25
          a. Equilibrium and Its Implications   25
          b. Arbitrary Test for a One-Compartment Model   28
          c. Determination of β and k_2 in the One-Compartment
             Open Model   28
            Sample Problem 4   29
            Practice Problem 4   31
       4. Multicompartment Open Models   33
            Sample Problem 5   34
            Practice Problem 5   35
    B. Active Transport   35
       1. Description   35
       2. Mixed Kinetics   37
          a. Zero-Order Kinetics   37

b.   Determination of Zero-Order Rate Constants   38
c.   First-Order Conditions in Active Transport   38
d.   Michaelis-Menten Kinetics   39
     Sample Problem 6   40
     Practice Problem 6   41

REFERENCES   42

I. INTRODUCTION

After a drug is introduced into a biological system it is subject to a number of processes whose rates control the concentration of drug in the elusive region known as the "site of action," thus affecting its onset, its duration of action, and the intensity of the biological response. Some knowledge of these rate processes governing the fate of a drug is therefore necessary for a full understanding of the observed pharmacological activity of the drug.

While presupposing no formal background in kinetics, pharmacokinetics, or calculus, this chapter is designed to teach the basic principles of compartmental modeling. A limited number of simple derivations are included in the text, but it is possible to make use of the results without having the mathematical skill to carry out the derivations. For those who have some proficiency in calculus there are a few more advanced derivations and brief discussions regarding their significance in the Appendix.

In assuming minimal experience on the part of the reader, the chapter presents the subject using a "self-study" approach. Each topic is followed by a sample problem for which a method of solution is provided. A practice problem covering the same principles but including only the final answers follows each sample. Solutions to the samples and practice problems may appear obvious, but the experience acquired by working them through is prerequisite to a complete comprehension of the subject matter. You will need semilog paper (2 cycles × 10 to the inch and 1 cycle × 60 divisions) and coordinate paper (20 squares to the inch). A natural log table is included at the end of this book.

II. TRANSPORT OF DRUGS

A. Passive Diffusion

1. Two-Compartment Closed Model

Consider the case where both compartments in Fig. 1 contain equal volumes of water. Both compartments are therefore equivalent in all respects. Let us dissolve some drug in the water contained in compartment A. Since the barrier is permeable to drug, we would expect drug molecules to pass freely from compartment A to compartment B and vice versa. However, there will be a net

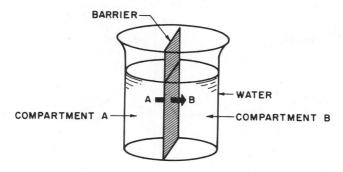

Fig. 1 Model illustrating passive transfer of a drug from compartment A to B through a permeable membrane.

transfer of drug from compartment A to B during the process. This transport of drug from the solution of higher concentration to that of lower concentration is indicated by the arrow in Fig. 1. The arrow is not meant to imply that the passage of molecules through the membrane is a one-way process, but rather that the net transfer of drug is from the high-concentration solution to the low-concentration solution. We shall refer to this as a *passive transport process*, meaning that a net transfer of drug will occur from compartment A to B until the concentrations in both compartments become equal. At that time the system will be in equilibrium, which is to say that although there is movement across the barrier in both directions there is no net transfer in either direction. The concentrations in each compartment then remain equal.

In pharmacokinetics we will be concerned with the amount of drug transferred across a membrane and the rate of transfer. That is, we are interested in both the equilibrium state and the rate of achieving equilibrium. We shall consider both of these aspects and their analysis in the following sections. (For a discussion of the relationship of Fick's law rate constants to be observed first-order constants discussed in this chapter, see the Appendix.)

a. Time Course for Concentration in A and B. Let us define the concentration of drug in compartment A as A and that in compartment B as B. The transport of drug may then be illustrated as

$$A \longrightarrow \!\!\!\!\!\!\!\!\!\!\! \longrightarrow B \tag{1}$$

The rate of transfer of drug may be examined by observing the way in which A

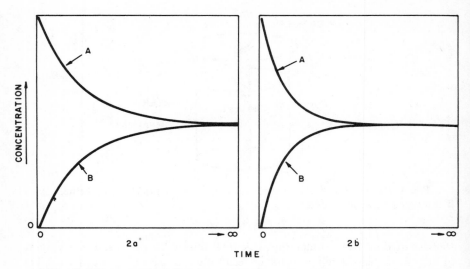

TIME

Fig. 2 Concentration time course for drug in compartments A and B following introduction of drug into compartment A in Fig. 1. The barrier employed in Fig. 2a is thicker than in Fig. 2b.

decreases with time or B *increases* with time. This rate of transport may be expressed as $-dA/dt$ or $+dB/dt$.

Figure 2 illustrates typical results for the transport process defined in Eq. (1). A comparison of the two figures will reveal that the *rate process* represented in Fig. 2a is slower than that in Fig. 2b. This is obvious from the fact that the latter is finished sooner. But how much faster is it? It is not easy to compare rates per se. Since plots of concentration versus time are really curves, the rate values, such as $-dA/dt$, are not constant throughout the process but are continuously diminishing. The value can only be defined at a particular time t, since it will have a different value at any other time. It would be convenient if one could compare some parameter which is constant for a given rate process.

b. The Rate Constant: A Time-Independent Parameter. Often a rate process may be found experimentally to behave according to the general expression

$$\frac{dX}{dt} = -kX^n \tag{2}$$

where the variable X may be defined as the *transferable concentration* and the constant k represents the proportionality constant associated with the net transfer rate process as illustrated by Eq. (1). Equation (2) states that the rate of change in the concentration of transferable drug at time t is equal to the product of a proportionality constant k times the transferable concentration raised to the n-th power. The constant k is referred to as the *rate constant* and the power, n, defines the *order* of the process. These parameters are usually determined graphically and will be the subject of subsequent sections.

It is imperative that the reader clearly understand the physical meaning of the variable X. Equation (2) illustrates that X is a variable that changes with time. It is defined as the transferable concentration remaining at any given time. An equilibrium or t_∞, X will always be equal to zero. In terms of Eq. (1) and Figs. 1 and 2, we can calculate X at any given time from the expression $(A_t - A_\infty)$. Since A_∞ represents the final concentration left in compartment A, the concentration yet to be transferred at any time t is the difference between the concentrations at times t and ∞ or $(A_t - A_\infty)$. By employing the material balance equation $A_t + B_t = A_0$, one can calculate the variable X from data representing the B compartment. Since $(A_0 - A_\infty) = B_\infty$, we can substitute first for A_t and then for $(A_0 - A_\infty)$ to obtain $(B_\infty - B_t)$. Thus the variable X is *transferable concentration* and may be calculated according to the equation

$$X = (A_t - A_\infty) = (B_\infty - B_t) \tag{3}$$

It is apparent from Eq. (2) that a rate process may have a convenient parameter associated with it in the form of the rate constant, k. Since this is a numerical constant, it will not be time-dependent. Thus we will have only one rate constant associated with the overall rate process. Two rate processes, of the same order, may conveniently be compared by comparison of their rate constants. The calculation of first-order rate constants is discussed in the following section.

c. *The Determination of First-Order Rate Constants.* For a first-order process the value of n in Eq. (2) will be one. Equation (4) represents the differential equation for a first-order process,

$$\frac{dX}{dt} = -k_1 X \tag{4}$$

where k_1 is the first-order rate constant. Separating the variables yields

$$\frac{dX}{X} = -k_1 dt \tag{5}$$

which integrates to

$$\ln X \Big|_{X_0}^{X_t} = -k_1 t \Big|_0^t \tag{6}$$

yielding

$$\ln X_t = \ln X_0 - k_1 t \tag{7}$$

Equation (7) is the *working equation* which we will use to calculate the value of the first-order rate constant, k_1. If we are using data for decrease in A with time, we can simply substitute for X in terms of A according to Eq. (3) to yield

$$\ln (A_t - A_\infty) = \ln (A_0 - A_\infty) - k_1 t \tag{8}$$

For the case presented in Fig. 1, $B_0 = 0$. Therefore, $B_t = A_0 - A_t$ and $B_\infty = A_0 - A_\infty$. Substituting in Eq. (8) yields

$$\ln (B_\infty - B_t) = \ln B_\infty - k_1 t \tag{9}$$

Equation (9) can be used to solve for k_1 from data representing the increase in drug concentration in the B compartment as a function of time.

According to Eq. (7), a plot of the natural logarithm of the variable X, where X is $(A_t - A_\infty)$ or $(B_\infty - B_t)$, versus time will be linear with slope $-k_1$ and intercept in X_0. The intercept is thus the natural logarithm of the total concentration change which can occur. Thus we can apply Eq. (7) to data to determine whether or not the rate process is described by Eq. (4). If a good first-order plot results, we may conclude that the process is first-order and calculate the first-order rate constant from the slope of the plot. This is illustrated in the following example.

Sample Problem 1

A drug is dissolved in the water contained in compartment A in the beaker illustrated in Fig. 1. Calculate the first-order rate constant for transfer using the concentration in compartment A, measured as a function of time, as given in Table 1.

Solution: The first-order rate constant for transfer from A to B may be calculated from a plot based on Eq. (7). In this problem the variable $X = (A_t - A_\infty)$, where A_∞ is equal to 5.00 since the compartments are equivalent. The values for X, calculated in this way, may be plotted on semilog paper as shown in Fig. 3a. The rate constant is calculated from this plot as follows:

$$k_1 = \frac{\ln 5.00 - \ln 0.98}{50 \text{ min}}$$

Table 1

Decrease in Drug Concentration (mg%) in
Compartment A as a Function of Time

t (min)	Conc (mg%)	t (min)	Conc (mg%)
0	10.00	100	5.20
10	8.56	110	5.17
20	7.58	120	5.14
30	6.88	130	5.11
40	6.35	140	5.09
50	5.98	150	5.06
60	5.70	160	5.04
70	5.51	170	5.02
80	5.39	180	5.01
90	5.29	190	5.00

$$k_1 = 3.26 \times 10^{-2} \ min^{-2}$$

There are some important guidelines to observe in estimating rate constants by this graphical method. Generally it is best to limit the plot to values of X that are greater than $0.2X_0$ to avoid using data representing small differences in relatively large numbers. Figure 3a exceeds this limit, since it includes the value $0.1X_0$ at 70 min. The graph paper should be chosen and labeled in such a way that the plot is expanded over the maximum distance. The slope should be calculated from the line which best fits the data and not from experimental plots. The reason for this approach is illustrated in Fig. 3b, where the data points do not fall on the line of best fit.

Practice Problem 1

A drug-transfer experiment was conducted in a beaker arranged as in Fig. 1. A solution containing 100 mg of drug in 100 ml of buffer was put into compartment A, with 100 ml of the same buffer in compartment B. The concentration of drug in B was assayed as a function of time (Table 2).

(a)   What is the rate constant for the transfer of drug from A to B?
      Answer: $k_1 = 2.12 \times 10^{-2} \ min^{-1}$

(b)   What value would be obtained for k_1 using a plot based on data for the A compartment?
      Answer: $k_1 = 2.12 \times 10^{-2} \ min^{-1}$

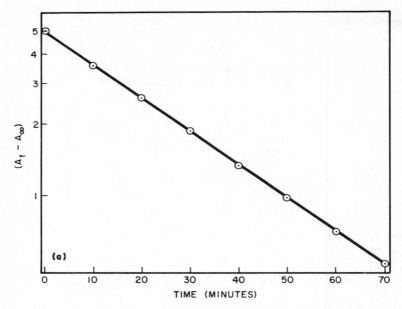

Fig. 3a First-order plot for data in Sample Problem 1. The variable $X = (A_t - 5.00)$ is plotted on semilog paper as a function of time.

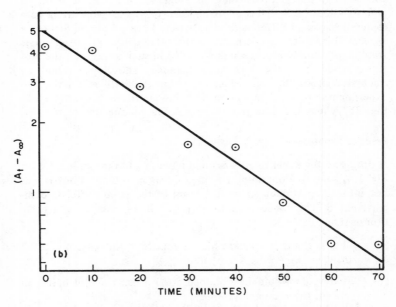

Fig. 3b First-order plot for data which illustrate experimental error. The rate constant for the line of best fit is identical to that in Fig. 3a. Any pair of experimental points, chosen from this data, will not provide the value for $-k_1$.

Table 2

Drug in Compartment B as a Function of Time

t (min)	Conc (mg%)
0	0
10	9.2
20	18.5
35	27.0
60	35.3
80	41.0
115	45.5
240	50.4
360	49.7

d. Nonequivalent Compartments. Since a system such as that described by Fig. 1 is reversible, it is more accurate to write Eq. (1) as

$$A \overset{k_f}{\underset{k_r}{\rightleftarrows}} B \tag{10}$$

where k_f is the first-order rate constant for the forward rate process and k_f is the first-order rate constant for the reverse process. The rate expression may be written

$$\frac{-dA}{dt} = k_f A - k_r B \tag{11}$$

It is evident, then, that the apparent first-order rate constant k_1 is actually a combination of the microconstants k_f and k_r. The exact nature of this relationship will be defined later. First, we will examine the system at equilibrium.

At equilibrium, the concentrations in compartments A and B remain constant. That is,

$$\frac{-dA}{dt} = 0 = k_f A_\infty - k_f B_\infty$$

or

$$k_f A_\infty = k_r B_\infty \tag{12}$$

Upon rearrangement, we obtain

$$\frac{k_f}{k_r} = \frac{B_\infty}{A_\infty} = K \tag{13}$$

where K is the apparent equilibrium constant. Note that in the previous cases of equivalent compartments, $A_\infty = B_\infty$, and necessarily, $k_f = k_r$. Now however, we are considering nonequivalent compartments, so that the concentrations of *total* drug in A and B are not necessarily equal when equilibrium is attained. On the other hand, the concentrations of *transferable* species *are* always equal at equilibrium, since that species determines the concentration gradient for diffusion. (See Appendix A.)

Since $B_t = A_0 - A_t$, this may be combined with Eqs. (11) and (12) to derive

$$\ln(A_t - A_\infty) = -(k_f + k_r)t + \ln(A_0 - A_\infty) \tag{14}$$

which becomes

$$\ln(A_t - A_\infty) = -(k_f + k_r)t + \ln A_\infty \tag{15}$$

for the case of equivalent compartments where $B_\infty = A_\infty$. A comparison of Eqs. (14) and (8) shows that the observed first-order rate constant, k_1, calculated from the slope of plots such as that shown in Fig. 3 is defined by

$$k_1 = k_f + k_r \tag{16}$$

This relationship is derived in several kinetics texts [1-4]. The values for the individual constants may be calculated from Eqs. (13) and (16), since both k_1 and K may be determined experimentally. Thus the apparent first-order rate constant for the reverse rate process may be determined from

$$k_r = \frac{k_1}{K + 1} \tag{17}$$

and for the forward rate process from

$$k_f = \frac{k_1 K}{K + 1} \tag{18}$$

or from Eq. (16).

Sample Problem 2

A weakly acidic drug is dissolved in compartment A of a beaker arranged as in Fig. 4. The results are given in Table 3. Compartment B has a pH of 4, and the pK_a of the drug is 3. Only un-ionized drug may pass through the membrane.

Table 3

Decrease in Drug Concentration in Compartment A
as a Function of Time

t (min)	Total conc (mg%)	t (min)	Total conc (mg%)
0	6.60	40	0.68
5	4.15	50	0.63
10	2.69	60	0.61
15	1.89	70	0.60
20	1.32	80	0.60
30	0.85	90	0.60

(a) Calculate the value of the apparent first-order rate constant, k_1.
   Solution: A semilog plot of $(A_t - A_\infty)$ vs t, similar to that shown in Fig. 3, is linear with slope equal to -1.06×10^{-1} min^{-1}. It follows that $k_1 = 1.06 \times 10^{-1}$ min^{-1}. Note that a plot of data for the B compartment would yield an identical line.

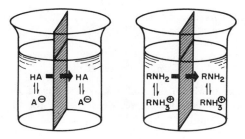

Fig. 4 Passive transport is limited to uncharged species in this model. Transfer of a weak acid, HA, or an amine base, RNH_2, will be influenced by the pH of compartments A and B since the concentration of uncharged species must be equal when the two compartments achieve equilibrium.

(b) What is the value of the apparent equilibrium constant, K?
What is the value of the equilibrium constant if the concentration of un-ionized drug only is considered?
Solution: In the first instance,

$$K = \frac{B_\infty}{A_\infty} \quad \text{(Eq. 13)}$$

$$K = \frac{6.00}{0.60} = 10$$

In the second case, however, we know that at equilibrium the concentration of transferable species in each compartment must be equal, so

$$K' = 1$$

(c) Solve for k_f and k_r.
Solution: We know that $K = 10$ and $k_1 = 1.06 \times 10^{-1}$ min^{-1}. Using Eq. (17), which states

$$k_r = \frac{k_1}{K + 1}$$

$$k_r = 0.964 \times 10^{-2} \text{ min}^{-1}$$

and from Eq. (16),

$$k_f = 9.64 \times 10^{-2} \text{ min}^{-1}$$

(d) What is the pH of the A compartment?
Solution: This can be solved by employing the Henderson-Hasselbach equation:

$$pH = pK_a - \log \frac{\text{protonated drug}}{\text{unprotonated drug}}$$

We know the pH of B, and pK_a of the drug, and the total concentration in B. Therefore, we can solve for the concentration of transferable species (HA), which is the same in B as in A at equilibrium.

$$HA = \frac{6.00 \text{ mg\%}}{11} = 0.545 \text{ mg\%}$$

This value may be substituted into the equation

$$pH \text{ of A} = 3 - \log \frac{HA}{A^-}$$

to yield

$$\text{pH of A} = 3 - \log 9.9 \cong 2$$

Practice Problem 2

Sulfadimethoxine is placed into compartment A, which contains human blood serum. A membrane separates it from compartment B, which contains only water. The experiment is illustrated in Fig. 5. Free sulfadimethoxine, S_f, passes through the membrane, while the protein-bound sulfa, S-P, does not. The initial total concentration of sulfonamide in compartment A is 62 mg%. The data for the transfer process are found in Table 4.

Table 4

The Concentration of Sulfadimethoxine Transferred
from the Blood Plasma Compartment as a Function of Time

t (min)	mg% total sulfa in B	t (min)	mg% total sulfa in B
0	0.00	180	6.52
15	1.02	240	7.16
30	1.92	300	7.53
45	2.73	360	7.73
60	3.42	400	7.85
90	4.55	640	8.00
120	5.40	880	8.00
150	6.04		

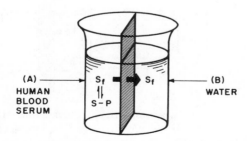

Fig. 5 In this model, passive transport is limited to unbound (free) sulfadimethoxine. The concentration of free (S_f) is assumed to be in equilibrium with that bound to plasma protein (S-P).

(a)   What is the first-order rate constant?
      Answer: $k_1 = 9.36 \times 10^{-3}$ min^{-1}

(b)   What is the apparent K?
      Answer: 1.48×10^{-1}

(c)   What are the values for k_f and k_r?
      Answer: $k_f = 1.21 \times 10^{-3}$ min^{-1}, $k_r = 8.15 \times 10^{-3}$ min^{-1}

(d)   What is the mg% bound in A at t_∞?
      Answer: 46 mg%

2. Two-Compartment Open System

a. Time Course for Concentration in B, T, and C. The two-compartment open model may be illustrated as in Fig. 6. The central compartment (which will be referred to as blood), composed of blood and well-perfused tissues, is designated by B, and the tissues or the rest of the body by T. All drug removed from the body, regardless of the route of elimination, is represented by compartment C. The central compartment is open in the sense that elimination occurs from this compartment by excretion and/or metabolism. Thus the entire system is open, since the drug passes reversibly from blood to tissue. Contrast this system to that given in Fig. 1. In that case no drug could leave the system, so an equilibrium state had to be reached eventually. With an open system, drug is always being lost from one compartment, so that, depending on the rate of equilibration, the ratio of drug in the tissues to drug in the plasma may or may not reach its equilibrium value.

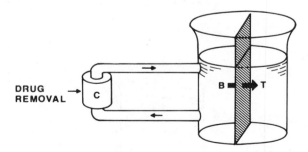

Fig. 6   A model for the two-compartment open model. Drug placed in compartment B undergoes passive transport to T and is simultaneously removed as the solution circulates through C at a constant rate. The beaker has two compartments which contain drug remaining in the system. The model is open compared with Fig. 1, since drug removed by C is considered lost from the system (the beaker).

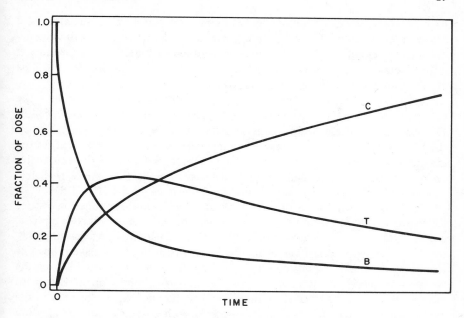

Fig. 7 Time course for drug in each compartment following introduction of a dose in B of Fig. 6. Drug is initially lost from B to both T and C and eventually from both B and T to C so that $B_\infty = T_\infty = 0$ and $C_\infty = 1$. In a closed system $T_\infty = KB_\infty$ (See Fig. 2, where $K = 1$ and $B_\infty = A_\infty = 0.5$.)

The time course of the drug in each of these compartments is shown in Fig. 7, where, contrary to the case of the closed system shown in Fig. 2, the amounts of drug in B and T do not reach constant levels.

b. Rate Constants. Another way of depicting the two-compartment open model is by means of Eq. (19).

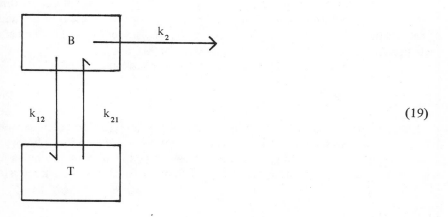

$$(19)$$

Rate constants for drug transfer between compartments 1 and 2, the blood and tissues, are represented by k_{12} and k_{21}, and k_2 is the rate constant for elimination of drug from the blood. It is important to realize that k_2 is not the same as β, the overall rate constant for elimination from the body. The difference will be illustrated in the calculations which follow.

 c. *Determination of Rate Constants.* A drug placed directly into the bloodstream will undergo simultaneous elimination and distribution processes. The resulting decrease in drug concentration in the blood will be described by the kinetics for transport to parallel compartments. A general treatment for the kinetic analysis of competing first-order rate processes will be presented later under the discussion of elimination. Diffusion into the tissues is a reversible process with two microconstants, as discussed previously in Sec. II.A.1.d.

 If the concentration of drug in the blood is measured as a function of time following a rapid intravenous injection, it may be possible to observe a biphasic curve. Although in truth all rate processes are occurring simultaneously throughout the curve, appropriate values for the constants in Eq. (19) make it possible to observe both a "distribution phase" and an "elimination phase." During the distribution phase the fraction of dose in the tissue compartment is seen to increase to a maximum value as shown in Fig. 8. The fraction of dose in the blood decreases due to simultaneous loss to both tissue (T) and elimination (C). During the elimination phase, drug content decreases in both the tissue and blood compartments as a function of time. If these same data are plotted on semilog paper, the elimination phase will become linear. Figure 9 illustrates such a plot. Note that these data for blood and tissue result in parallel lines, indicating that the common value for their slope represents the negative value of the rate constant for loss from the entire body, which is composed of compartments B and T in this model. A reference line, representing the sum of B plus T, is also included in the figure. This line also becomes parallel to the others during the elimination phase. It is important to note (and to remember) that the ratio of tissue fraction to blood fraction [5] has approached a constant value during the elimination phase. (We shall not consider exceptions to this case in this text.) The elimination phase is also referred to as the β phase, and the negative value of the slope of its log plot is β. The reason for this nomenclature should become clear from the following mathematics.

 A system such as this may be described by the equation

$$P = Ae^{-\alpha t} + Be^{-\beta t} \tag{20}$$

where P is the concentration of drug in plasma. Equation (20) has been derived previously by several authors [6-8]. This biexponential equation illustrates why the decrease in plasma drug concentration as a function of time is a biphasic curve. The constants, α and β, however, are complex functions of all three rate

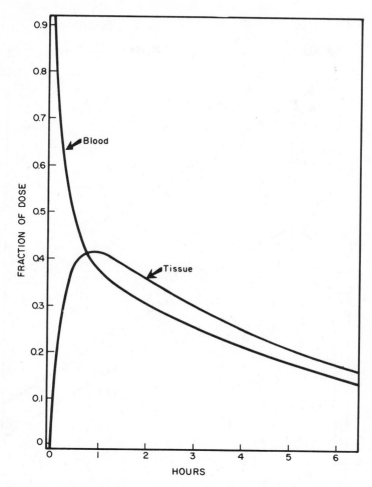

Fig. 8 Time course for a drug in blood and tissue compartments of Eq. (19) following a rapid intravenous injection. The distribution phase occurs during the first 1.5 hr and is followed by an elimination phase characterized by parallel loss from both blood and tissues.

constants, k_{12}, k_{21}, and k_2. The solution to α and β are given here simply to illustrate their complexity:

$$\alpha = \frac{c_1 + \sqrt{c_1^2 - 4c_2}}{2} \tag{21}$$

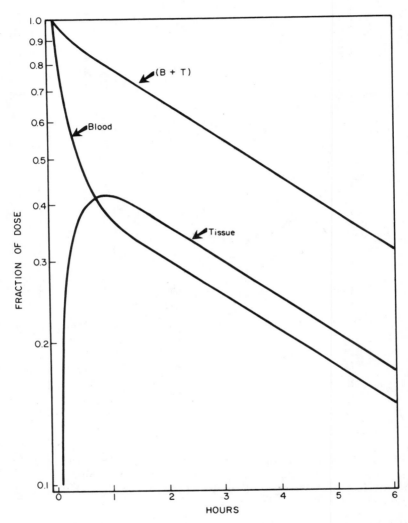

Fig. 9   A semilog plot for the data shown in Fig. 8. Loss of drug from the blood and tissue compartments is represented by parallel lines during the elimination phase. This represents loss from the entire body since the sum, B + T, is also parallel. Blood data representing the elimination phase can therefore be used to describe loss from the entire body.

and

$$\beta = \frac{c_1 - \sqrt{c_1^2 - 4c_2}}{2} \tag{22}$$

where $c_1 = k_{12} + k_{21} + k_2$ and $c_2 = k_{21}k_2$.

In spite of the imposing appearance of these terms, it is not a difficult matter to solve for k_{12}, k_{21}, and k_2 from blood level vs time data. It is simply necessary to obtain values for α, β, A, and B from a plot of ln P vs. time such as

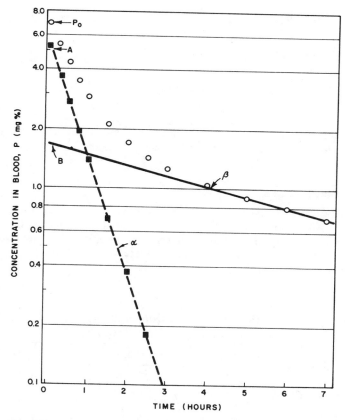

Fig. 10 "Feathering" blood level data. The best-fit line for the β phase is drawn first to obtain the slope, $-\beta$, and intercept, B. The second line represents the difference between the β line and the experimental points. The slope, $-\alpha$, and intercept, A, are obtained from this difference plot. The values A, α, B, β are used in Eqs. (23) through (28) to calculate the values for k_{12}, k_{21}, and k_2.

the one illustrated in Fig. 10. The following equations can then be employed to calculate the values of the individual rate constants from the blood concentration data.

$$A + B = P_0 \tag{23}$$

$$A' = \frac{A}{P_0} \tag{24}$$

$$B' = \frac{B}{P_0} \tag{25}$$

$$k_{21} = A'\beta + B'\alpha \tag{26}$$

$$k_2 = \frac{1}{A'/\alpha + B'/\beta} = \frac{\alpha\beta}{k_{21}} \tag{27}$$

$$k_{12} = \frac{A'B'(\beta - \alpha)^2}{k_{21}} = \alpha + \beta - k_2 - k_{21} \tag{28}$$

The use of these equations in pharmacokinetic analysis of plasma drug concentration data is illustrated in the following problems.

Sample Problem 3

A drug was administered by rapid intravenous injection into an adult male. An indwelling venous catheter was used to withdraw blood samples over a 7-hr period. Samples were assayed for intact drug and results are given in Table 5. Calculate the values for k_2, k_{21}, and k_{12}.

Table 5

Concentration of Drug in Blood
Following Intravenous Administration

t(hr)	Conc (mg%)	t (hr)	Conc (mg%)
0.00	7.00	2.50	1.43
0.25	5.38	3.00	1.26
0.50	4.33	4.00	1.05
0.75	3.50	5.00	0.90
1.00	2.91	6.00	0.80
1.50	2.12	7.00	0.70
2.00	1.70		

Solution: Construct a first-order plot representing drug concentration in the blood as shown in Fig. 10. The negative slope of the second phase, β, is derived from the best line drawn through the terminal portion of the plot. The intercept of this line with the y axis is B. (Note that semilog paper is used). The α line, marked by solid squares in Fig. 10, is obtained as follows. From each data point (open circles) in the initial phase of the curve is subtracted the value at the corresponding time on the extrapolated portion of the β line. A plot of these values yields a line of slope equal to minus α and intercept equal to A.

The following values were obtained from Fig. 10:

$$A = 5.25 \text{ mg\%} \qquad B = 1.75 \text{ mg\%} \qquad P_0 = 7.00 \text{ mg\%}$$

$$\alpha = 1.34 \text{ hr}^{-1} \qquad \beta = 0.13 \text{ hr}^{-1}$$

Application of Eqs. (24) through (28) leads to:

$$k_2 = 0.40 \text{ hr}^{-1} \qquad k_{21} = 0.43 \text{ hr}^{-1} \qquad k_{12} = 0.64 \text{ hr}^{-1}$$

Practice Problem 3

A drug was administered by intravenous injection into a patient, and the blood level data given in Table 6 were obtained. Calculate the values for k_2, k_{21}, and k_{12}.

Answer: $k_2 = 0.39 \text{ hr}^{-1}$, $k_{12} = 0.84 \text{ hr}^{-1}$, $k_{21} = 0.61 \text{ hr}^{-1}$

Table 6

Concentration of Drug in Blood as a Function of Time

t (hr)	μg/ml	t (hr)	μg/ml
0.2	5.65	2.0	1.78
0.4	4.58	3.0	1.43
0.6	3.80	4.0	1.22
0.8	3.23	5.0	1.06
1.0	2.78		

3. Pre-Equilibrium or One-Compartment Open Model

a. Equilibrium and Its Implications. Equation (20) describes the time course of a drug that is introduced into compartment B in Eq. (19). Analysis of these data as illustrated in Fig. 10 indicates that the initial slope, α, is due primarily to the distribution of drug throughout the body. If the distribution of drug throughout the body is very rapid relative to the rate of elimination, then $\alpha \gg \beta$, and Eq. (20) will approach the limit

$$P = Be^{-\beta t} \tag{29}$$

which is a monoexponential expression. This does not imply that the drug is distributed in a manner that is any different from that shown in Eq. (19). It simply means that if a single plot is made using a given time axis which will accommodate the β slope, the α slope will be too fast to be displayed on the same plot. In fact, if samples were removed at sufficiently early time periods following injection and an expanded plot of the initial time were made, the α slope could be evaluated. This one-compartment open model is therefore actually an approximation or simplification used to describe the two-compartment open model when $\alpha \gg \beta$. Since the α phase is completed very early in the process, the approximation based on Eq. (29) is valid over nearly all of the time course of the drug in the body. Indeed, it might be preferable to portray a one-compartment system as

$$\boxed{\begin{array}{c} B \\ \text{and} \\ T \end{array}} \xrightarrow{\ \ \beta\ \ } C \tag{30}$$

since the partitioning between blood and tissue is not observed unless very early samples are taken.

This very rapid α phase has some important consequences. The magnitude of α is, as was mentioned, largely dependent on the rate of the distribution of drug between B and T relative to the rate of elimination to C. The rate of distribution, in turn, depends on the sum of the forward and reverse rate constants, $k_{12} + k_{21}$. When the sum of these microconstants becomes large enough relative to k_2, distribution takes place so rapidly that even though elimination is occurring at the same time, the blood and tissue compartments will approach an equilibrium ratio. That is,

$$\frac{k_{12}}{k_{21}} \simeq \frac{T'}{P'} \simeq K \tag{31}$$

where T' is the amount of drug in the tissues, P' is the amount of drug in the central compartment, and K is the equilibrium constant as discussed under Eq. (13). This is illustrated in Fig. 11, where $\alpha \gg \beta$ and the ratio of k_{12}/k_{21} is 3/1. If equilibrium is achieved, the ratio of drug in tissues to that in plasma should also be 3/1. This relationship is seen to be true in Fig. 11, since the dashed line representing $3 \times P$ is identical to the time course for T. This figure also illustrates the approximate nature of Eq. (29), since the α phase is indeed present but it is too fast to display on the same time scale as the β phase.

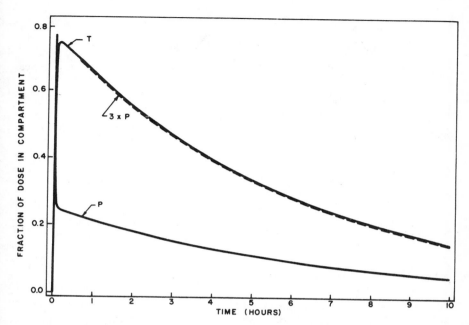

Fig. 11 A two-compartment model resembles a one-compartment model when distributions is rapid relative to elimination. The ratio $k_{12}/k_{21}/k_2$ is 90/30/1 in this example. The rate constant for distribution is therefore 120 [Eq. (16)] and the equilibrium constant, K, is 3 [Eq. (13)]. The dashed line, $3 \times P$, demonstrates the agreement between the equilibrium prediction and the observed data.

Under what condition does Eq. (29), or equilibrium, apply? As a *first approximation* it may be assumed that Eq. (29) will apply when

$$k_{12} + k_{21} \geq 20k_2 \tag{32}$$

In such cases the distribution is sufficiently fast to compete favorably with elimination and establish what has been referred to here as a pre-equilibrium state. In Fig. 11 the ratio $(k_{12} + k_{21})/k_2$ is 120. The ratio of T'/P' is thus equal to the equilibrium constant, k_{12}/k_{21}. The ratio of T'/P' is also constant during the β phase of a two-compartment open model, but it is not equal to the value k_{12}/k_{21} (Eq. 39a, Appendix B).

The relationship between β, the rate constant for elimination from the whole body, and k_2 is a simple one for a drug distributed by a one-compartment model. The rate of loss of drug from the body may be written as

$$- \frac{dD}{dt} = \beta D = k_2 P' \tag{33}$$

where D represents the total amount of drug remaining in the body. Since

$$D = T' + P' \tag{34}$$

substitution for T' from Eq. (31) and then for D in Eq. (33) yields

$$\beta P'(1 + K) = k_2 P' \tag{35}$$

which reduces to

$$\beta = \frac{k_2}{1 + K} = k_2 f_p \tag{36}$$

where the fraction in the blood is $f_p = [P'/(P' + T')]$.

   b.   *Arbitrary Test for a One-Compartment Model.* A simple test commonly employed to determine the number of required compartments consists of
examining a first-order plot of plasma level data for the existence or nonexistence of an α phase. Of course, if the time between the injection and the first
blood sample is long enough, any drug will appear to be described by a one-
compartment model. Thus it may be appropriate to sample shortly after injection to determine the relative rate of distribution as compared to elimination.
If early sampling fails to detect an α phase, a one-compartment model will
describe the data. If analysis of the α and β portion indicates that Eq. (31) is
in effect, it may still be appropriate to acknowledge that pre-equilibrium exists
and use a one-compartment model to describe the biphasic data. A cardinal rule
in modeling or compartmental analysis is to use the fewest number of compartments necessary to describe the data adequately [9] .

   Depending on the purpose of the study, this number may differ. For example, Baggot [10]' has compared the elimination of amphetamines from
numerous animal species using a one-compartment analysis wherein the first
plasma assay, taken at 30 min, lies on the β line in all cases although the $t_{1/2}$
values varied from 0.6 to 6 hr. Conversely, Kaplan [11] has determined all of
the constants in Eq. (19) by determining five points during the first 20 min in a
study which required 12 hr to describe the β phase.

   c.   *Determination of β and k_2 in the One-Compartment Open Model.*
Equation (29) may be rewritten as

$$\ln P = \ln B - \beta t \tag{37}$$

indicating that the slope of a semilogarithmic plot of blood concentration vs time will be $-\beta$. The intercept of a semilog plot is B.

Substitution of Eq. (31) into Eq. (36) yields

$$\beta = \frac{k_2 k_{21}}{k_{12} + k_{21}} = k_2 f_p \tag{38}$$

Therefore, if we knew the values of k_{12} and k_{21} we could easily calculate k_2 from β. However, in the case of a one-compartment model, there are many instances when k_{12} and k_{21} cannot be determined because the α phase either was not or could not be determined. It would be possible to calculate k_2 if the volume of B were known. Equation (27) may be rewritten as

$$k_2 = \frac{1}{A/\alpha P_0 + B/\beta P_0} \tag{39}$$

which simplifies to

$$k_2 = \frac{P_0}{B} \beta \tag{40}$$

for the one-compartment model, since $A/\alpha \ll B/\beta$. We know B from the first-order plot of the blood level data. P_0 is a hypothetical value equal to the concentration in the central compartment at time zero if all the drug remained in the central compartment. This may be easily calculated from the dose and the volume of the central compartment if this value is known. If the central compartment is assumed to be the plasma, as is often done, the volume will be approximately 5% of the body weight.

The value of the equilibrium constant, K, may also be determined from P_0 and B. Combining Eqs. (38) and (40) and rearranging yields

$$\frac{P_0}{B} - 1 = \frac{k_{12}}{k_{21}} \tag{41}$$

which of course is equal to K.

Sample Problem 4

A drug is administered to a 70-kg man and the fraction of the dose in each of three compartments is determined as a function of time with the results shown in Table 7.

Table 7

Fraction of Dose, f, in Blood, Urine, and as
Metabolities Following Intravenous Injection

Time (hr)	Blood	Urine	Metabolites
	f		
1.0	0.28	0.11	0.05
2.0	0.24	0.18	0.09
3.0	0.21	0.24	0.12
4.0	0.18	0.30	0.15
5.0	0.16	0.35	0.17
6.0	0.14	0.39	0.20
8.0	0.10	0.46	0.23
10.0	0.08	0.50	0.25
48.0	0.00	0.67	0.33

(a)   Is this drug described by a one- or a two-compartment model?
Solution: A first-order plot of the data does not show an α
phase. From the data at hand the most reasonable choice is
therefore the one-compartment open model.

(b)   What is the value of β, the overall rate constant for elimination
from the body? Calculate this value using urine and metabolite
as well as blood data.
Solution: First-order plots of blood, urine, and metabolite
data yield three parallel lines. Thus, any of these sets of data
may be used to calculate β. (See the discussion concerning rate
constants for elimination.)

$$\text{slope} = -\beta$$

$$\beta = 1.41 \times 10^{-1} \ hr^{-1}$$

(c)   What is the value of k_2, the specific elimination constant for
loss of drug from the central compartment?
Solution: We know from Eq. (40) that

$$k_2 = \frac{\beta P_0}{B}$$

Since the data are in fractions rather than concentration, P_0
must equal 1 and the intercept of the semilog plot of blood
data gives a value for B of 0.32. Therefore,

$$k_2 = \frac{0.141}{0.32} = 4.41 \times 10^{-1} \ hr^{-1}$$

(d)   What is the ratio k_{12}/k_{21}?

Solution: For a one-compartment model

$$\frac{k_{12}}{k_{21}} = \frac{\text{tissue content}}{\text{blood content}} = \frac{T'}{P'}$$

Values for P' are given in the data, and T' may be calculated easily since

$$\text{Total drug} = 1 = T' + P' + \text{urine} + \text{metabolites}$$

For example, at 4 hr,

$$P' = 0.18$$

$$T' = 1 - 0.18 - 0.30 - 0.15 = 0.37$$

$$\frac{k_{12}}{k_{21}} = \frac{2}{1}$$

The same value will be obtained at any other time.

Practice Problem 4

A drug was given by intravenous injection. Blood samples were taken and analyzed as a function of time with the results shown in Table 8.

Table 8

Concentration of Drug in Blood Following
Intravenous Injection

t (hr)	Conc (mg%)	t (hr)	Conc (mg%)
0.05	26.4	1.00	7.2
0.10	17.4	1.50	6.4
0.15	13.6	2.00	5.8
0.20	11.3	3.00	4.6
0.30	9.2	4.00	3.7
0.40	8.5	5.00	3.0
0.50	8.1	6.00	2.3
0.75	7.6	7.00	1.9

(a)   Is the time course for this drug best described by a one-or a two-compartment model?

Answer: A two-compartment model is suggested by a first-order plot of this data as shown in Fig. 12. However, most of the time profile is in the β phase, since the α phase is complete within 0.5 hr while the β phase is not finished in 7 hr.

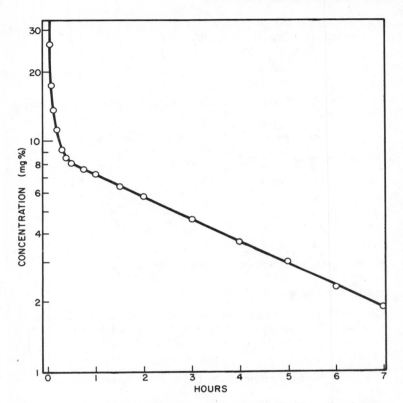

Fig. 12   A first-order plot of the data in Practice Problem 4. The system may be described by a one- or two-compartment model as discussed in the answer to this problem. If the first sample were drawn at 30 min, the α phase would not be observed and the remaining data would be treated as a one-compartment model. Analysis of the early data provides estimates for k_{12}, k_{21}, and k_2 values.

Therefore, a one-compartment model might be sufficient if equilibrium is achieved. The values for the microconstants can be used to make this appraisal as shown in part (b).

(b) What are the values for the microconstants?
      Answer: Since $\alpha \gg \beta$, it is difficult to feather this data. The results are roughly A = 35 mg%, B = 9 mg% and the rate constants in hr^{-1} are $\alpha = 12.8$, $\beta = 0.22$, $k_{12} = 9.22$, $k_{21} = 2.79$, and $k_2 = 1.01$. The ratio $(k_{12} + k_{21})/k_2 = 12$ indicates a two-compartment model. This is approaching the value of 20 [see Eq. (32)] so that a one-compartment approximation with

K = 3.3 might be adequate for some purposes. Theophylline dosage regimens in adults (Chap. 7, Sec. III.B.4) illustrate a similar simplification.

4. Multicompartment Open Models

As has been noted [9,12], the preferred compartmental model is the one containing the fewest compartments which adequately describe the data. While one-compartment and two-compartment models accommodate a great many drugs, there are a number of cases where these are not sufficient. Significant distribution of drug in deep tissues such as bone or fat, or strong binding to any tissue, may result in the appearance of a triexponential blood level curve, indicating the presence of a third compartment.

More than three compartments are also possible, but there are practical limits on the detection of new compartments. The addition of each new compartment requires an additional phase in the first-order plots employed in the classical pharmacokinetic approach. Deciding how many phases actually exist can be a problem. At this stage in the development of pharmacokinetics, the data seldom warrant proposing anything more complex than a three-compartment open model for intact drug. One alternative approach is based upon the rate at which the plasma flow perfuses various organs. Methotrexate, thiopental, and arabinosylcytosine are drugs which have been analyzed using this approach [13-16]. While this method may have certain advantages [17], it has the disadvantage of requiring sacrifice of the animal to determine actual organ levels of drug in order to test the validity of the proposed model. Our discussion will be limited to the classical approach for compartmental analysis using the intact animal as its own control.

A triexponential equation describing the time course of drug in the central compartment for the three-compartment model is

$$P = Ae^{-\alpha t} + Be^{-\beta t} + Ge^{-\gamma t} \tag{42}$$

which is the same as the equation for the two-compartment model with an additional term. The mathematics and treatment of this model [6,18-21] and more complex models [6,20] have been discussed in some detail.

The three-compartment model has been proposed for several drugs. Doherty and Perkins[22] found a triexponential curve for serum levels of tritiated digoxin in humans after intravenous administration. This curve suffers from the disadvantage of being constructed from average values for 11 patients, but a later paper [23] shows the same type curve using data from one patient. Nagashima *et al.* [21] have published an interesting study of bishydroxycoumarin in which the first compartment of the three-compartment model is proposed to be the plasma only, rather than the usual plasma plus well-perfused tissues. Tubocurarine in human adults [24] appears to fit a three-compartment model, as does the antitumor agent 5-(dimethyltriazo)-imidazole-4-carboxamide (DIC) when administered intravenously to dogs [19].

Sample Problem 5

A healthy subject weighing 70 kg was given 150 mg of bishydroxy-coumarin, by intravenous injection. From the data in Table 9, taken from Ref. 21, calculate the slopes of the three phases of the plasma level vs time plot.

Table 9

Concentration of Bishydroxycoumarin (BHC) in the
Plasma After Intravenous Injection

t (hr)	BHC (mg/liter)	t (hr)	BHC (mg/liter)
0.17	36.2	3.0	13.9
0.33	34.0	4.0	12.0
0.50	27.0	6.0	8.7
0.67	23.0	7.7	7.7
1.0	20.8	18.0	3.2
1.5	17.8	23.0	2.4
2.0	16.5		

Solution: Three different phases of the curve can be resolved in a manner analogous to that used for the two-compartment open model. A semilogarithmic plot of the data shows a terminal linear portion with slope equal to $-\gamma$. The extrapolated portion of this line is subtracted from the corresponding experimental points to yield a biphasic curve with a final slope of $-\beta$. Finally, the extrapolated portion of the β line is subtracted from the nonlinear portion of this second plot to give the α line. The slopes and y intercepts for the lines obtained by this process are:

Slopes	Intercepts
$\alpha = 3.1 \ hr^{-1}$	A = 23.5 mg/liter
$\beta = 0.44 \ hr^{-1}$	B = 10.5 mg/liter
$\gamma = 0.078 \ hr^{-1}$	G = 14.0 mg/liter

The microconstants for this system may be determined as outlined in Ref. 21.

Practice Problem 5

A drug is administered by intravenous injection. The plot of blood concentration vs time is found to have three phases with negative slopes of 0.75, 0.30, and 0.085 hr^{-1}.

(a) Draw a compartmental scheme which describes the data.
Answer:

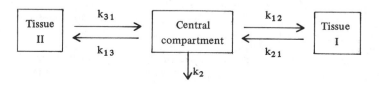

(b) What process might be responsible for each slope?
Answer: The first slope results primarily from distribution to the tissue compartments. The second slope reflects elimination following establishment of steady-state conditions. When the less tightly held drug has been eliminated, the drug remaining in the deep tissues is not released rapidly enough to maintain a plasma-to-tissue ratio as high as in the second phase. This results in a second and slower elimination phase. You may suggest alternative descriptions which are kinetically equivalent. Try it.

B. Active Transport

1. Description

Up to this point, all the rate processes discussed have been examples of passive transport. That is, the membrane itself did not actively participate in the transfer process, but instead it simply provided a physical barrier which permitted the formation of a concentration gradient when the drug was introduced into one of the compartments. However, there are many cases where the membrane plays an active role, transporting solute molecules against an electrochemical or concentration gradient. Molecules transported in this manner include naturally occuring substances, with sodium and potassium ions representing the best-known examples. Others are amino acids [25], sugars [26], uracil [27], and thymine [28]. Some foreign molecules, such as 5-fluoro- and 5-bromouracil [29] are also actively transported.

A number of discussions of transport mechanisms have been published [18,25,30–33]. The distinctions between passive and active transport can be briefly summarized by comparing their major properties.

Passive transport may be characterized by the following:

1. Drug molecules move from a region of relatively high concentration to one of relatively low concentration.
2. The rate of transfer is proportional to the concentration gradient between the compartments involved in the transfer.
3. The transfer process achieves equilibrium when the concentration of the transferable species is equal on both sides of the membrane.
4. Drugs which are capable of existing in both a charged and a noncharged form approach an equilibrium state primarily by transfer of the noncharged species across the membrane.

In contrast to the above, an active process involves active participation by the membrane in the transfer of molecules between compartments. A "carrier," which may be an enzyme or other component of the membrane, is responsible for effecting the transfer by a process which may be represented as follows:

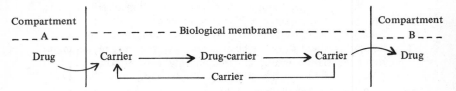

Here the drug in compartment A is picked up by the carrier in the surface of the membrane. The drug-carrier complex then moves across the membrane and the drug is discharged to compartment B at the membrane surface open to B. The carrier then returns to the A compartment surface for another drug molecule.

A transfer system like this quite naturally has characteristics decidedly different from those listed for the passive system:

1. This process consumes *energy*. There is energy involved in the work done by the carrier.
2. Since the transport involves consumption of energy, it may be subject to *poisoning* by such metabolic poisons as fluorides, dinitrophenol, lack of oxygen, and so on.
3. Unlike the passive transfer process, which is dependent upon a concentration gradient, an active transfer process can work *against the concentration gradient*. That is, the carrier may transport all of the drug from one compartment to the other without any regard for an "equilibrium state" which was the endpoint in the case of a passive transport process. Indeed, the carrier transfer system will generally be a "one-way" transport process.

4. The system will be relatively *structure-specific*. The carrier will be designed to transport a specific chemical structure. Thus, it will not be completely indiscreet in its activity.

5. However, the carrier system may transport a chemical structure which is sufficiently similar to the one for which it is allegedly "specific." The transfer system is thus subject to *competition* between similar chemical structures.

6. Since there are a finite number of carriers available, the system is capacity-limited. If the total number of transferable molecules exceeds the number of carrier sites available for transfer, the system will become *saturated*. The system will then be working at full capacity and the transfer of drug may thus occur at a constant rate until the concentration of drug falls below that of the capacity limit of the system.

2. Mixed Kinetics

a. Zero-Order Kinetics. A system in which transfer occurs at a constant rate is described by zero-order kinetics. An example of such a system is the saturated active transport system just described.

When n, the order of the rate process, becomes zero, Eq. (2) becomes

$$\frac{dX}{dt} = -k_0 \tag{43}$$

where k_0 is the zero-order rate constant. Separating variables and integrating between the limits of $t = 0$ and t, and X_0 and X_t yields

$$X_t = X_0 - k_0 t \tag{44}$$

Equation (44) is the working equation which we will use to calculate the value of the zero-order rate constant, k_0. Before we consider typical data for the calculation of a zero-order rate constant, let us briefly review some properties of a zero-order rate process.

The properties of first-order rate processes, which have previously been discussed, do not apply to zero-order processes. This will be quite evident upon examination of the zero-order rate expression. According to Eq. (43), the rate of a zero-order transfer process will be equal to a constant, k_0. On the other hand, we have previously seen how the rate of a first-order process decreases with time, being at a maximum at time zero and decreasing to a zero rate asymptotically. Notice that equal initial rates for a zero-order and a first-order process very quickly result in a faster zero-order rate, since the first-order rate process decreases as the material is transferred and the zero-order process continues at a rate equal to the initial rate (Fig. 13a).

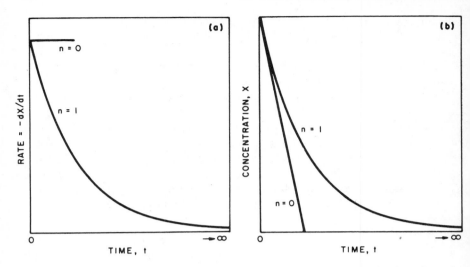

Fig. 13 (a) Rate of loss, $-dX/dt$, from compartment A as a function of time for a zero-order process, $n = 0$, and a first-order process, $n = 1$. (b) Decrease in drug concentration in compartment A as a function of time for a first-order process, $n = 1$, and a zero-order process, $n = 0$.

b.   Determination of Zero-Order Rate Constants.   A comparison of Eqs. (44) and (7) reveals a method for distinguishing between zero- and first-order data. Equation (44) indicates that if the data are zero-order, a plot of X vs t will be a straight line of slope equal to $-k_0$ and intercept equal to X_0. First-order data plotted in this way will not yield a straight line. This situation is illustrated in Fig. 13b. The type of deviation from linearity which is observed is worth noting. First-order data on a zero-order plot show a *positive* deviation from linearity. Conversely, zero-order data on a first-order plot show a definite *negative* deviation (see also Sample Problem 6).

The zero-order rate constant is easily calculated from the slope of a graph such as that shown in Fig. 13b.

c.   First-Order Conditions in Active Transport.   The active transport system considered in the previous example may also behave according to a first-order rate process. Consider the same transfer system under conditions where the number of sites greatly exceeds the amount of drug available for transport. The transfer process will not operate at its maximum capacity under these conditions since it is dependent upon the availability of drug. When a fruitful collision occurs between drug and carrier, then the transport of drug across the membrane as a drug-carrier complex occurs in the same manner as previously outlined. However, at any given moment there is a large number of available sites not in operation. The rate is thus far below the rate at saturation.

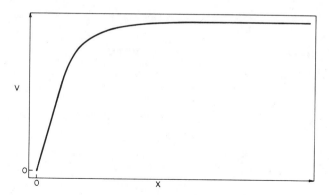

Fig. 14   Rate of transport, V, as a function of transferable concentration, X, for an active transport system at first-order conditions (low X) and pseudo zero-order conditions (high X) where the carrier system is saturated.

Now let us imagine that the concentration of drug is doubled but that the available sites remain in large excess of transferable drug. We would expect the rate to increase, since on a statistical basis there are now twice as many collisions and thus twice as many chances for a fruitful carrier-drug collision. An increase in concentration will result in an equal increase in rate as long as the carrier system does not become saturated and the solutions remain sufficiently dilute so that an increase in concentration is paralleled by an increase in thermodynamic activity. In Eq. (4) we have seen that a process is first-order when the transfer rate is proportional to the concentration of transferable drug. Thus an active transport system can behave by a first-order rate process when the concentration of drug is sufficiently dilute to be the limiting factor rather than the capacity of the transfer system itself. Figure 14 illustrates the change in kinetic order when drug concentration is increased from dilute conditions to those of capacity-limited transfer.

 d. *Michaelis-Menten Kinetics.* The above discussions of zero- and first-order kinetics, as indicative of saturated and nonsaturated active transport systems, are analogous to the Michaelis-Menten approach to enzyme-catalyzed reactions [34]. Processes are said to behave in accordance with Michaelis-Menten kinetics when the rate, V, can be described by the equation

$$V = \frac{V_{max}[X]}{K_m + [X]} \tag{45}$$

where V_{max} is the maximum possible rate (see Fig. 14) and $[X]$ is the concentration of drug that may undergo change. The Michaelis constant, K_m, is identical with that value of $[X]$ which will result in $V = V_{max}/2$. When $[X]$ is much smaller than K_m the denominator approaches the value of K_m and Eq. (45) becomes

$$V = \left(\frac{V_{max}}{K_m}\right)[X] \tag{46}$$

Since (V_{max}/K_m) is constant, this equation is of the form $-dX/dt = k[X]$ which, like Eq. (4), is apparent first order. The rate is therefore proportional to concentration of drug when $[X] < 0.1\,K_m$ as illustrated in Fig. 14.

At sufficiently high drug concentrations where $[X] \gg K_m$, Eq. (45) becomes

$$V = V_{max} \tag{47}$$

which is a constant rate as shown in Fig. 14 when $[X] > 10\,K_m$. When $[X]$ is in the intermediate region $(0.1\,K_m < [X] < 10\,K_m)$, then Eq. (45) must be employed and the approximations given in Eqs. (46) and (47) do not suffice.

The elimination of a highly metabolized drug from the body is frequently found to exhibit what is called nonlinear kinetics. This terminology means that deviation from first-order behavior is observed at sufficiently high doses. These nonlinear data may sometimes be adequately described by an equation of the form of Eq. (45). In such a case the elimination is said to behave according to Michaelis-Menten kinetics. The K_m values have no simple theoretical significance. However, the approach has often proved to be of practical value in successfully characterizing complex kinetic systems. Phenytoin multiple dose calculations provide an excellent example of the analysis of nonlinear elimination kinetics using the Michaelis-Menten equation. (See Chap. 7, Section III.B.1.)

Sample Problem 6

A drug is being transferred from compartment A to compartment B during two experiments which are conducted under different sets of experimental conditions. In both cases the appearance of drug in the B compartment is measured as a function of time. The volume of the B compartment is identical to that of A, and the results are given in terms of the amount of drug transferred rather than the concentration of drug in the B compartment. Results are given in Table 10.

(a) What is the order of the transfer process in experiments 1 and 2?
Solution: A plot of $B_\infty - B_t$ on coordinate graph paper results in a straight line for data from experiment 2, while data from experiment 1 are nonlinear. The same data on semilog paper, however, are linear in the case of experiment 1. Therefore,

Table 10

Appearance of Drug in Compartment B During the
Transfer Process from Compartment A

Total amount transferred (μg) Experiment			Total amount transferred (μg) Experiment		
t (min)	No. 1	No. 2	t (min)	No. 1	No. 2
0	0	0	25	97	42
3	34	5	30	98	50
5	51	8	35	99	58
10	76	17	40	99	67
15	88	25	50	100	83
20	94	33	60	100	100

experiment 1 illustrates a first-order process, and experiment 2 a zero-order process.

A first-order plot of data covering the first 15 min of each experiment (this includes almost 90% of the total process in experiment 1, but only 25% of the total in experiment 2) is linear for experiment 1, and is very nearly linear for experiment 2 as well. This emphasizes the importance of plotting data covering at least 50% of a process when trying to determine its order.

(b) What are the rate constants associated with both experiments?
Solution: In experiment 1,

$$k_1 = -\text{slope} = \frac{\ln 100 - \ln 24.2}{10 \text{ min}}$$

$$k_1 = 1.42 \times 10^{-1} \text{ min}^{-1}$$

In experiment 2,

$$k_0 = -\text{slope} = \frac{100 \,\mu g - 0 \,\mu g}{60 \text{ min}}$$

$$k_0 = 1.67 \,\mu g/\text{min}$$

Practice Problem 6

Two separate experiments are carried out infolving the active transport of a drug through a biological membrane. In each case the

drug remaining in compartment A is assayed as a function of time.
Results are agiven in Table 11.

Table 11
Loss of Drug from Initial Compartment at Two Dosage Levels

t (min)	mg%	mg%	t (min)	mg%	mg%
0	10.0	100.0	60	0.02	32.6
5	6.0	94.5	70	0.00	21.4
10	3.5	89.0	80	0.00	10.0
15	2.1	83.5	85	–	6.0
20	1.2	77.8	90	0.00	3.5
25	0.70	72.0	95		2.1
30	0.41	66.5	100		1.2
35	0.24	60.8	105		0.7
40	0.14	55.0	110		0.4
50	0.05	43.8	115		0.0

(a) What is the order of the transport process at the 10 mg% dose
level?
Answer: First order

(b) What is the value of the rate constant?
Answer: 1.04×10^{-1} min^{-1}

(c) What is the order of the transport process at the 100 mg% dose
level?
Answer: Zero order

(d) What is the value of the rate constant?
Answer: 1.1 mg%/min

(e) What is occurring between 80 and 115 min following the 100
mg% dose? (You might find it helpful to construct a plot of
mg% vs t in answering this question.)
Answer: At 80 min, when the concentration in A drops to 10
mg%, the active transport system is no longer saturated, so the
process becomes first order.

REFERENCES

1. W. P. Jencks, *Catalysis in Chemistry and Enzymology*, McGraw-Hill Book
Company, New York, 1969, pp. 586–589.
2. K. J. Laidler, *Chemical Kinetics*, 2nd Ed., McGraw-Hill Book Company,
New York, 1965.

3. S. W. Benson, *The Foundation of Chemical Kinetics*, McGraw-Hill Book Company, New York, 1960, pp. 27–29.

4. A. A. Frost and R. G. Pearson, *Kinetics and Mechanism*, 2nd Ed., John Wiley and Sons, New York, 1961, pp. 160–162, 166–172, 186.

5. P. R. Byron and R. E. Notari, Critical Analysis of "Flip-Flop" Phenomenon in Two-Compartment Pharmacokinetic Model, *J. Pharm. Sci. 65*, 1140 (1976).

6. M. Mayersohn and M. Gibaldi, Mathematical Methods in Pharmacokinetics. II. Solution of the Two-compartment Open Model, *Am. J. Pharm. Educ. 35*, 19 (1971).

7. A. Rescigno and G. Segre, *Drug and Tracer Kinetics*, Blaisdell Publishing Co., Waltham, Mass., 1966, pp. 24 ff., 91 ff.

8. S. Riegelman, J. C. K. Loo, and M. Rowland, Shortcomings in Pharmacokinetic Analysis by Conceiving the Body to Exhibit Properties of A Single Compartment, *J. Pharm. Sci. 57*, 117 (1968).

9. E. R. Garrett, Basic Concepts and Experimental Methods of Pharmacokinetics, in *Advances in the Biosciences 5: Schering Workshop on Pharmacokinetics* (G. Raspe, ed.), Pergamon Press-Vieweg, New York, 1970, p. 7.

10. J. D. Baggot, A Comparative Study of the Pharmacokinetics and Biotransformation of Amphetamine, Thesis, The Ohio State University, Columbus, Ohio, 1971.

11. S. A. Kaplan, R. E. Weinfeld, S. Cotter, C. W. Abruzzo, and K. Alexander, Pharmacokinetic Profile of Trimethoprim in Dog and Man, *J. Pharm. Sci. 59*, 358 (1970).

12. J. G. Wagner, *Biopharmaceutics and Relevant Pharmacokinetics*, Drug Intelligence Publications, Hamilton, Ill., 1971, pp. 237–238.

13. K. B. Bischoff, R. L. Dedrick, and D. S. Zaharko, Preliminary Model for Methotrexate Pharmacokinetics, *J. Pharm. Sci. 59*, 149 (1970).

14. K. B. Bischoff, R. L. Dedrick, D. S. Zaharko, and J. A. Longstreth, Methotrexate Pharmacokinetics, *J. Pharm. Sci. 60*, 1128 (1971).

15. K. B. Bischoff and R. L. Dedrick, Thiopental Pharmacokinetics, *J. Pharm. Sci. 57*, 1346 (1968).

16. R. L. Dedrick, D. D. Forrester, and D. H. W. Ho, In Vitro-in Vivo Correlation of Drug Metabolism—Deamination of 1-β-D-Arabinofuranosylcytosine, *Biochem. Pharmacol. 21* (1972).

17. D. S. Zaharko, Pharmacokinetics, *Cancer Chemother. Rep.*, Part 3, *3*, 21 (1972).

18. G. A. Portman, Pharmacokinetics, in *Current Concepts in the Pharmaceutical Sciences: Biopharmaceutics* (J. Swarbrick, ed.), Lea and Febiger, Philadelphia, 1970, pp. 11–12, 67–70.

19. T. L. Loo, B. B. Tanner, G. E. Housholder, and B. J. Shepard, Some Pharmacokinetic Aspects of 5-hr (Dimethyltriazeno)-imidazole-4-carboxamide in the Dog, *J. Pharm. Sci. 57*, 2126 (1968).

20. L. Z. Benet, General Treatment of Linear Mammillary Models with Elimination from Any Compartment as Used in Pharmacokinetics, *J. Pharm. Sci 61*, 536 (1972).

21. R. Nagashima, G. Levy, and R. A. O'Reilly, Comparative Pharmacokinetics of Coumarin Anticoagulants, IV. Application of a Three-compartmental Model to the Analysis of the Dose-dependent Kinetics of Bishydroxy-coumarin Elimination, *J. Pharm. Sci. 57*, 1888 (1968).

22. J. E. Doherty and W. H. Perkins, Studies with Tritiated Digoxin in Human Subjects After Intravenous Administration, *Am. Heart J. 63*, 528 (1962).

23. J. E. Doherty, W. H. Perkins, and W. J. Flanigan, The Distribution and Concentration of Tritiated Digoxin in Human Tissues, *Ann. Int. Med. 66*, 116 (1967).

24. M. Gibaldi and G. Levy, Dose-dependent Decline of Pharmacologic Effects of Drugs with Linear Pharmacokinetic Characteristics, *J. Pharm. Sci. 61*, 567 (1972).

25. W. Wilbrandt and T. Rosenberg, The Concept of Carrier Transport and Its Corollaries in Pharmacology, *Pharmacol. Rev. 13*, 109 (1961).

26. T. H. Wilson and B. R. Landau, Specificity of Sugar Transport by the Intestine of the Hamster, *Am. J. Physiol. 198*, 99 (1960).

27. L. S. Schanker and D. J. Tocco, Characteristics of the Pyrimidine Transport Process of the Small Intestine, *Biochem. Biophys. Acta 56*, 469 (1962).

28. L. S. Schanker and D. J. Tocco, Active Transport of Some Pyrimidines Across the Rat Intestinal Epithelium, *J. Pharmacol. Exp. Therap. 128*, 115 (1960).

29. L. S. Schanker and J. J. Jeffrey, Structural Specificity of the Pyrimidine Transport Process of the Small Intestine, *Biochem. Pharmacol 11*, 961 (1962).

30. W. Wilbrandt, Possible Mechanisms of Active Transport, in *Enzymes and Drug Action* (J. L. Mongar and A. V. S. DeReuck, eds.), J. and A. Churchill, London, 1962, pp. 43–59.

31. W. D. Stein, *The Movement of Molecules Across Cell Membranes*, Academic Press, New York, 1967.

32. W. A. Ritschel, *Applied Biopharmaceutics I*, University of Cincinnati, Cincinnati, Ohio, 1969, pp. 138–143.

33. T. Teorell, General Physico-chemical Aspects of Drug Distribution, in *Advances in the Biosciences 5: Schering Workshop on Pharmacokinetics* (G. Raspe, ed.), Pergamon Press-Vieweg, New York, 1970, pp. 21–37.

34. J. G. Wagner, Properties of the Michaelis-Menton Equation and Its Integrated Form Which Are Useful in Pharmacokinetics, *J. Pharmacokin. Biopharm. 1*, 103 (1973).

Chapter 3

PRINCIPLES OF PHARMACOKINETICS

I.   INTRODUCTION   46

II. PHARMACOKINETIC PARAMETERS   48
     A. Biological Half-life   48
         1. Half-life   48
             a. First order   48
             b. Zero Order   50
                 Sample Problem 1   50
                 Practice Problem 1   52
         2. Determination of Biological Half-life   52
             Sample Problem 2   54
             Practice Problem 2   54
     B. Apparent Volume of Distribution   55
         1. Methods for Determination   56
             a. Mass Balance   56
             b. Extrapolation   57
             c. Area Under the Curve (AUC)   57
             d. Steady-State Infusion   58
         2. Variation in Vd Estimates by the Various Methods   58
             Sample Problem 3   59
             Practice Problem 3   60
         3. Other Factors Affecting Volume of Distribution   61
             Sample Problem 4   61
             Practice Problem 4   62
     C. Clearance   62
         1. The Meaning of Clearance   62
         2. Renal Clearance   64
         3. Nonrenal Clearance   68
             Sample Problem 5   68
             Practice Problem 5   69

D. Rate Constants for Elimination   70
    1. Parallel Drug Loss   70
        Sample Problem 6   73
        Practice Problem 6   74
    2. Metabolism and Excretion: One-Compartment Model   75
    3. Metabolism and Excretion: Two-Compartment Model   76
    4. Dose-Dependent Changes in Elimination Kinetics   77
        a. Capacity-Limited Systems   77
        b. Other Dose-Dependent Kinetics   79
        Sample Problem 7   80
        Practice Problem 7   82
E. Supply Constants   82
    1. General Model   82
    2. Blood Level Curves   83
        Sample Problem 8   88
        Practice Problem 8   89
    3. Calculation of Absorption Rate Constants   90
        a. Simple Case   90
        b. Rate-Determining Step   91
        c. The Loo-Riegelman and Wagner-Nelson Equations   94
        d. First-Order Loss of Drug from Depot   97
F. Intravenous Infusion   98
        Sample Problem 9   102
        Practice Problem 9   103

REFERENCES   103

I. INTRODUCTION

One of the problems in arriving at a more accurate dosage regimen or a more meaningful interpretation of a biological response to a dose is inaccessibility of the drug concentration at the active site. In order to approximate a solution to this problem the technique of *compartmental analysis* has come into use. This is an attempt to define quantitatively what has become of the drug as a function of time from the moment it is administered until it is no longer in the body. Although widespread practice of compartmental analysis is relatively recent, the principle has been with us since at least 1937, when Teorell offered a compartmental scheme. His model was virtually ignored for years because of the complexity of the kinetic equations necessary for its solution. With the advent of computers and the increased interest in understanding drug action, models such as his have been successfully employed in the pharmacokinetic analysis of many drugs. The essential components of a typical compartmental scheme are shown here.

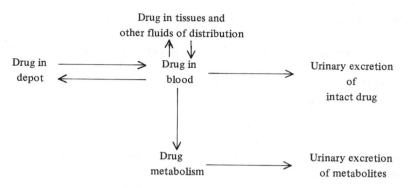

Many modifications of this scheme have been used and certainly no single scheme will apply to all drugs. For example, if protein binding occurs in the plasma, one must consider the equilibrium between bound and unbound drug and its effect on distribution which occurs by diffusion of free drug into tissues. Although many different models may be required to describe a large variety of drugs, there are some generalizations which can be made relative to this approach.

All schemes describe the distribution of drug within "compartments." Compartments generally include the blood and urine. However, while a compartment may be an anatomical entity, this is not a requirement. A compartment is defined as a kinetically distinguishable "pool" in terms of the drug concentration–time profile. If the data indicate the loss of a certain fraction of drug to some sites, as a function of time, this site would constitute a compartment in the scheme regardless of whether or not the anatomical or physiological significance were known. In other words, it is possible to know the amount of drug in a compartment as a function of time without really knowing where that compartment is physically located.

In humans, the studies are generally limited to *blood* and *urine concentration* studies. This is coupled with a knowledge of the dose and other information which can be assessed separately, such as binding phenomena.

When a drug or metabolite moves from one compartment to another, there are one or more *rate constants* associated with the transfer process. In general, these rate processes will be *first order*. Exceptions will occur in cases where a capacity-limited transport system or metabolic route may become saturated and behaves as a zero-order rate process. Schemes are drawn by employing the *fewest possible number of compartments* that are compatible with the experimental results. Generally, data are tested for "best fit."

In brief, pharmacokinetics is concerned with quantitatively accounting for the whereabouts of a drug after it has been introduced into the body. The analysis is carried out throughout the entire time course for the drug in the body. By analyzing the content of accessible fluids, one uses kinetics to make deductions regarding the amount of drug in nonaccessible regions—perhaps even the site of action. The most widely sampled fluids are blood and urine, which are often analyzed for both drug and drug metabolic products. These data are used to produce a compartmental analysis. The relative volumes of distribution and rate constants derived from the analysis are significant parameters in the comparison of analogs of a given drug or a variety of dosage forms. This chapter will be devoted to the methods for determining these parameters using the technique of compartmental analysis.

Pharmacokinetic parameters may be vital to ensure a successful protocol in the clinic as well as in research on laboratory animals. Often the clinical evaluation of drugs or drug products is carried out on the basis of some secondary response because of the nonexistence of a directly measurable parameter which is related to the treatment of the disease by the drug. Many times no response is measured at all, and the clinician attempts to make objective and subjective assessments of the patient's general welfare. A dosage regimen for a new drug may in fact be based on such an evaluation and may or may not include a comparison with a standard drug or analog. Even with proper experimental design, a dosage regimen based upon such studies can be only a rough approximation at best. This point is well illustrated if one compares sulfonamide dosage regimens calculated from pharmacokinetic data to those commonly used in the clinic [1].

II. PHARMACOKINETIC PARAMETERS

A. Biological Half-Life

1. Half-Life

   a. *First Order*. The half-life of a first-order process is a constant for a given rate process. It can be defined by considering the previously defined variable, X. The half-life is the time required for X_t to become equal to one-half of X_0. Thus, it is the time required for the variable X to decrease to one-half of its initial value, Equation (7) in Chap. 2 can be rearranged to give

$$\ln \frac{X_t}{X_0} = -k_1 t \tag{1}$$

By the definition of half-life, X_t/X_0 equals 0.5 at $t_{1/2}$, so

$$t_{1/2} = \frac{0.693}{k_1} \tag{2}$$

since ln (0.5) equals −0.693.

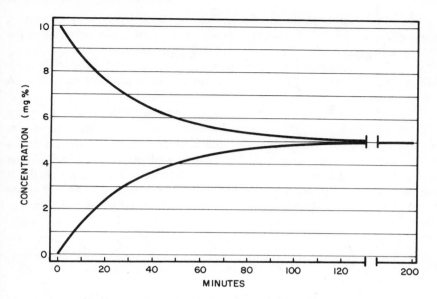

Fig. 1 Data from Sample Problem 1 in Chap. 2.

From Eq. (2) it is obvious that one way to calculate a first-order half-life is by using the rate constant determined from a first-order graph of the data. This method is most accurate, but half-lives may also be estimated directly from plots of raw data.

Figure 1 is a plot of the data from Sample Problem 1 in Chap. 2 on co-ordinate paper. According to the definition, the half-life is the time it takes for half of the observed change to occur. In this problem the total change is 5 mg%. Starting at zero time, the $t_{1/2}$ is therefore the time required to decrease from 10 to 7.5 mg%, or 21 min. This is the same value as that obtained using Eq. (2). What result is obtained when a different point on the curve is used as the initial value? If the time corresponding to 8 mg% drug in the A compartment, and 2 mg% in B is chosen as the starting point, the half-life is the time for a change of 1.5 mg%, or 21 min again. Try it.

This example illustrates some important points. The $t_{1/2}$ is independent of initial concentration. This can easily be understood by examining Eq. (1). Regardless of what value you choose for X_0, the value for X_t will be $0.5X_0$. Substituting into Eq. (1) yields

$$\ln \frac{0.5X_0}{X_0} = -k_1 t_{1/2} \tag{3}$$

which reduces simply to the ln of 0.5. Thus Eq. (2) will always describe the $t_{1/2}$ independent of the initial value of X chosen to make the calculation. Although the $t_{1/2}$ is independent of X_0, it is easier and more accurate to estimate the $t_{1/2}$ value from the earlier part of the process. To test this, try calculating the half-life as illustrated above, but using 6 mg% as the initial concentration in the A compartment and 4 mg% in the B compartment of Fig. 1.

A process which behaves according to first-order mathematics will have a uniform value for the $t_{1/2}$ throughout the entire process. This requirement can serve as a quick test to determine the adherence to first-order principles from a plot of the raw data. Although $t_{1/2}$ is commonly used, one could define the time to reach any desired fraction and this would be a constant for that process if it is indeed first-order. For example, the time for 10% loss can be defined as the time required to reach 90% of the original transferable material. In this case $t_{0.9}$ would be equal to $(\ln 0.9)/ - k_1$ or

$$t_{0.9} = \frac{0.105}{k_1} \tag{4}$$

b. Zero Order. The half-life of a zero-order process is not like that just discussed for a first-order process. Applying the definition of half-life to the zero-order equation yields

$$0.5X_0 = X_0 - k_0 t_{1/2} \tag{5}$$

which rearranges to

$$t_{1/2} = \frac{0.5X_0}{k_0} \tag{6}$$

From Eq. (6) we can see that $t_{1/2}$ is not independent of the initial concentration. In fact, the larger the initial concentration, the longer is the half-life. This difference can be used to distinguish between a zero- and first-order process by varying the initial concentration (or dose) and measuring the resulting half-life.

Sample Problem 1

Two different drugs are administered to a patient by intravenous injection on six different occasions. The time between each test is 1 week. In each case the time for elimination of one-half the dose is determined. Answer the questions using the data shown in Table 1.

Table 1
Changes in Half-Life with Increasing Dose

Dose (mg)	Drug 1 $t_{1/2}$ (hr)	Drug 2 $t_{1/2}$ (hr)
40	10	3.47
60	15	3.47
80	20	3.47

(a) What is the order of the elimination rate process of drug 1 and drug 2?
    Solution: Drug 2 has a constant $t_{1/2}$, while the $t_{1/2}$ for drug 1 increases with the dose. Therefore, drug 1 must be eliminated by a zero-order process, and drug 2 by a first-order process.

(b) What is the value of the rate constant and the units of that constant for drug 1 and drug 2?
    Solution: Solving Eq. (6) for k_0,

$$k_0 = \frac{0.5 X_0}{t_{1/2}}$$

At a dose of 40 mg, drug 1 has a $t_{1/2}$ of 10 hr, so

$$k_0 = \frac{(0.5)(40 \text{ mg})}{10 \text{ hr}}$$

$$k_0 = 2 \text{ mg/hr}$$

The other doses give the same answer. The rate constant for drug 2 may be calculated from Eq. (2):

$$k_1 = \frac{0.693}{t_{1/2}}$$

$$k_1 = 0.20 \text{ hr}^{-1}$$

(c) If a dose of 10 mg were given to the same patient, how much time would be required to eliminate 2 mg in the case of drug 1 and drug 2?
    Solution: For drug 1, Eq. (44) in Chap. 2 may be rearranged and solved:

$$t = \frac{X_0 - X_t}{k_0}$$

$$t = \frac{10 \text{ mg} - 8 \text{ mg}}{2 \text{ mg/hr}}$$

$t = 1$ hr

In the case of drug 2, Eq. (1) may be solved for t to give

$$t = \frac{\ln(X_0/X_t)}{k_1}$$

$$t = \frac{\ln(10/8)}{0.20 \text{ hr}^{-1}}$$

$t = 1.1$ hr

Practice Problem 1

Use your data and graphs from Sample Problem 6 in Chap. 2 to answer these questions.

(a) What is the half-life in experiment 1 starting at $t = 0$? Starting at $t = 5$ min?
   Answer: 4.9 min

(b) What is the half-life in experiment 2 starting at $t = 0$? Starting at $t = 30$ min?
   Answer: 30 min, 15 min

2. Determination of Biological Half-Life

The biological half-life may be defined using the blood concentration data as a point of reference or from the standpoint of an observed biological response. In reading the literature one must be aware of this ambiguity and determine which criterion is used by the author. The half-life based on biological response may or may not be the same as that determined from the blood. They will agree only when there is a direct relationship between the blood concentration and the biological response. For the purpose of developing this treatment of pharmacokinetics, we will define the biological half-life on the basis of blood level data.

A drug being eliminated by a first-order process will have a half-life which is constant and independent of the initial concentration or dose. This biological half-life may be defined as the time required for the body to eliminate one-half of the drug which it contains. Since we are considering elimination from the body, this half-life will be the half-life which is associated with the rate constant for overall elimination, β, according to

$$t_{1/2} = \frac{0.693}{\beta} \tag{7}$$

where $-\beta$ is the slope of the first-order plot based on the equation for a one-compartment model or the final slope of the biphasic plot based on the equation for a two-compartment model. The value of $t_{1/2}$ is *not* equal to $0.693/k_2$. This would be true only for the trivial case where drug distribution is limited to the blood and therefore $k_2 = \beta$. However, since drugs are distributed into body fluids, the overall elimination is reflected by β rather than by k_2 — which was previously defined as the specific rate constant for elimination from the central compartment. A model-independent equation relating k_2 and β is [2]

$$\beta = k_2 f_p \tag{8}$$

where f_p is the fraction of drug in the blood under postdistributive conditions, relative to the total drug in the body.

In addition to dose independence, biological half-life defined in this manner should be independent of the route of administration. Figure 2 illustrates two typical blood level patterns following I.V. and oral doses of the same drug. Note that the curves become parallel in the later time periods of the graph. At this

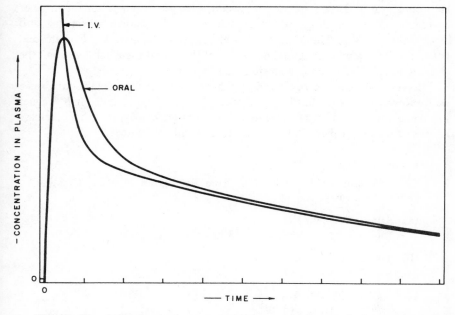

Fig. 2 Blood level curves representing equal doses of the same drug administered by two different routes (I.V. and oral). The drug behaves according to a two-compartment model with values $k_1 = k_{12} = 9$, $k_{21} = 3$, and $k_2 = 2$.

time both curves reflect the elimination of drug from the body. In the case of the I.V. dose the distribution phase has been completed prior to the parallel portion. In the case of the oral dose both distribution and absorption have been completed. Since the β phase curves are parallel, the half-lives calculated from them are equal. However, it is preferable to calculate $t_{1/2}$ from blood level data following I.V. administration if possible. If absorption is slow the observed terminal slope following oral administration may represent the absorption step. This phenomenon is called "flip-flop" and will be discussed in Chap. 6, Sec. IV.B.3.a.

In order to be valid, a value of $t_{1/2}$ calculated from a dose placed in an extravascular depot must be calculated from data representing the time when *both* absorption and distribution are complete. This time may be difficult to determine, since independent data for drug in the depot are generally not available. The fact that the data yield a straight line when plotted on semilog paper does not necessarily mean that the depot is empty. This uncertainty makes the calculation of $t_{1/2}$ from such data risky.

The half-life of a drug will be affected by any factors which change β. As might be imagined, therefore, intersubject variations may be quite large. Renal insufficiency is one possible cause of increased half-life. Metabolic differences because of age or disease are also important. Changes in the pH of the urine or co-administration of drugs which stimulate or inhibit metabolism can also change the half-life. These changes all affect β by changing k_2. Pagliaro and Benet [3] have published an extensive list of drugs and their half-lives, and the changes due to renal or hepatic dysfunction.

However, β may also be altered by changes in the distribution of durg, since we know from Eq. (22) in Chap. 2 that k_{12} and k_{21} are included in β. Wagner [4] has pointed out that a change in distribution rate constants with an increase in dose could change β even when k_2 is independent of the dose.

Sample Problem 2

Calculate the biological half-life from data given in each of the following in Chap. 2.

(a) Sample Problem 3.
   Solution: $t_{1/2} = 0.693/\beta = 5.33$ hr

(b) Sample Problem 4.
   Solution: $t_{1/2} = 4.91$ hr

(c) Practice Problem 4.
   Solution: $t_{1/2} = 3.15$ hr

Practice Problem 2

(a) A drug was administered to a 70-kg patient by an I.V. injection of 100 mg. All of the patient's urine was collected by

Table 2

Intact Drug Appearing in the Urine as a
Function of Time Following I.V. Injection

t (hr)	Cumulative amount of drug in urine (mg)	t (hr)	Cumulative amount of drug in urine (mg)
0	0	12	91
1	18	14	94
2	33	16	96
3	45	18	97
4	55	20	98
5	64	24	100
6	70	30	100
8	80	36	100
10	87		

catheterization over a period of 30 hr. The urine samples were assayed for drug content. Calculate the biological half-life using the results as given in Table 2.

Answer: $t_{1/2} = 3.43$ hr

(b) What is the value for β?

Answer: $\beta = 0.20$ hr^{-1}

B. Apparent Volume of Distribution

The apparent volume of distribution of a drug, Vd, is not literally a volume at all. That is, it should not be regarded as a particular physiological space within the body. It might be hypothetically defined as the volume of body water which would be required to contain the amount of drug in the body if it were uniformly present in the same concentration in which it is in the blood. However, all compartments which contain the drug may not have equal concentrations, so any volume calculated utilizing the drug concentration in only one compartment can be only an *apparent* volume. In the long run, it appears most useful to avoid all analogies to volumes and consider Vd simply as a proportionality factor which, when multiplied by the concentration of drug in the blood, yields the amount of drug present in the body, or

$$D_t = Vd\, P_t \qquad\qquad (9)$$

where D_t and P_t represent the total amount of drug in the body and the concentration of drug in the blood at some time, t. It has been common practice to associate calculated values for Vd with known values for the volumes of body water compartments. For example, the average volumes for body water compartments are roughly (in percent v/wt of body weight), plasma 5%, extracellular fluid 20%, and total body water 70%. The inadequecy of interpreting Vd values in terms of body "space" will become apparent after studying the limitations of the Vd calculations themselves. Consideration of this conceptual problem has led Benet and Ronfeld [5] to suggest that the distribution of a drug ought simply to be described by amounts in the central and tissue compartments instead of by misleading volume terms. In any case, volumes of distribution do figure prominently in the literature, so it is important to have some appreciation of the problems and inherent errors associated with the calculation of these numbers.

1. Methods for Determination

There are a number of ways of calculating Vd when dealing with a drug that is described by a *one-compartment model,* all of which yield the same value. Derivations for the equations are given in Appendix B. This Vd value, calculated from these equations, fulfills the requirement that it accurately predicts the amount of drug in the body. This is because we have defined the one-compartment model as a condition of instantaneous equilibrium wherein $(T'/P') \approx (k_{12}/k_{21})$. This ratio is independent of the route of administration.

In the case of a *two-compartment model,* the (T'/P') ratio can be influenced by the route of administration. During the beta phase following rapid I.V. administration $(T'/P') \approx [k_{12}/(k_{21} - \beta)]$. (See Appendix B.) This is not the equilibrium expression that is in effect for the one-compartment model. However, in Sec. II.F below ("Intravenous Infusion"), it will be shown that $(T'/P') = (k_{12}/k_{21})$ for both one- and two-compartment drugs during the time of steady-state plasma levels, P_{inf}, that are achieved by constant rate I.V. infusion. Thus the (T'/P') ratio, which is constant for a one-compartment drug, decreases for a two-compartment model drug when comparing the β-phase to the steady state. Therefore, unlike the one-compartment case, the Vd values calculated by the various methods are not equal. This observation and the reasons behind it have been discussed at some length by several authors [6–10] and a short discussion of pertinent mathematical relationships is provided in Appendix B.

a. Mass Balance. This method requires data for the amount of drug remaining in the body, D_t, and the corresponding plasma concentration, P_t, at $t > t_d$ where t_d is the time required for distribution. From Eq. (9) it follows that

$$Vd = \frac{D_t}{P_t} \tag{10}$$

In order to know the amount of drug remaining in the body it is necessary to perform mass balance experiments. If a rapid intravenous dose is given, then the amount put into the body is known. The amount of drug lost from the system by excretion and metabolism up to time t would have to be determined. If the drug is eliminated solely by urinary excretion the method may prove to be practical. Mass balance may not be feasible when several metabolites are formed or when analysis of nonrenal excretion is difficult.

b. Extrapolation. In the application of mass balance it is necessary to know both the amount in the body and the concentration in the blood at the same time in order to calculate Vd. Using blood level data alone, this is possible only at time zero following an intravenous injection. Then, at time zero, D_t is the size of the dose and P_t is defined by B, the intercept of the linear terminal line of a semilog plot. For a two-compartment model this would be the beta line intercept (Fig. 10, Chap. 2). In a one-compartment case the intercept, B, is equivalent to the plasma concentration at time zero where the distribution of drug is instantaneous. This method of obtaining the volume of distribution by the *extrapolation method* may be expressed by

$$Vd = \frac{D_0}{B} \qquad (11)$$

and the value calculated in this way is often called Vd,extrap. The extrapolation method has the disadvantage of being a single-point determination. The accuracy might be increased by repeating the calculation at more than one dose, but the determination of blood concentrations at more than one level can present a problem is the concentration becomes too dilute. When data for the amount of drug eliminated are available Eq. (10) may be used to calculate Vd at times other than time zero.

c. Area Under the Curve (AUC). When the kinetics are first order the area under the curve (AUC) from time zero to infinity will be a linear function of dose (see Fig. 5). The AUC values following rapid I.V. injections can be used as follows:

$$Vd = \frac{D_0}{(AUC)\,(\beta)} \qquad (12)$$

which is often called Vd,area or Vd,β. This equation is also useful for routes of administration other than rapid intravenous injections since the area is independent of the route of administration if absorption of the dose is complete [2]. If absorption is incomplete but the fraction absorbed, F, is known, then the numerator may be corrected to yield FD_0. Methods for calculating AUC values for plasma level curves are given in the Appendix (for rapid intravenous injections) and Sec. II.E.2 (for any route of administration).

d. Steady-State Infusion. The theory and applications associated with constant-rate I.V. infusion will be discussed in Sed. II.F of this chapter and in Sec. IV.A of Chap. 4. Looking ahead at Fig. 15 will demonstrate how drug blood levels approach a constant value using this technique. These steady-state blood levels, P_{inf}, can be used to calculate Vd,area from

$$Vd = \frac{k_0}{(P_{inf}) (\beta)} \tag{13}$$

where k_0 is the zero-order rate of drug input. Since the blood level (and thus T'/P') remains constant, the calculation may be repeated at more than one time interval without loss in assay sensitivity. This value should not be confused with Vd_{inf} which is the volume of distribution operative during the steady state [10]. The amount of drug in the body during the steady state is calculated from $D_{inf} = (P_{inf}) (Vd_{inf})$ where $Vd_{inf} = Vp\{1 + [k_{12}/k_{21}]\}$ as shown in Appendix B. This relationship may be used to estimate Vd_{inf} for a two-compartment model drug wherein $Vp = (dose)/(A + B)$ following a rapid I.V. injection (Fig. 10, Chap. 2). The estimate obtained in Eq. (12) is equivalent to $Vd,area = Vp\{1 + [k_{12}/(k_{21} - \beta)]\}$ making this value larger than that for Vd_{inf} in the case of a two-compartment model. As mentioned earlier, one-compartment model estimates are independent of the route of administration.

The value for Vd_{inf} may be determined for any model wherein elimination occurs only from the central compartment by using

$$Vd_{inf} = \frac{(dose)}{(P_{inf})} \left\{ 1 - \frac{(AUC)_t}{(AUC)_\infty} \right\} \tag{14}$$

where t is the time at which the infusion is stopped, dose is the amount infused up to time t, P_{inf} is the steady-state plasma level, and AUC is the area under the curve from time zero to t or to ∞. [See also Eq. (64) and its discussion.]

2. Variation in Vd Estimates by the Various Methods

One-compartment model estimates are independent of the method used since $(T'/P') = (k_{12}/k_{21})$ regardless of the route of administration. The distribution of a two-compartment model drug can change from $(T'/P') = (k_{12}/k_{21})$ during the steady state to $(T'/P') = k_{12}/(k_{21} - \beta)$ during the β phase following rapid I.V. injections. This has caused considerable confusion in the literature concerned with Vd values for two-compartment model drugs. The values obtained by extrapolation, Eq. (11), can differ significantly from either Vd,area, Eq. (12) or (13), or Vd_{inf}, Eq. (14). It can be shown from the relationships in

Appendix B.2 that Vd,extrap > Vd,area > Vd_{inf} > Vp for a two-compartment model drug. More important, only the values calculated by Eq. (10) or Eqs. (12) and (13) will correctly predict the amount of drug in the body during the final, or β phase following intravenous injection of a two-compartment model drug. The extrapolation Vd [Eq. (11)] overestimates the amount of drug in the body except in the trivial case at zero time, and Vd_{inf} underestimates the amount of drug except during the steady state of an infusion when it alone gives the correct answer.

An understanding of the conditions which affect the Vd allows us to explain some clinical findings which might otherwise appear anomalous. A number of drugs, including cephalexin, colistimethate, lincomycin, methicillin, and insulin, show decreased apparent volumes of distribution (calculated using areas) in patients with renal failure as compared to normal patients [11,12]. Also, administration of probenecid, an inhibitor of renal tubular secretion of organic acids, reduces the apparent volume of distribution of penicillin derivatives [12,13].

These observations are not surprising if we recognize certain facts. First, remember that the observed changes may not reflect any change in the tissues through which the drugs are distributed, since Vd does not necessarily represent a real volume at all. Second, changes in elimination may reduce k_2 while apparently not significantly altering the values for k_{12} and k_{21}. The difference between a one- and two-compartment model (in this text) is in the rate of distribution relative to the rate of elimination. Therefore decreasing k_2 while leaving k_{12} and k_{21} the same will shift a two-compartment toward a one-compartment model. This is equivalent to changing distribution from $(T'/P') = [k_{12}/(k_{21} - \beta)]$ toward $(T'/P') = (k_{12}/k_{21})$, which is the equilibrium and steady-state ratio. Thus Vd,area will approach the smaller value of Vd_{inf}. If renal failure causes a reduction in k_2 alone, then the calculated value for the apparent volume of distribution would be expected to decrease as (T'/P') approaches (k_{12}/k_{21}).

Sample Problem 3

A physician wishes to inject sufficient drug to achieve a plasma level equal to 0.10 mg/ml in a patient weighing 70 kg. The apparent volume of distribution for the drug is given as 18% v/w. How many milligrams of drug must be injected into the blood in order to have a plasma level of 0.10 mg/ml after distribution, assuming that 10% of the dose is excreted unchanged by the kidney and no drug is lost via biotransformation during this time, t?

Solution: The apparent volume of distribution is

Vd = 0.18(70 kg) = 12.6 liters

To achieve the desired concentration in the plasma, the amount that must be present in the body after distribution is complete is given by

$$D_t = Vd\ P_t \qquad \text{[from Eq. (10)]}$$

$$D_t = (12.61)(0.10\ \text{g/liter}) = 1.26\ \text{g}$$

Since 10% of the dose has been lost by this time, the dose given must be

$$D_0 = \frac{D_t}{0.90}$$

$$D_0 = 1.40\ \text{g}$$

Practice Problem 3

The pharmacokinetic parameters of a new drug are being studied. Blood level and elimination data following a 1.4-g dose were collected, with the results shown in Table 3.

Table 3
Blood and Elimination Data
Following I.V. Injection

t (hr)	Blood conc (mg/liter)	Total amount eliminated (mg)
1.0	80.0	—
2.0	51.0	—
3.0	36.5	—
4.0	29.3	—
5.0	25.0	555
7.0	20.8	—
9.0	18.2	730
12.0	15.5	835
15.0	13.0	920
18.0	11.2	995

(a) What is the estimated value for Vd by extrapolation?
    Answer: Vd = (1400 mg)(29.5 mg/liter) = 47.5 liters

(b) Compare the value for Vd obtained by mass balance to that obtained by the area method. Note, as shown in Appendix C: AUC = $(A/\alpha) + (B/\beta)$.
    Answer: At $t > t_d$ mass balance provides the estimate Vd = 37 liters. Vd,area = (1400 mg)/[700 mg/liter)(0.0536)] = 37 liters.

(c) What is the calculated value for Vd_{inf}?
    Answer: Vp = $D_0/(A + B)$ = (1400 mg)/(140 mg/liter) = 10

liters; $(k_{12}/k_{21}) = (0.40/0.20) = 2$; $\dot{V}d_{inf} = Vp[1 + (k_{12}/k_{21})]$
= 30 liters

(d) Which value will correctly predict the amount of drug in the body from blood level data obtained during the β phase following rapid I.V. injection of the drug?
Answer: 37 liters

3. Other Factors Affecting Volume of Distribution

In Chap. 2 we discussed equilibrium between nonequivalent compartments, and how primarily un-ionized drug or unbound drug can pass through a biological membrane. This has important consequences in the calculation of Vd since many drugs, such as erythromycin, sulfonylureas, salicylates, and coumarin anticoagulants are bound to plasma protein. The apparent volume of distribution should be calculated on the basis of freely diffusing drug, so a correction must be made for the fraction bound. If this correction is not made, two types of error can occur. When the assay method determines only free drug, the bound drug will be counted with drug distributed to the tissues and the Vd calculated will be too large. On the other hand, if the assay is for total drug, the denominator in Eq. (10) or (11) will be too large, and the value of Vd too small. If corrections are not made for protein binding, Vd values calculated at different doses for a drug whose extent of binding varies with dose will also vary [14].

Sample Problem 4

Ten grams of sodium salicylate are given I.V.
(a) What is the Vd if B is found to be 40 mg%?
Solution:

$$Vd = \frac{D_0}{B} \quad \text{Eq. (11)}$$

$$Vd = \frac{10 \times 10^3 \text{ mg}}{4.0 \times 10^2 \text{ mg/liter}}$$

$$Vd = 25 \text{ liters}$$

(b) What is the Vd if 20 g is given I.V. and B is 55 mg%?
Solution:

$$Vd = \frac{20 \times 10^3 \text{ mg}}{5.5 \times 10^2 \text{ mg/liter}}$$

$$Vd = 36 \text{ liters}$$

(c) Offer an explanation for this difference.
Solution: Total salicylate—bound and unbound—is being measured. When 20 g are given, some binding sites may have become

saturated so that a smaller fraction of the total is bound. More drug is free to distribute to the tissues so that B is proportionately less. [If the extent of binding were the same as in part (a), B would equal 80 mg%.] Therefore, Vd appears larger.

(d) If only *free drug* were assayed, which Vd would be larger—that in part (a) or part (b)?
Solution: Since drug bound to protein would be counted with drug distributed to tissues, and since a larger fraction of drug in (a) is bound, Vd calculated in part (a) would be larger.

Practice Problem 4

One gram of aspirin is administered to each of two subjects. Extrapolation of the first-order plots representing the final slope of the blood level curves yields the following results [14]:

| | *Initial* | |
Subject	Serum Level (mg/liter)	Body Wt (kg)
A	74	83
B	123	83

(a) What is the calculated value for Vd based on this data?
Answer: Subject A, Vd = 13.5 liters
Subject B, Vd = 8.13 liters

(b) If the assays are for total salicylate in the blood, what explanation can be offered for the difference in the calculated values for Vd?
Answer: Since a large portion of salicylate in the blood is bound to serum albumin, a relatively high albumin concentration in subject B would account for the smaller Vd. Reference 14 discusses these data.

C. Clearance

1. The Meaning of Clearance

A clearance value is simply another way of expressing the rate constant for loss of drug. The rate of loss from the body (R_{ex}) at some time, t, assuming first-order elimination, is given by the equation

$$R_{ex\ t} = \beta D_t = \beta\, Vd\, P_t \tag{15}$$

Since β and Vd are both constants for a given subject and a given mode of administration, their product is a new constant with units of volume per unit time, which we will call clearance. Clearance, C, is therefore written

$$C = \frac{R_{ex\ t}}{P_t} = \frac{(\text{amount eliminated per unit time})_t}{P_t} \tag{16}$$

The relationship between C and β suggests an alternative way of calculating biological half-life. Since

$$C = \beta Vd = \frac{0.693\ Vd}{t_{1/2}} \tag{17}$$

then

$$t_{1/2} = \frac{0.693\ Vd}{C} \tag{18}$$

Consideration of the earlier discussion on rates of first-order processes suggests one difficulty in the determination of clearance values; the rate is constantly changing with time, so it is difficult to determine accurately. For example, a graph of amount of drug in the body vs time may resemble Fig. 3.

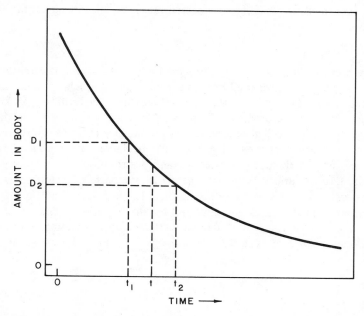

Fig. 3. Time course for the total amount of drug in the body following a rapid I.V. injection of a one-compartment model drug.

Calculation of the rate of loss at a particular time involves finding the slope of the curve at that time. This is a difficult task. The procedure usually followed involves taking two measurements quite close together and essentially linearizing the curve between them. This process is illustrated in Fig. 3, where the rate at time t would be approximated by

$$R_{ex\,t} = \frac{D_1 - D_2}{t_2 - t_1} \qquad (19)$$

Determination of clearance values also requires a value for the concentration of drug in the blood. The most representative plasma value is the one corresponding to time t, the point midway between t_1 and t_2, since that point provides roughly an average value for the time period. Clearly, the longer the time interval between t_1 and t_2, the less chance that the calculated rate will be representative of the actual rate at time t, and hence the more inaccurate the clearance value.

There is a way to circumvent this problem however, through the use of a zero-order intravenous infusion. When the rate of elimination becomes equal to the rate of infusion, the plasma concentration remains constant, as discussed in the section on infusion. At this time, therefore, the denominator in Eq. (16) will be unambiguous. Also, determination of the rate of elimination will no longer involve assessment of the slope of a curved line since this rate equals the rate of infusion, which is a constant.

2. Renal Clearance

We have seen where drugs placed into the body will undergo distribution and elimination. Elimination is used here as a general term to include metabolism or excretion from the body by the skin, alimentary tract, lungs, or kidney. Although some volatile drugs such as anesthetics may be removed primarily by the lungs, the kidney will generally serve as the primary route for excretion. The kidney is responsible for removal of organic nonvolatile constituents, inorganics which are not retained by the body, and waste products of nitrogenous metabolism (urea, uric acid, etc.). The basic approach to determining *renal clearance* will be explained here, noting that this parameter may (in theory at least) be determined by analogous methods for any route of elimination.

Renal clearance, C_R, may be defined as that volume of plasma, in milliliters, which is cleared of a substance by the kidneys in 1 min. This may be calculated from

$$C_R = \frac{UV}{P} \qquad (20)$$

where U is the concentration in the urine (mg/ml), V is the volume in milliliters of urine excreted during 1 min, and P is the concentration in the plasma (mg/ml). This is equivalent to defining C_R as (the amount excreted in 1 min)/ (amount contained in 1 ml of plasma). Thus the units resulting from the of Eq. (20) are milliliters per minute, which agree with the definition of C_R as the volume of blood cleared in 1 min.

The functional unit of the kidney is the nephron, which is composed of glomerulus and tubule. Urinary excretion of drugs may involve any or all of the following processes:

1. Glomerular filtration
2. Active tubular secretion
3. Passive tubular resorption

The relative importance of these processes in elimination of a drug may be indicated to some extent by the clearance value obtained. Before discussing the meaning of clearance values, it is instructive to consider some tests employed for kidney function. The substances creatinine, inulin, mannitol, and sodium thiosulfate are completely *filtered by the glomeruli* and excreted in the urine. The term filtration is perhaps an unfortunate one here. Actually, water and all the dissolved material from plasma pass through the glomeruli, leaving behind only proteins and colloidal material. The filtrate is thus the same concentration as the blood itself. However, most of the water is resorbed from the tubules. The normal clearance value for such substances is thus equal to the glomerular filtrate formed per minute or 125 to 130 ml.

Creatinine clearance values are often useful for individualizing a dosage regimen for a patient with renal impairment. Normal creatinine clearance values are in the range of 97 to 140 ml/min for men and 85 to 125 ml/min for women. Since the clearance value varies with body size, it is often normalized by multiplying the observed clearance value by the fraction (1.73/patient's surface area in m^2). The value 1.73 corresponds to an observed clearance value of 120 ml/min. In cases of severe impairment, clearance values are included as part of the patient's profile, while less serious cases more commonly include creatinine serum levels obtained as part of blood analyses. Garamycin dosing information, for example, includes a table which allows the adjustment dosage using either creatinine serum levels or clearance values.

Low-threshold substances such as urea, uric acid, certain phosphates and sulfates, are *filtered by the glomeruli* and *passively resorbed* in the tubules. Since the resorption is passive, there is an approach to equilibrium involved and thus some of the substance will be excreted. The amount will be less than the previous case. Normally the clearance value for urea is less than 75 (approximately 73). The urea is not injected for this test, since it is already present in the blood.

High-threshold substances such as glucose, ascorbic acid, Na, K, Ca, Mg, P, Cl, and S are normally completely resorbed by *active tubular resorption*. The glucose clearance test thus has a normal value of zero.

Diodrast (TM), hippuran, and *para*-aminohippurate (PAH) are substances which are completely removed from the plasma in a single passage through the kidneys when present in blood in low concentrations. These are *actively secreted by the tubules* in addition to glomerular filtration. Thus, as long as the capacity of the active system is not exceeded, the blood will be completely cleared. The clearance value (650 to 700 ml/min) is therefore equivalent to the plasma flow in the kidneys. When a dose of PAH sufficient to provide a 1 mg% plasma level is administered, the clearance value is equal to the plasma flow. However, a dose providing 50 mg% is capable of saturating the capacity-limited active tubular secretion. The C_R value obtained will therefore decrease. Although the clearance value is less at the dose which is above saturation, tubular secretion is nevertheless operating at maximum capacity. Thus the C_R value at the 50 mg% dose can be used as a measure of overall kidney function since it will reflect tubular secretion at maximum capacity plus glomerular filtration.

Thus we may use the renal clearance value for a given drug as a first approximation of how the kidney is excreting that particular drug. In general, a value of 130 ml/min would indicate *glomerular filtration,* a value greater than 130 ml/min would indicate both *filtration* and *secretion,* and a value less than 130 would then indicate *passive resorption.* It should be noted here that this is only a first approximation, since combinations can give clearance values which are misleading. However, if a value is large, such as the case of $C_R = 650$ ml/min, there is no doubt that active secretion is involved. Since this is an active transport system it will be subject to all of the properties discussed in Sec. II.D. We have already discussed the *saturation* of the system at high doses of PAH. This same principle can be responsible for a change in the apparent kinetic order of elimination and thus the apparent half-life. At low doses, filtration and secretion will be first-order and $t_{1/2} = 0.693/\beta$. However, if secretion becomes saturated due to a large dose, then elimination will be the sum of apparent zero-order secretion and first-order filtration. Thus the effect of dose on the $t_{1/2}$ will depend upon the relative contribution of secretion to the overall elimination process.

If secretion is saturated, it cannot increase any further in rate with increased dose. Filtration rate, however, can increase, since it is a function of plasma concentration. Thus at sufficiently high plasma concentrations, the elimination rate may again become apparent first-order if the primary component of the elimination process becomes filtration. Similarly, a dose which was just sufficient to saturate the secretion process would result in mixed kinetics only until the plasma level had decreased to the point where the elimination system was no longer saturated. At that time it would return to a first-order process.

This active secretion will also be subject to *competition*. That is, two drugs which are sufficiently similar to be secreted by the same active process will enter into competition for the available enzymes. It is important to realize that any drug with a large clearance value, indicating active secretion, is potentially capable of competing with other actively secreted drugs. The coadministration of two actively secreted drugs can, in effect, increase the $t_{1/2}$ for both drugs, since the total available sites for transfer are decreased in number. This factor can change the pharmacokinetic picture for a drug whose $t_{1/2}$ was established by independent studies. This could result in accumulation of drug and untoward effects from an otherwise normal dosage regimen.

Competition for tubular secretion has actually been put to theraputic usage. The compound probenecid is actively secreted and is thus capable of competitively inhibiting the tubular secretion of other acidic compounds which are excreted by this route. It has therefore been employed as an adjuvant in penicillin therapy, where it inhibits penicillin tubular secretion and thus increases the biological half-life of the antibiotic. It also inhibits excretion (renal or hepatic) of such agents as p-aminosalicylic acid (PAS), p-aminohippuric acid (PAH), phenosulfonphthalein (PSP), pantothenic acid, 17-ketosteroids, sodium iodomethamate, and sulfobromophthalein (BSP). The PSP excretion test may be used to determine the adequacy of probenecid blood levels for penicillin therapy. The PSP renal clearance is reduced to about one-fifth the normal value when probenecid levels are sufficient to inhibit penicillin secretion. Probenecid also inhibits tubular resorption of urate. Thus serum uric acid levels are decreased, and probenecid is useful in gout and gouty arthritis.

Substances which undergo passive resorption in the tubules will be subject to the principles previously discussed under passive transport. Tubular resorption will be predominantly by passive diffusion of the uncharged species. Accordingly, resorption will be a function of the pH of the urine and the pK_a of the drug. For example, the $t_{1/2}$ of salicylic acid may be increased by acidifying the uring with NH_4Cl and thus enhancing passive resorption of undissociated salicylic acid. Conversely, alkalinization of the urine with sodium bicarbonate will decrease the $t_{1/2}$ of salicylic acid by increasing the salicylate concentration and thus decreasing the passive resorption. This latter approach has been employed to treat cases of salicylate poisoning. Similar results have been demonstrated upon adjustment of the pH of the urine during sulfonamide excretion, where the $t_{1/2}$ was shortened from 11 to 4 hr upon alkalinization of the urine [15].

The use of infusion to study renal clearance has other advantages in addition to those discussed in the previous section. A minor clearance route may be detected by comparing urinary drug output with infusion input during steady state, whereas a minor elimination route might be overlooked in a single dose type of study. Examining clearance at several steady-state blood levels allows the recognition of capacity-limited processes.

3. Nonrenal Clearance

As has already been mentioned, compounds may be eliminated in a number of ways other than by the kidneys. However, although theoretically possible, calculation of clearance values for nonrenal elimination routes are seldom performed. Reasons for this are easy to understand. While collection of drug eliminated by the kidney is a simple matter, allowing relatively easy determination of the rate of renal elimination, drug eliminated by other routes is more difficult to measure. Reuning and Schanker [16] have successfully determined clearance values for biliary excretion of ouabain in rats. For most classes of drugs, the most important alternate route is metabolism. It is not our purpose to go into the mechanism and chemistry of metabolism, since the subject is complex and there have been several good reviews published on the subject [17–21]. This complexity makes clearance studies difficult. For example, if we wished to study the clearance value for elimination of a drug by formation of a certain metabolite, we would be hampered by the difficulty of collecting the metabolite as it is formed. Even if the compound were formed entirely in the liver, there is no simple, painless way to collect it. Besides this, the required enzymes are probably present in other tissues as well, making loss of drug by this route virtually impossible to follow.

Of course, if drug is lost by only one route, whether it be renal or not, the clearance value for this route is the same as the value for total clearance from the body and may be calculated as indicated for Fig. 3.

If more than one elimination pathway is present, it seems most reasonable to abandon the concept of clearance and compare the efficiencies of the various paths by comparing their rate constants, as will be discussed in the following section. Renal clearance has been in use for many years, and from that standpoint at least it is useful to be familiar with the concept, but the application of clearance to other routes does not seem to offer any advantages.

Sample Problem 5

Assume the normal glomerular filtrate is 130 ml/min. Of this about 106 ml are reabsorbed in the proximal tubule. Another 9 ml are absorbed in the thin segment. The distal tubule further reabsorbs "actively" about 14 ml of this. Assume that PAH is injected I.V. at a rate that gives a plasma level of 1 mg/100 ml. At the end of 3 min, 19.5 mg of PAH is excreted in the urine.

(a) Calculate the renal clearance for PAH.
    Solution:

$$C_R = \frac{\text{rate of appearance in urine}}{\text{plasma conc}}$$

$$C_R = \frac{(19.5 \text{ mg}/3 \text{ min})}{(0.01 \text{ mg/ml})}$$

$$C_R = 650 \text{ ml/min}$$

(b) What is the renal plasma flow and why?
Solution: PAH is actively secreted. At low doses, such as this one, the capacity of the system is not exceeded, so the blood is completely cleared. Therefore, plasma flow equals the clearance value, or 650 ml/min.

(c) Would you expect this value to change at a PAH plasma level of 50 mg/100 ml? How would it change and why?
Solution: At this concentration the capacity-limited system would be expected to be saturated. In this case C_R will decrease, since the rate of excretion will be lower relative to the plasma concentration than it was in part (b).

Practice Problem 5

(a) A table of data is presented below for six hypothetical drugs. Assuming that no biotransformation is involved, rank the drugs in the order of decreasing $t_{1/2}$.

Drug	Vd (liters)	C_R (ml/min)
A	50	130
B	50	40
C	50	700
D	15	700
E	50	1
F	70,000	1

Answer: $F > E > B > A > C > D$

(b) Compare each of the drugs with A. In each case choose one or more of the following reasons as probable explanations for the difference in elimination rates.

List of Reasons

A   Renal tubular resorption
B   Renal tubular secretion
C   Low Vd
D   Extensive tissue binding
E   Poor absorption
F   Decreased glomerular filtration

Answer:

Drug	Reason
B	A, F
C	B
D	C, B
E	A, possibly F
F	A, D, possibly F

D. Rate Constants for Elimination

1. Parallel Drug Loss

In Chap. 2 we examined the transfer of drug from one compartment to another. The final concentration gradient was shown to be dependent upon the solvent system in each compartment and the dissociation or the binding properties of the drug. We shall now consider the case where the drug is *completely transferred* from compartment A into two compartments, B and C, as illustrated in Fig. 4. For the case in point the transfer process to each compartment will be defined as a first-order process, and the first-order rate constants will be designated as k_B and k_C for transfer to compartments B and C, respectively. This model is especially important in the pharmacokinetics of a drug eliminated from the body by more than one route, so it is necessary to develop a sound understanding of the meaning of the observed rate constant for this case. However, the kinetics associated with this model are usually surprising on first examination. The problems at the end of the section are therefore particularly useful in demonstrating the validity of the equations to be derived here.

The simultaneous transfer of drug from compartment A to B and C may be illustrated as

$$C \xleftarrow{\quad k_C \quad} A \xrightarrow{\quad k_B \quad} B \tag{21}$$

Fig. 4. Parallel first-order transfer processes. Drug placed in compartment A is simultaneously and in time completely transferred to compartments B and C.

As will be demonstrated in the following derivation, the apparent first-order rate constant obtained from consideration of any compartment—A, B, or C— is the same, and is equal to the sum of k_B and k_C.

The rate of loss from A may be written

$$\frac{dX}{dt} = -(k_B + k_C)X \tag{22}$$

where X equals $(A_t - A_\infty)$. Since by definition in our present example, A_∞ equals zero, Eq. (22) becomes

$$\frac{-dA}{dt} = (k_B + k_C)A_t \tag{23}$$

Separating variables and integrating between the limits of A_0 and A_t and zero and t yields

$$\ln A_t = \ln A_0 - (k_B + k_C)t \tag{24}$$

or, in nonlogarithmic form,

$$A_t = A_0 e^{-(k_B + k_C)t} \tag{25}$$

The rate of appearance in B is given by

$$\frac{dB}{dt} = k_B A_t \tag{26}$$

or, applying Eq. (25),

$$\frac{dB}{dt} = k_B A_0 e^{-(k_B + k_C)t} \tag{27}$$

This integrates to

$$B_t = \left(\frac{k_B A_0}{k_B + k_C} \right) [1 - e^{-(k_B + k_C)t}] \tag{28}$$

between the limits of $B_0 = 0$ and B_t and zero and t. At t_∞, B_t becomes

$$B_\infty = \frac{k_B A_0}{k_B + k_C} \tag{29}$$

Substituting Eq. (29) into Eq. (28),

$$(B_\infty - B_t) = B_\infty e^{-(k_B + k_C)t} \tag{30}$$

which may be written

$$\ln (B_\infty - B_t) = \ln B_\infty - (k_B + k_C)t \tag{31}$$

A similar derivation for the rate of increase of drug in C gives

$$\ln (C_\infty - C_t) = \ln C_\infty - (k_B + k_C)t \tag{32}$$

A comparison of the form of Eqs. (24), (31), and (32) indicates that a first-order plot of data for compartment A, B, or C will have a slope of $-(k_B + k_C)$. Thus, the apparent first-order rate constant, k_a, is the sum of the parallel first-order rate constants, or

$$k_a = k_B + k_C \tag{33}$$

The individual rate constants may be determined from a knowledge of the yields and the overall rate constant, k_a. For example, Eq. (29) may be rearranged to calculate k_B according to

$$k_B = \frac{k_a B_\infty}{A_0} \tag{34}$$

and a similar equation can be written for k_C using C_∞. The ratio of B_t to C_t can be expressed using Eq. (28) and a similar equation for C_t. The resulting expression,

$$\frac{B_t}{C_t} = \frac{k_B}{k_C} \tag{35}$$

shows that the ratio of the concentration in B to that of C at any time will be the same as the ratio of the rate constants.

Although the present example involves transfer to only two compartments, the principles remain the same for simultaneous transfer to any number of parallel compartments. It should also be noted here that we have considered only the case where *transfer is complete*. If the transfer to either one or both of the compartments is not complete, the simplified approach derived above will not satisfactorily describe the resulting kinetics. Derivations for these more complex cases [22] as well as more detailed derivations for the simple case presented are given in various kinetics texts.

Sample Problem 6

A drug of the type HA is dissolved in compartment A as shown in Fig. 4. The concentration of drug in compartments A and B is measured as a function of time. The results are given in Table 4.

Table 4

Concentration of Drug in Compartments A and B as a
Function of Time During the Transfer Process C ← A → B

t (hr)	Conc (mg%)		t (hr)	Conc (mg%)	
	A	B		A	B
0.0	10.0	0.0	8.0	0.7	6.2
0.5	8.4	1.0	10	0.3	6.4
1.0	7.1	1.9	12	0.2	6.5
1.5	6.0	2.6	14	0.1	6.6
2.0	5.0	3.3	16	0.0	6.7
3.0	3.6	4.2	18	0.0	6.7
4.0	2.5	4.9	20	0.0	6.7
6.0	1.3	5.8	22	0.0	6.7

(a) Make a first-order plot of A data and calculate the overall rate constant, k_a. Do the same for B and C data.
Solution: For the A compartment, a semilog plot of A_t vs t has a slope equal to $-k_a$, so that

$$k_a = \frac{(\ln 10 - \ln 1.82)}{5 \text{ hr}}$$

$$k_a = 0.34 \text{ hr}^{-1}$$

Similar plots of $(B_\infty - B_t)$ and $(C_\infty - C_t)$ vs t yield the same rate constant.

(b) What is the calculated value of $t_{1/2}$ for each compartment?
Solution: For A, B, and C,

$$t_{1/2} = \frac{0.693}{0.34 \text{ hr}^{-1}}$$

$$t_{1/2} = 2.0 \text{ hr}$$

(c) What are the individual rate constants, k_B and k_C?
Solution: Using Eq. (34),

$$k_B = \frac{(0.34 \text{ hr}^{-1})(6.7 \text{ mg\%})}{10 \text{mg\%}}$$

$$k_B = 0.23 \text{ hr}^{-1}$$

Since $k_a = k_B + k_C$,

$$k_C = 0.34 \text{ hr}^{-1} - 0.23 \text{ hr}^1$$

$$k_C = 0.11 \text{ hr}^{-1}$$

Note that

$$\frac{k_B}{k_C} = \frac{2}{1} = \frac{B_t}{C_t}$$

Practice Problem 6

A drug was administered to a 70-kg patient by an intravenous injection of 150 mg. All of the patient's urine was collected by catheterization over a period of 36 hr. The urine samples were assayed for drug content. The resulting data are found in Table 5. The drug is eliminated by metabolism and excretion. Only the unmetabolized drug was assayed in the urine.

Table 5

Intact Drug Appearing in the Urine as a
Function of Time Following I.V. Injection of 150 mg

t (hr)	Cumulative amount of drug in urine (mg)	t (hr)	Cumulative amount of drug in urine (mg)
0	0	12	91
1	18	14	94
2	33	16	96
3	45	18	97
4	55	20	98
5	64	24	100
6	70	30	100
8	80	36	100
10	87		

(a) Plot the data for amount in urine as function of time on coordinate graph paper. Make the appropriate first-order plot and calculate the apparent first-order rate constant.

Answer: $k_a = 0.20 \, hr^{-1}$

(b) What are the values of the apparent first-order rate constants for excretion and for metabolism?

Answer: $k_e = 13 \, hr^{-1}$, $k_m = 0.07 \, hr^{-1}$

(c) There are three compartments involved in this transfer process: the body, urine, and metabolism. In part (a) you constructed a coordinate plot of amount in the urine vs time. Complete that plot by graphing the amount remaining in the body and the cumulative amount metabolized vs time.

(d) Determine the $t_{1/2}$ from each of the three plots which you constructed in the above problem. What is the value of the apparent first-order rate constant calculated from the $t_{1/2}$?

Answer: $t_{1/2}$ in each case is 3.5 hr, $k_a = 0.20 \, hr^{-1}$

Note: The symbols k_a, k_e, and k_m were used to relate this problem to the illustration given in Sample Problem 6. These will be replaced with the symbols β, β_e, and β_m to describe the kinetics of loss from the body.

2. Metabolism and Excretion: One-Compartment Model

The rate constant β represents the overall first-order elimination constant for loss of drug from the body by all routes. For example, if drug is eliminated by urinary excretion and metabolism the one-compartment case may be written

$$U \xleftarrow{\quad \beta_e \quad} \boxed{\begin{array}{c} B \\ and \\ T \end{array}} \xrightarrow{\quad \beta_m \quad} M \qquad (36)$$

where β_m and β_e are first-order rate constants for metabolsim and excretion, respectively. This corresponds to the general Eq. (21) for parallel irreversible first-order processes. Therefore, β is defined by

$$\beta = \beta_m + \beta_e \qquad (37)$$

As in the case of the beaker (Fig. 4) just discussed, the fraction of dose recovered as metabolite or intact drug can be used to calculate the individual rate constants if elimination is first order. When D_t becomes zero,

$$\beta_e = \frac{\beta U_\infty}{D_0} \qquad (38)$$

and

$$\beta_m = \frac{\beta M_\infty}{D_0} \tag{39}$$

where U_∞ is the total amount excreted intact and M_∞ is the total amount metabolized. Alternatively, the constants can be calculated by substituting into Eq. (37) from

$$\frac{U_t}{M_t} = \frac{\beta_e}{\beta_m} \tag{40}$$

In general, k_2 is not known for a one-compartment model drug, so its component parts, k_e and k_m are not calculable. However, if the proper information were available, these constants could be determined, as will be demonstrated later in Sample Problem 7.

Elimination by simultaneous first-order processes has the following characteristics:

1. The ratio of drug to metabolite is independent of time.
2. The ratio of drug to metabolite is independent of dose.
3. The percent of drug eliminated at a given time is independent of the dose.
4. The percent of drug either metabolized or excreted at a given time is independent of the dose.
5. The total fraction metabolized (or excreted) is independent of the dose.

3. Metabolism and Excretion: Two-Compartment Model

Values for β_m and β_e may be calculated in the manner described for a one-compartment model. However, because of the existence of an observable α phase, we are also able to calculate the specific rate constant for loss from the blood, k_2, as described in Sec. II.A.2 of Chap. 2. When both metabolism and excretion take place, the two-compartment model becomes

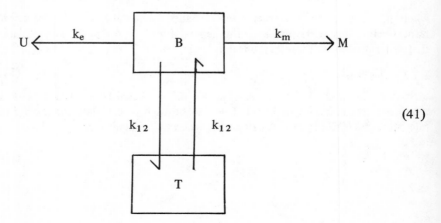

$$(41)$$

where k_e and k_m are the specific rate constants for drug loss from the blood by way of excretion and metabolism. By analogy to Eq. (33),

$$k_2 = k_e + k_m \tag{42}$$

Values for k_e and k_m may be calculated in the same way as β_e and β_m using the following equations, which correspond to Eqs. (38) through (40):

$$k_e = \frac{k_2 U_\infty}{D_0} \tag{43}$$

$$k_m = \frac{k_2 M_\infty}{D_0} \tag{44}$$

$$\frac{U_t}{M_t} = \frac{k_e}{k_m} \tag{45}$$

4. Dose-Dependent Changes in Elimination Kinetics

a. Capacity-Limited Systems. The previous discussion was limited to first-order elimination. It is also possible to encounter a capacity-limited elimination route and to saturate this system by a large dose. A more detailed coverage of the kinetics of capacity-limited systems may be found in a discussion by Levy [23].

We have already discussed one case of this type in our consideration of active secretion by the kidney. If this process (or a capacity-limited metabolic transformation) is the only method for removal of a drug, the compartmental scheme at saturation might be written

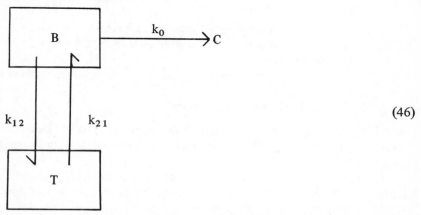

$$\tag{46}$$

where k_0 is the apparent zero-order rate constant for loss of drug from the body.

Under these conditions the biological half-life would increase with dose. Indeed, one method to test for saturation of a capacity-limited elimination process is to examine the effect of dose size on the apparent half-life.

Another possibility is that of elimination by two simultaneous routes where one is capacity-limited. An example is elimination of a drug by urinary excretion and metabolism where the capacity of the enzyme system involved in the metabolic process has been exceeded. This may be represented as

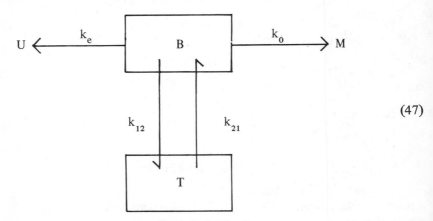

$$(47)$$

where k_0 is the zero-order rate constant for metabolism and k_e is the first-order rate constant for excretion. Figure 13a in Chap. 2 illustrated how a zero-order rate process will predominate over a first-order rate process of equal initial rate as the substrate concentration decreases. Thus simultaneous zero-order and first-order elimination processes will behave quite differently from the parallel first-order processes described earlier. Elimination described by Eq. (47) would have the following properties:

1. The ratio of metabolite to intact drug would increase with time.
2. The ratio of metabolite to intact drug at a given time would decrease with increasing dose.
3. The percent metabolized after complete elimination would decrease with increasing dose.
4. The half-life would not be dose-independent.

Levy [24] has described a related situation in which a single metabolite is formed by simultaneous zero- and first-order processes and urinary excretion is first-order.

An example of a system similar to that shown in Eq. (47) is salicylic acid elimination. Salicylic acid is eliminated both intact and as the metabolites, salicyluric acid and salicyl glucuronide. The major route of loss is through salicyluric acid formation, which is a capacity-limited process. The following characteristics have been demonstrated for this elimination [25,26]:

1. *Saturation.* We have previously discussed why a saturated rate process will behave by apparent zero-order kinetics. It appears that the formation of salicyluric acid is capacity-limited at doses of 1 g and above. The apparent half-life for decrease in salicylic acid blood concentration following I.V. sodium salicylate administration increases with dose. The values of $t_{1/2}$ are 2.4 hr at 0.25-g doses, 6.1 hr at 1.3-g doses, and 19 hr at 10- to 20-g doses. However, since elimination has both zero- and first-order components, the $t_{1/2}$ is not described by the simple zero-order expression, $t_{1/2} = 0.5X_0/k_0$.

It was demonstrated in Chap. 2 (Sample Problem 6) that a first-order plot of zero-order data will show a negative deviation from linearity. A semilogarithmic plot of plasma salicylate concentration following a 3-g dose of sodium salicylate curves downward for almost 30 hr.

2. *Competition.* Co-administration of *para*-aminobenzoate effectively blocks the formation of salicyluric acid. The elimination of sodium salicylate then occurs by the first-order processes of salicylic acid secretion and salicyl glucuronide formation. Thus a semilogarithmic plot of plasma concentrations following a 3-g dose of sodium salicylate together with *para*-aminobenzoate is linear.

3. *Change in fraction metabolized.* Under conditions where salicyluric acid formation is not saturated, one would expect to find elimination described by a simple first-order process, and the percent metabolized to salcyluric acid at t_∞ would be defined as

$$\% \text{ met } = \frac{100\beta_{\text{met}}}{\beta} \tag{48}$$

Thus as long as the process remains first-order, the ratio of metabolite to dose will be constant. However, if the metabolism becomes capacity-limited and thus zero-order, the fraction β_{met}/β would be expected to decrease with increasing dose. Indeed, the fraction of salicylurate decreases with increasing dose when the dose exceeds about 0.5 g in adults.

b. Other Dose-Dependent Kinetics. A number of drugs are eliminated from the body by an apparent first-order process, yet show an apparent decrease in the first-order rate constant for elimination with increasing dose. Among these compounds are phenylbutazone, discoumacetate, probenecid, phenytoin, and bishydroxycoumarin [27-29]. Although the reasons for this behavior have not been determined, several mechanisms have been put forward, including substrate inhibition of metabolizing enzymes [27,28,30], and inhibition of biotransformation by metabolic products [29].

Sample Problem 7

Assume the therapeutic blood level of sulfaethylthiadiazole (SETD) is 12 mg% as total sulfa. The drug is eliminated by both urinary excretion and metabolism. The first-order biological half-life ($t_{1/2}$) is 6 hr. A single 2.0-g dose is required to reach the therapeutic blood level in a 70-kg man. The amount excreted in the urine is 180 mg when the blood has reached 12 mg%. The drug is 100% absorbed, and 90% remains in the body when the desired level is achieved.

(a) What is the first-order rate constant for total elimination (β)?
Solution:

$$\beta = \frac{0.693}{t_{1/2}} = \frac{0.693}{6 \text{ hr}}$$

$$\beta = 0.116 \text{ hr}^{-1}$$

(b) What is the rate constant for excretion (β_e) and for metabolism (β_m)?
Solution: When the blood concentration reaches 12 mg%, 90% of the drug remains in the body, therefore 10%, or 200 mg, has been eliminated. At this time 180 mg is found in the urine, so 20 mg must have been metabolized. According to Eq. (40),

$$\frac{\beta_e}{\beta_m} = \frac{U_t}{M_t} = \frac{180}{20} = \frac{9}{1}$$

therefore

$$\beta_e = 9\beta_m$$

since

$$\beta = \beta_e + \beta_m = 10\beta_m$$

$$\beta_m = \frac{\beta}{10} = 0.012 \text{ hr}^{-1}$$

and

$$\beta_e = 0.104 \text{ hr}^{-1}$$

(c) What is Vd if the β phase is in effect when the desired plasma level is achieved?
Solution:

$$Vd = \frac{D_t}{P_t}$$

$$Vd = \frac{(2,000 \text{ mg} - 200 \text{ mg})}{120 \text{ mg/liter}} = 15 \text{ liters}$$

(d) What is the amount of drug (P', T', U, and M) in each compartment when the blood level is 12 mg%, assuming a volume of 3.5 liters for the central compartment?

Solution: The amount in the central compartment is given by

$$P' = V_p P$$

$$P' = (3.5 \text{ liters}) \, 120 \text{ mg/liter} = 420 \text{ mg}$$

therefore, the tissues contain

$$T' = D_t - P'$$

$$T = 1,800 \text{ mg} - 420 \text{ mg} = 1,380 \text{ mg}$$

U and M are given in part (b).

(e) Assuming that the drug is distributed according to a one-compartment model, what are the values for k_2, k_e, k_m, and the relative values for k_{12} and k_{21}?

Solution: In a one-compartment model k_2 may be calculated from Eq. (36) in Chap 2,

$$k_2 = \beta \left(1 + \frac{k_{12}}{k_{21}} \right)$$

since

$$\frac{k_{12}}{k_{21}} = \frac{T'}{P'} = K$$

$$\frac{k_{12}}{k_{21}} = \frac{1,380}{420} = 3.3$$

then

$$k_2 = (0.116 \text{ hr}^{-1})4.3 = 0.50 \text{ hr}^{-1}$$

The constants k_e and k_m are determined from Eqs. (42) and (45) with the results

$$k_e = 0.45 \text{ hr}^{-1}$$

$$k_m = 0.050 \text{ hr}^{-1}$$

Practice Problem 7

A drug fitting a one-compartment open model was found to be eliminated from the plasma by the following pathways with the corresponding rate constants for loss from the plasma:

Metabolism, $\beta_m = 0.175 \text{ hr}^{-1}$
Excretion by the kidney, $\beta_e = 0.150 \text{ hr}^{-1}$
Excretion through the bile, $\beta'_e = 0.50 \text{ hr}^{-1}$
Excretion by the salivary glands, $\beta''_e = 0.01 \text{ hr}^{-1}$

Answer the following questions from the data provided:
(a) What is the half-life of the drug?
  Answer: $t_{1/2} = 0.83 \text{ hr}$

(b) What would be the half-life of the drug if the metabolism of the drug were completely blocked?
  Answer: $t_{1/2} = 1.05 \text{ hr}$

(c) If the patient suffered from liver disease such that biliary flow were completely blocked, what would be the half-life of the drug?
  Answer: $t_{1/2} = 2.07 \text{ hr}$

(d) If one were to assay for the drug (not metabolites) in the urine, the feces, and the saliva, what would be the ratio of drug to be found in these biological samples? Express your answer as the ratio feces:urine:saliva.
  Answer: 50:15:1

(e) If the amount of drug-metabolizing enzyme were increased such that the rate of drug metabolism were doubled, what would be the plasma half-life of the drug?
  Answer: $t_{1/2} = 0.69 \text{ hr}$

E. Supply Constants

1. General Model

Up to now we have considered the analysis of blood level curves obtained following rapid intravenous administration of a drug. Essentially, this simplifies our modeling by eliminating the added complexity of an absorption phase. In practice, however, dosage forms which exhibit an absorption phase are very important, and it is useful to be able to interpret the time course for drug in the blood under these conditions.

When a drug is put into a depot, such as the stomach, intestines, or muscle, it is usually absorbed by a first-order process. Of course, because of design of the dosage form, the possibility of active absorption, or the nature of the chemical itself, absorption may not appear first-order. In most cases, though, the first-order assumption fits the data well. This discussion is limited to first-order absorption. A general scheme fitting such a model is shown here:

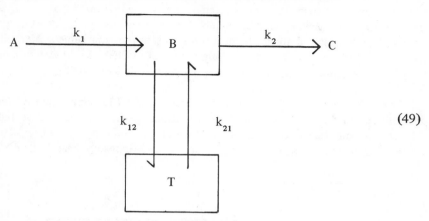

$$(49)$$

The apparent first-order rate constant for absorption from depot A may be a complex constant. In the case of a solid dosage form it can be affected not only by the ease with which the compound itself is absorbed from the depot, but also by such factors as the rate of tablet disintegration and rate of dissolution of the solid. If a prodrug, such as an ester, is administered, k_1 for the appearance of active drug in the blood may also reflect hydrolysis of the ester. Details of factors influencing k_1 will be discussed in later chapters. Blood level curves following extravasal administration are, of course, quite different from those obtained from intravenous administration, and we will now briefly discuss their qualitative interpretation.

2. Blood Level Curves

An alteration in any one of the rate processes shown in Eq. (49) will be reflected in the blood level curve. Thus, the plasma concentration-time profile for a drug that is described by this compartmental scheme can vary in shape because of variations in:

1. Release rate from the depot
2. Rate of metabolism
3. Rate of urinary excretion
4. Amount released from the depot
5. The distribution of drug between blood and tissues
6. Binding to various sites

Each of these variables will show a unique effect on the blood level pattern. If any or all of these variables change simultaneously, as is the case when different drugs are administered, no simple deductions regarding the relative magnitudes of the variables may be drawn by comparing the curves. That is, it is impossible simply to compare such parameters as amount absorbed or the ratio of drug in tissue to drug in plasma by comparing blood level curves for two different drugs, even when administered under identical conditions to the same subject. Methods for the comparison of different drugs are discussed in Chap. 6 in the section on penicillins. Different dosage forms of the *same drug,* however, will be compared here.

For a given drug, certain of the rate constants in Eq. (49) may be considered constant regardless of the mode of administration. These, as might be expected, are the constants that depend largely on the molecular identity of the drug. The distribution constants, k_{12} and k_{21}, are in this category. An individual,

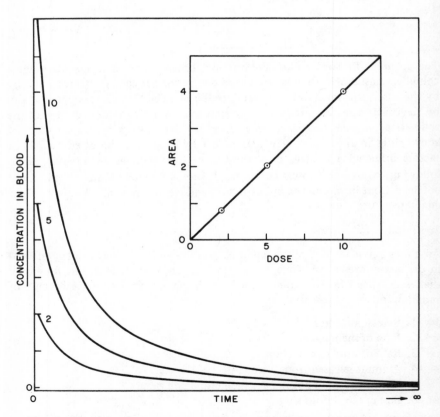

Fig. 5   Blood level curves representing rapid I.V. doses of 10, 5, and 2 for a two-compartment model drug. The insert illustrates that the area under such a curve is proportional to the administered dose.

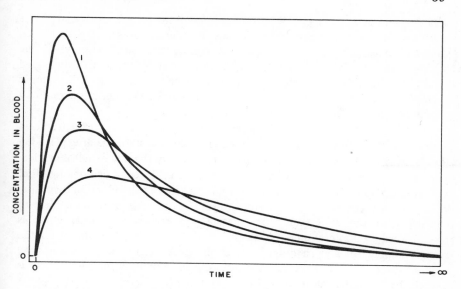

Fig. 6 The effect of the first-order rate constant for supply of drug to the blood. The values decrease from top to bottom: $k_1 = 6$ (curve 1), 3 (curve 2), 2 (curve 3), and 1 (curve 4). Other constants have been held constant: $k_{12} = k_{21} = 2$; $k_2 = 3$.

assuming his physiological condition remains stable, would not be expected to show vastly different values for k_{12} and k_{21} each time a drug is given. The elimination constant, k_2, will also remain stable if conditions such as urine pH, biological variation, and the possibility of enzyme induction are controlled. Thus the area under a blood level curve following a rapid intravenous injection is proportional to the dose (Fig. 5). Since drug is injected directly into the bloodstream, only the dose size alters the curves. On the other hand, in Eq. (49) both of the absorption parameters, k_1 and available dose, are easily changed by alterations in formulation or route of administration. Therefore, we will now briefly examine how changes in k_1 and the size of the dose absorbed alter blood concentration curves in order to indicate the kind of judgments possible when comparing different routes of administration, or different forms of the drug administered by the same route.

Figure 6 shows four examples of blood level patterns where only the first-order rate constant for release from the depot has been changed. This could occur if, for example, a change was made from one crystalline form of a drug to another with a different dissolution rate, or if absorption from an elixir was compared to that from a tablet. The rate constants for distribution have been held constant at $k_{12} = k_{21} = 2$ and the rate constant for elimination at 3. The units are reciprocal time. The rate constant for release from the depot has been given the values 6 in curve 1, 3 in curve 2, 2 in curve 3, and 1 in curve 4. The following characteristics are evident. As the rate constant for supply is increased for a given drug, the peak value is increased and the time to achieve this value is decreased. In addition to this, the blood is cleared of drug sooner in the case of a high peak than it is for a lower peak.

In spite of the dramatic differences in the shapes of these curves, the area under each curve from t_0 to t_∞ is identical. In each case all of the drug placed in the depot was released into the bloodstream and only the rate of release varied. The identical areas under the curves can be used as evidence to demonstrate that the same amount of drug was released from the depot to the blood in each case. When the rate constant for supply of drug is the only rate constant subject to change, then the area under the plasma concentration vs time curve is proportional to the total amount released from the depot. Thus, increasing the rate of supply of a given drug increases the peak height, decreases the time required to reach the peak, and decreases the total time during which there is drug in the blood. It does not effect the area under the curve.

An intravenous injection is really a limiting case of this model. "Absorption" is instantaneous, so the peak occurs at zero time. Since we know that the entire dose reaches the bloodstream, we can compare the area under a rapid intravenous curve (Fig. 5) with the areas under curves obtained after the same dose by other routes to determine the amounts absorbed by these routes.

The areas may be obtained in several ways. One is by use of a planimeter. Another involves plotting data for the different routes on the same scale, then cutting out the curves and weighing them. The areas may be calculated from the weights if the weight of one unit area of the paper is known. In a third method, the area under a curve is estimated by dividing the curve into sections that approximate a series of trapezoids with a triangle at each end as shown in Fig. 7. The individual areas of the trapezoids, $a(c + d)/2$, and the triangles, $ab/2$, are summed to obtain the area under the curve. It is necessary to have the same units of concentration and time in order to compare different curves. However, it is not necessary to have the same scale. In fact, one of the advantages of the trapezoidal method is that the curves can be drawn to occupy the maximum amount of space on the graph paper, therefore improving the estimates of the lengths of the sides involved in the calculations. In the method involving cutting and weighing, a small blood level profile would be less accurate than the larger one that might be used for comparison.

The other parameter easily changed is the size of the available dose. This may change because the amount actually placed in the depot changes, or because of some physical or chemical interaction at the site of administration such as the failure of the drug to dissolve completely. Thus Fig. 8 is a typical pattern for five

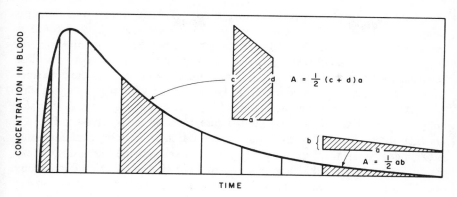

Fig. 7 The total area under a curve may be estimated by summing the areas of the trapezoids and triangles which approximately comprise it.

different doses of the same drug placed in a depot which releases drug by a first-order process. In this example the rate constants have been kept constant as follows: $k_1 = 1$, $k_{12} = k_{21} = k_2 = 2$. The dose, or the amount released from the depot, has been set at 10 in curve 1, 8 in curve 2, 6 in curve 3, 4 in curve 4, and 2 in curve 5. Since we are considering a single drug with fixed rate constants, the

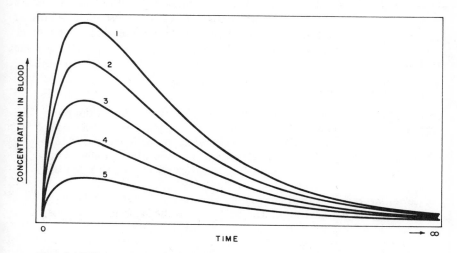

Fig. 8 Effect of the size of the available dose administered by an extravascular route. From top to bottom the relative dose is: 5 (curve 1), 4 (curve 2), 3 (curve 3), 2 (curve 4), and 1 (curve 5). Rate constants have been held constant at $k_1 = 1$ and $k_{12} = k_{21} = k_2 = 2$.

area under a curve is proportional to the dose. That is, the ratio of the areas under the curves, curve 1/curve 2/curve 3/curve 4/curve 5, is 10:8:6:4:2 in direct proportion to the dose released. In this example, where k_1 is the same for each curve, the peak heights are also found to be proportional to the dose released. As would be expected, the initial rate is proportional to the dose since k_1 is constant, but the product $k_1(A_0)$ is decreasing with decreasing available dose, A_0. Unlike Fig. 6, the peak times for the curves in Fig. 8 are all the same and, therefore, independent of the initial dose. Since all the processes in Eq. (49) are first-order, the time for the blood concentration to reach its maximum value is dependent upon the first-order rate constants and not the initial dose. It can also be observed that the time required to clear the blood of drug is directly related to the peak height. This is in direct contrast to the curves in Figs. 5 and 6, which showed more rapid drug loss with increased peak height.

Thus, comparisons of blood level curves for the same drug may be summarized by two observations. A change in the time required to reach the peak indicates a change in k_1. A change in the area under the curve indicates a change in the amount absorbed. Application of these principles will be demonstrated in the problems which follow.

We have discussed idealized blood level curves following drug administration under controlled conditions. Most clinical studies are done with groups of people. This leads to the problem of individual variations which may cause all the rate constants to change from subject to subject. When data from these studies are to be used in comparisons such as those just discussed, it is therefore important that proper experimental design be employed so that effects of individual variation will be minimized. Wagner [31] has discussed the designs of clinical studies and their analysis. Several additional references on the subject are cited in that paper.

Sample Problem 8

While testing a new drug, a pharmacologist administered the same dose both intramuscularly and subcutaneously to his test animals. He found the ED_{50} for the intramuscular route to be about 25% lower. A study using the same experimental conditions produced the blood level curves shown in Fig. 9. Offer an explanation for the observed difference in ED_{50}.

Solution: Both curves are for the same drug. Therefore, k_{12}, k_{21}, and k_2 are held constant. The peak time is the same in both cases, indicating that k_1 is the same for both routes. However, the areas under the curves appear different. Because k_1 remains constant, we can use peak height to compare areas, and we find that subcutaneous administration shows 25% less area under the curve, indicating 25% less drug absorbed. Therefore, the change in amount absorbed will explain the difference in ED_{50}.

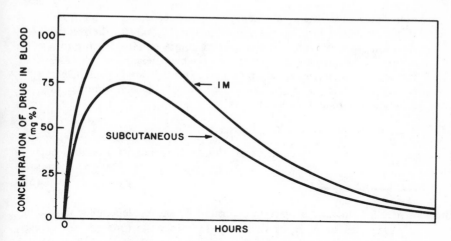

Fig. 9 Time course for drug in the blood following administration of equal doses by two different routes as described in Sample Problem 8.

Practice Problem 8

Capsules of the amorphous and crystalline forms of a new drug were administered to healthy volunteers in a crossover study. Nearly all of those receiving the amorphous form showed some toxicity, while those who received equal doses of the crystals had no side effects. In

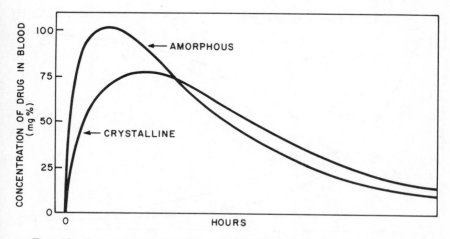

Fig. 10 Time course for drug in the blood following equal oral doses administered as the amorphous and crystalline forms as described in Practice Problem 8.

both cases all of the administered drug was recovered in the urine. Using the blood level curves shown in Fig. 10, explain the results. *Answer:* The amorphous form dissolves more rapidly, leading to a larger k_1. An increase in k_1 increases the peak height and decreases the peak time, as observed in the figure. This increase in peak height accounts for the toxic symptoms even though the same amount of drug was absorbed in each case.

3. Calculation of Absorption Rate Constants

   a. Simple Case. In chemical kinetics, a sequence of reactions such as

$$A \xrightarrow{k_1} B \xrightarrow{k_2} C \tag{50}$$

may be handled in various ways to determine k_1 and k_2 depending on whether data are available for A, B, or C. Figure 11 shows the time course for each component for the case where the first-order constants are equal. This scheme resembles, in an overall way, Eq. (49), with B representing the total drug in the body. We will not go into the analysis of systems like Eq. (50), since this is discussed in other texts [22]. It is sufficient to say that the calculation of k_1, which is analogous to the absorption constant, is most simply done if data for A are available, since

$$\ln A_t = \ln A_0 - k_1 t \tag{51}$$

so that a plot of $\ln A_t$ vs t has a slope of $-k_1$.

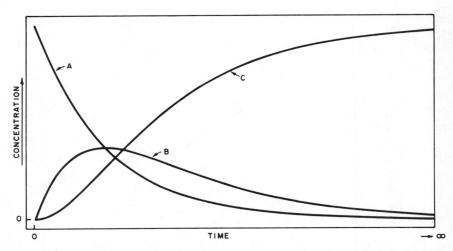

Fig. 11 Time course for each component in consecutive, irreversible first-order processes: $A \xrightarrow{k} B \xrightarrow{k_2} C$, where $k_1 = k_2$.

Unfortunately, in pharmacokinetic studies, the amount of drug remaining in the depot is not usually available for direct measurement. Instead, data for plasma or blood concentration of the drug are most commonly collected. The methods we will discuss for the calculation of k_1 allow us to calculate a measure of the amount in the depot from blood concentration data so that this may be plotted to obtain the desired constant.

These methods, developed by Wagner and Nelson [32], and Loo and Riegelman [33], are applicable to one- and two-compartment model drugs, respectively. Other methods for calculation of absorption rates from blood or urine data have been published [34,35]. Vaughn and Dennis [36] have applied the techniques of numerical deconvolution to absorption rate calculations.

   b. *Rate-Determining Step.* The overall rate process, from beginning to end, is limited by the slowest step in the sequence provided that one step is sufficiently slower than the rest. This may be likened to a bucket brigade with one lethargic member. In a simple series of consecutive, irreversible first-order rate processes [Eq. (50)], either step may become rate-limiting.

If the initial step is rapid, it may be possible to calculate both k_1 and k_2 from data for B or C. This is illustrated in Fig. 12, where two different time scales have been chosen to display the same data. It is obvious that data for A will always provide an estimate for k_1. However, data for B may be used to calculate k_2 by a simple first-order plot of the data shown in Fig. 12a or to calculate k_1 using the data in Fig. 12b, where the variable X_t would be defined as $(A_0 - B_t)$. This estimate for k_1 will be reasonable as long as $k_1/k_2 > 10$. The data for C can also be used to calculate k_2 by applying a first-order treatment to the data in Fig. 12a, where X_t would be defined as $(A_0 - C_t)$. A method which can be applied to cases where $2 \leqslant k_1/k_2 \leqslant 10$ with reasonable success ($\pm 10\%$) is that of "feathering." This is illustrated in Fig. 13. The first-order plot for the terminal portion of the B data is extrapolated to zero time and a difference plot is made using the line and the experimental points. It is necessary that A_t be equal to zero and $k_1 > k_2$ for the plot of $\ln B_t$ vs t to yield k_2. Linearity of this plot is not sufficient evidence for the acceptability of the slope. This problem was discussed previously as a warning and that biological half-life values from data following oral administration of drug may not be accurate.

If the second step is sufficiently rapid, the initial step will become rate-determining. When $k_2 \gg k_1$, Eq. (50) approaches the steady-state case since B_t becomes constant and approximately equal to zero. This is illustrated in Fig. 14, where $k_2/k_1 = 20$. It can readily be observed in this figure that data for A, B, or C all provide estimates for the slower constant, k_1. Generally one would not expect to analyze B data in the steady state, since the values would be very small and nearly constant by definition. However, it may not be necessary to have the case where B is actually in the steady state in order to obtain k_1 estimates from first-order plots for loss of B. The apparent biological $t_{1/2}$ values estimated from

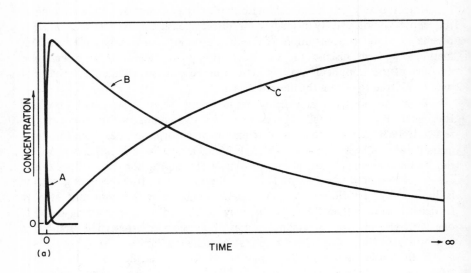

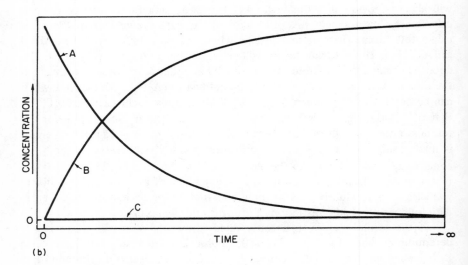

Fig. 12   Consecutive, irreversible first-order processes where the initial step is rapid. In this example for $A \xrightarrow{k_1} B \xrightarrow{k_2} C$, $k_1/k_2 = 500$. (a) This time scale illustrates primarily the second step. (b) This time scale illustrates the first step in the sequence.

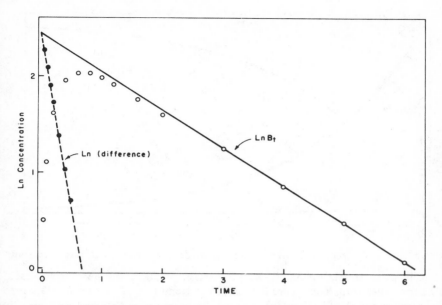

Fig. 13 "Feathering" data for concentration of B in the consecutive first-order processes $A \overset{k_1}{\rightarrow} B \overset{k_2}{\rightarrow} C$ to obtain estimates for both k_1 and k_2. The negative value for the slope of the terminal portion of $\ln B_t$ vs t will estimate k_2 provided that $k_1 > k_2$ and A_t has approached zero. The value for k_1 is estimated from the dashed line, which is a first-order plot of the natural logarithm of the difference between the experimental values and the extrapolated values (antilogarithm values from the solid line).

first-order loss from blood following four intramuscular penicillin dosage forms were found to agree more closely with the absorption half-lives than with those for elimination following rapid intravenous injection [37]. The ratio of β/k_1 varied from 1.5 to 3.3 for the four cases, indicating a rapid second step though not a steady state. The cases with low ratios (1.5) provided $t_{1/2}$ estimates which were longer than either the absorption or the biological $t_{1/2}$. This would be expected when neither step can be regarded as rate limiting (see Sec. IV.B.3.a. in Chap. 6). In the general case (Fig. 11), the decrease in B is described as the net difference between its supply and loss, as can be seen from the equation

$$B_t = \left(\frac{A_0 k_1}{k_2 - k_1} \right) [e^{-k_1 t} - e^{-k_2 t}] \tag{52}$$

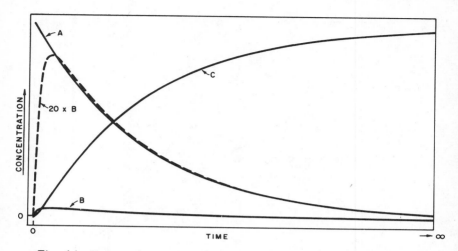

Fig. 14 Consecutive, irreversible first-order processes with rapid second step. In this example for A $\xrightarrow{k_1}$ B $\xrightarrow{k_2}$ C, k_2/k_1 = 20. In the steady-state case, B_t approaches zero. This figure illustrates the trend toward the steady state for the moderate ratio of k_2/k_1 = 20.

    c. The Loo-Riegelman and Wagner-Nelson Equations. These are both applied in much the same manner. Both of these equations allow us to calculate the percent of drug remaining unabsorbed at any time. This percentage is based on the *absorbable* fraction of the dose in the case of incomplete absorption [38]. An appropriate plot (first-order or zero-order) of this data allows calculation of the absorption rate constant (k_1 or k_0). We will first look at the application of the Loo-Riegelman equation [33] to a drug described by a two-compartment open model and absorbed by a first-order rate process. The first-order rate constant for absorption will be calculated from the data in Table 6.

    The equation to be used is

$$\left(\frac{A}{V_p}\right)_{tn} = P_{tn} + k_2 \int_{t_0}^{tn} P\,dt + T_{tn} \tag{53}$$

where $(A/V_p)_{tn}$ represents the total amount absorbed, A, at time tn, expressed in terms of V_p, the plasma volume. Concentrations of drug in plasma and tissue are given by P and T. The most convenient and simple way to explain the use of this equation is to work through an example.

    A drug is found to exhibit both an α and β phase following I.V. injection. The calculated values for the rate constants are k_{12} = 0.30, k_{21} = 0.40, and k_2 =

Table 6

Plasma Levels of Drug Following
Oral Administration of 490 mg

t (hr)	P (mg%)	t (hr)	P (mg%)
0.5	3.2	4.0	4.8
1.0	4.8	5.0	4.1
1.5	5.5	7.0	3.1
2.0	5.7	9.0	2.2
2.5	5.7	11.0	1.8
3.0	5.4	13.0	1.4

0.25 (hr^{-1}). The same drug was administered orally, and the data given in Table 6 were obtained. We will now use this information to calculate the three unknown quantities in Eq. (53), T_{tn}, $k_2 \int P \, dt$, and $(A/Vp)_{tn}$. The results of our stepwise calculations are entered in Table 7.

Step 1. Calculation of tissue concentrations as a function of time. The equation to be used is

$$T_{tn} = T_{tn-1} \, e^{-k_{21}\Delta t} + \left(\frac{k_{12}}{k_{21}}\right) P_{tn-1} \, [1 - e^{-k_{21}\Delta t}] + \frac{k_{12}\Delta P \, \Delta t}{2} \qquad (54)$$

This equation will be solved for each data point. In our example the first set of points is 0.5 hr, 3.2 mg%. Thus $\Delta t = 0.5$, $\Delta P = 3.2$, and $tn - 1$ is zero since it refers to the time of the previous data point. Thus P_{tn-1} and T_{tn-1} are also zero, since no drug is in the body at time zero. The first entry in our table under step 1 is calculated from

$$T_{0.5 \, hr} = 0 + 0 + \frac{(0.3)(3.2)(0.5)}{2} = 0.24 \qquad (55)$$

and the second entry from

$$T_{1.0 \, hr} = 0.24e^{-0.20} + \left(\frac{0.3}{0.4}\right) 3.2(1 - e^{-0.20}) + \frac{0.3(1.6)0.5}{2}$$

$$= 0.751 \qquad (56)$$

and so on. Each of the entries for T_{tn} is given in Table 7.

Step 2. Calculation of elimination as a function of time. We have now calculated the values for T_{tn}. Since we have data for P_{tn} there is only one part of Eq. (53) yet to be calculated and that is

Table 7

Answers to Stepwise Calculation for Loo-Riegelman Equation

	Step 1				Step 2				Step 3	
(1) t_n	(2) Δt	(3) P_{t_n}	(4) ΔP	(5) T_{t_n}	(6) Area t_{n-1} to t_n	(7) Area t_0 to t_n	(8) $k_2 \times$ col. 7	(9) $A/V_p =$ cols. 3 + 5 + 8	(10) $\%A/V_p$	(11) 100%– col 10
0.5	0.5	3.2	3.2	0.240	0.80	0.80	0.20	3.64	26.8	73.2
1.0	0.5	4.8	1.6	0.752	2.00	2.80	0.70	6.25	46.0	54.0
1.5	0.5	5.5	0.7	1.32	2.58	5.38	1.35	8.17	60.1	39.9
2.0	0.5	5.7	0.2	1.84	2.80	8.18	2.04	9.58	70.4	29.6
2.5	0.5	5.7	0.0	2.28	2.85	11.03	2.76	10.7	78.7	21.3
3.0	0.5	5.4	–0.3	2.62	2.78	13.81	3.45	11.5	84.6	15.4
4.0	1.0	4.8	–0.6	3.00	5.10	18.91	4.73	12.5	91.9	8.1
5.0	1.0	4.1	–0.7	3.09	4.45	23.36	5.84	13.0	95.6	4.4
7.0	2.0	3.1	–1.0	2.78	7.20	30.56	7.65	13.5	99.3	0.7
9.0	2.0	2.2	–0.9	2.26	5.30	35.86	8.96	13.4	98.5	1.5
11.0	2.0	1.8	–0.4	1.80	4.00	39.86	9.96	13.6	100.0	0.0
13.0	2.0	1.4	–0.4	1.43	3.20	43.06	10.8	13.6	100.0	0.0

$$k_2 \int_{t_0}^{tn} P\,dt \tag{57}$$

where the integral of $P\,dt$ represents the area under the plasma time curve from time zero to time tn. This can be done most easily by use of the trapezoidal rule as illustrated in Fig. 7. Thus the curve for P vs t must be drawn and the individual areas calculated for each trapezoid (or triangle) as described by the data points. The answers are illustrated in Table 7, column 6. These are the areas of the various trapezoids. However, the integral in Eq. (57) represents the total area up to tn. Therefore each area up to and including tn must be summed to obtain the value of the integral in Eq. (57) as shown in column 7. Each of these values is then multiplied by the elimination constant, $k_2 = 0.25$, to obtain the values in column 8.

Step 3. Calculation of A/V_p. The three component parts of Eq. (53) are now calculated (columns 3, 4, and 8) and are to be summed to obtain the values given in column 9. Examination of the entries in column 9 as a function of time will reveal that A/V_p appears to approach a maximum value of about 13.6. The values of A/V_p are next converted to a percent of this maximum value according to

$$\frac{\%A}{V_p} = \frac{(100A/V_p)}{13.6} \tag{58}$$

and the results are shown in column 10. Column 11 represents the percent of drug unabsorbed as a function of time and it is calculated by subtracting column 10 from 100%. The first-order plot of percent unabsorbed vs time yields a value of $0.60\ hr^{-1}$ for k_1.

The calculation of k_1 for a drug distributed according to a one-compartment model is done by means of the Wagner-Nelson [32] equation:

$$\left(\frac{A}{Vd}\right)_{tn} = P_{tn} + \beta \int_{t_0}^{tn} P\,dt \tag{59}$$

The procedure for solving this equation to obtain k_1 is basically the same as that just described.

d. First-Order Loss of Drug from Depot. The rate constant calculated using Eq. (53) or (59) does not truly represent absorption if part of the drug in the depot is lost to some parallel process that competes with absorption. Examples of such processes might be chemical degradation, biotransformation by enzymes or intestinal bacteria, or transfer to a compartment other than the blood. This kind of process can be shown schematically as

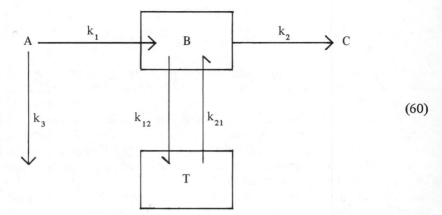

(60)

where k_3 represents the rate constant for drug loss by the competing process. In such a system, and where k_3 is a first-order rate constant, it has been shown that the rate constant calculated for absorption is the sum of k_1 and k_3 provided that these represent the only routes for loss of drug from the depot [38]. We can see that this system is similar to that discussed in Sec. II.D.1. The true rate constant for absorption may be obtained in a manner similar to that used earlier for obtaining the specific rate constants for metabolism and excretion from the apparent elimination constant. That is, adapting Eq. (34),

$$k_1 = \frac{k_a B_\infty}{D_0} = Fk_a$$

where k_a is the apparent rate constant for absorption and B_∞/D_0 represents the fraction absorbed. Loss of drug by a non-first-order process cannot be treated in this simple manner, however.

Thus, we recognize a potential problem in that false impressions of rapid absorption may result from a competing process such as rapid hydrolysis. Studies employing the Wagner-Nelson or Loo-Riegelman method should therefore include a calculation of the fraction of dose absorbed. If the drug is well absorbed, the calculated absorption rate constant should represent a good estimate of the actual value. If absorption is poor, the reason must be established before a physical meaning can be assigned to the apparent rate constant [38].

F. Intravenous Infusion

A constant intravenous infusion delivers a fixed amount of drug per unit time to the bloodstream. This represents a zero-order rate process. This kind of administration may be depicted by

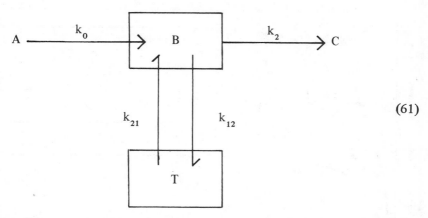

$$(61)$$

where k_0 is the zero-order rate constant for supply from the intravenous solution. Infusion allows the maintenance of a constant drug concentration in both blood and tissues. This can be used to advantage in designing pharmacokinetic experiments, since the steady-state body concentration provides a convenient device for accurate calculation of such parameters as clearance values or for obtaining data under capacity-limited and non-capacity-limited conditions. The influence of mode of administration on distribution may be quite significant, however, and should be taken into account when evaluating experimental data.

Figure 15 illustrates some typical blood level curves for a variety of infusion rates. After the infusion has been in effect for roughly five half-lives, the plasma level becomes constant. This stage will be referred to as the infusion steady state. At infusion steady state, as is shown in Appendix B,

$$k_0 = k_2 P_{inf} V_p = k_2 P'_{inf} \tag{62}$$

or the rate at which drug enters the body is equal to the rate at which it is removed. Rearranging Eq. (62), the plasma concentration at steady state is given by

$$P_{inf} = \frac{k_0}{k_2 V_p} \tag{63}$$

The elimination rate constant, k_2, is defined as first-order, and therefore is independent of blood concentration. Also, the volume of the central compartment, V_p, is postulated to be constant and independent of dose. Under these conditions, P_{inf} is proportional to the infusion rate.

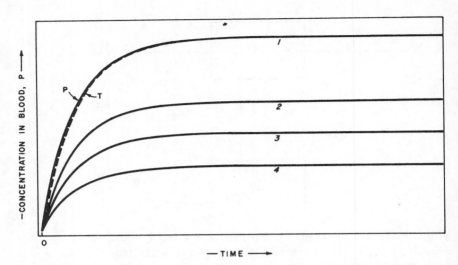

Fig. 15 Steady-state blood levels achieved by constant-rate intravenous infusion of drug distributed according to a two-compartment model. The steady-state levels (P_{inf}) are proportional to the infusion rates (k_0), which are (from top to bottom): 10 (curve 1), 6.6 (curve 2), 5 (curve 3), and 3.3 (curve 4). The values for the constants are $k_{12} = k_{21} = 10$, $k_2 = 1$. The steady-state ratio for the *amount* in the tissue relative to plasma is therefore $T'/P' = K = (k_{12}/k_{21}) = 1$ as shown in curve 1.

Examination of Fig. 15 also indicates that the time to reach the maximum plasma concentration is independent of the infusion rate. It is dependent only on the $t_{1/2}$ of the drug. Approximately 95% of the steady-state value is reached after four half-lives and 97% after five half-lives.

Probably the single most important characteristic of a constant intravenous infusion is that at the steady state, a two-compartment drug resembles a one-compartment drug. That is, for any drug, $T'/P' = k_{12}/k_{21}$, as demonstrated in Appendix B. This has several important implications which we will now examine.

First, as noted in Sec. II.B.2, the apparent volume of distribution calculated at the steady state is smaller than that obtained by the other methods if the drug in question fits a two-compartment model. It is, in fact, described by the same equation as Vd for a one-compartment model drug. In Sec. II.B.1 we have considered the application of steady-state infusion to the calculation of *Vd, area*, Eq. (13) and Vd_{inf}, Eq. (14). The value for Vd_{inf} is based on the steady-state equilibrium assumption $T'/P' = k_{12}/k_{21}$ so that $Vd_{inf} = Vp[1 + (k_{12}/k_{21})]$.

The value for Vd_{inf} may also be estimated from the assessment of the amount of drug in the body during the steady state, D_{inf}, using only blood level data since [9,10]:

$$D_{inf} = D_0 \left(1 - \frac{\int_0^t P\, dt}{\int_0^\infty P\, dt} \right) \qquad (64)$$

The integrals from time zero to t and from zero to ∞ represent the areas under the plasma level vs time curve from time zero to time t, when the infusion was stopped, and from zero until all drug was eliminated from the body. In this case, the value obtained for drug content in the body may be applied in Eq. (10) to find Vd_{inf}.

Second, at the steady state β_{inf} for a two-compartment model drug is similar to β for a one-compartment model. Since the supply rate equals the rate of loss, and if β is defined as an overall rate constant for elimination,

$$k_0 = \beta_{inf} D_{inf} = \beta_{inf} P_{inf} Vd_{inf} \qquad (65)$$

Combining with Eq. (63),

$$\beta_{inf} Vd_{inf} = k_2\, Vp \qquad (66)$$

Since $Vd_{inf} = V_p [1 + (k_{12}/k_{21})]$

$$\beta_{inf} = \frac{k_2 k_{21}}{k_{12} + k_{21}} = k_2 (f_p)_{inf} \qquad (67)$$

where $(f_p)_{inf}$ is the fraction of drug in the central compartment during infusion steady state. Equation (67) is equivalent to Eq. (38) in Chap. 2.

The value for β calculated after a rapid I.V. injection of a two-compartment model drug may be smaller than β_{inf}. This is because

$$\beta = k_2 (f_p)_\beta \qquad (68)$$

and, as discussed later in reference to Eqs. (69) and (70), $(f_p)_{inf}$ is more than $(f_p)_\beta$ which is the fraction of drug in the central compartment during the β phase. The β phase is illustrated by the parallel lines in Fig. 9 in Chap. 2. [It may be necessary to collect plasma concentration data through several log cycles for $(f_p)_\beta$ to approach a constant value for some multicompartment drugs (see Ref. 27).] Since β_{inf} may be more than β it would appear that the use of a β value to calculate the infusion rate necessary to maintain a desired plasma steady-state concentration, P_{inf}, using Eq. (65) would lead to an underestimation of the required k_0. However, the important term in Eq. (65) is the product of β and the volume of distribution. The product β Vd, calculated from a rapid intravenous dose, will equal k_2 Vp as in Eq. (66). Thus, as long as the values used were both determined by the same method the k_0 calculated will be correct.

Third, drug distribution in a two-compartment system is different during an infusion than after a single dose. As shown in Appendix B Eq. (39a), the tissue-to-plasma ratio during the β phase after a single dose is given by

$$\left(\frac{T'}{P'}\right)_\beta = \frac{k_{12}}{k_{21} - \beta} \tag{69}$$

Comparing this to the ratio at the steady state of an infusion, $(T'/P')_{inf} = k_{12}/k_{21}$, it is clear that

$$\left(\frac{T'}{P'}\right)_\beta > \left(\frac{T'}{P'}\right)_{inf} \tag{70}$$

so that of the total drug in the body, the fraction present in the tissues is greater following a rapid intravenous injection than during an infusion. Gibaldi [10] reports a 1.7-fold difference in these ratios for aspirin, and the possibility of a two- to threefold difference for penicillin G. Therefore, at equal plasma concentrations, the amount of drug in the peripheral compartment might be quite different for one mode of administration as compared to the other. This change in distribution may elicit different degrees of clinical response.

Some drugs, because of limited solubility, irritation, and so on, are not suitable for rapid intravenous injection. In these cases, therefore, the values of the pharmacokinetic parameters cannot be obtained in the usual manner. Methods have been devised [39, 40], however, for obtaining the various rate constants and the apparent volume of distribution from blood concentration curves obtained after cessation of an infusion. It should be noted that the parameters obtained in this way, including β and Vd, are the same as those obtained after rapid administration.

Sample Problem 9

A drug was given by intravenous injection and the following rate constants were determined: $k_{12} = 0.80$ hr^{-1}, $k_{21} = 0.60$ hr^{-1}, $k_2 = 0.40$ hr^{-1}, and $\beta = 0.14$ hr^{-1}. What is T'/P' after a single dose and during an infusion?

Solution: Since $k_{12} + k_{21} = 3.5 \times k_2$, this appears to be a two-compartment model. Therefore, after an injection $(T'/P')_\beta$ is given by Eq. (69):

$$\left(\frac{T'}{P'}\right)_\beta = 0.080/0.46$$

$$\left(\frac{T'}{P'}\right)_\beta = 1.7$$

During the steady state of an infusion,

$$\left(\frac{T'}{P'}\right)_{inf} = \frac{0.80}{0.60}$$

$$\left(\frac{T'}{P'}\right)_{inf} = 1.3$$

Practice Problem 9

Following rapid I.V. injection, the parameters for a group of related drugs were obtained as shown in Table 8.

Table 8

Pharmacokinetic Parameters

Drug	$t_{1/2}$ (hr)	Vd (%V/W)
W	1.0	12.9
X	0.7	13.6
Y	0.5	16.4
Z	0.4	18.6

(a) In each case, what rate of infusion is needed to maintain a plasma concentration of 10 mg% in a 70-kg man?
Answer: W, 630 mg/hr; X, 950 mg/hr; Y, 1,600 mg/hr; Z, 2,250 mg/hr

(b) After the infusion is started, in what order will they reach their steady-state concentration in the blood (first to last)?
Answer: Z, Y, X, W

REFERENCES

1. J.K. Seydel, Sulfonamides, Structure-Activity Relationships and Mode of Action, *J. Pharm. Sci., 57*, 1455 (1968).
2. M. Gibaldi, R. Nagashima, and G. Levy, Relationship Between Drug Concentration in Plasma or Serum and Amount of Drug in the Body, *J. Pharm. Sci. 58,* 193 (1969).
3. L.A. Pagliaro and L.Z. Benet, Critical Compilation of Terminal Half-Lives, Percent Excreted Unchanged and Changes of Half-Life in Renal and Hepatic

Dysfunction for Studies in Humans with References, *J. Pharmacokin. Biopharm. 3*, 333 (1975).

4. J.G. Wagner, Pharmacokinetics, in *Annual Reviews of Pharmacology*, Vol. 8, (H. W. Elliot, ed.), Annual Reviews, Inc., Palo Alto, Calif., 1968, pp. 85-86.

5. L. Z. Benet and R. A. Ronfeld, Volume Terms in Pharmacokinetics, *J. Pharm. Sci. 58*, 639 (1969).

6. R. Dominguez, Kinetics of Elimination, Absorption and Volume of Distribution in the Organism, in *Medical Physics*, Vol. II (O. Glasser, ed.), Year Book Publishers, Chicago, Ill., 1950, pp. 476-489.

7. J. G. Wagner and J. I. Northram. Estimation of Volume of Distribution and Half-life of a Compound After Rapid Intravenous Injection, *J. Pharm. Sci. 56*, 529 (1967).

8. D. S. Riggs, *The Mathematical Approach to Physiological Problems*, Williams and Wilkins Co., Baltimore, Md., 1963, pp. 193-214.

9. S. Riegelman, J. Loo, and M. Rowland, Concept of a Volume of Distribution and Possible Errors in Evaluation of this Parameter, *J. Pharm. Sci. 57*, 128 (1968).

10. M. Gibaldi, Effect of Mode of Administration on Drug Distribution in a Two-compartment Open System, *J. Pharm. Sci. 58*, 327 (1969).

11. M. Gibaldi and D. Perrier, Drug Distribution and Renal Failure, *J. Clin. Pharmacol. 12*, 201 (1972).

12. M. Gibaldi and D. Perrier, Drug Elimination and Apparent Volume of Distribution in Multicompartment Systems, *J. Pharm. Sci. 61*, 952 (1972).

13. M. Gibaldi and M. Schwartz, Apparent Effect of Probenecid on the Distribution of Penicillins in Man, *Clin. Pharmacol. Ther. 9*, 345 (1968).

14. L. Hollister and G. Levy, Some Aspects of Salicylate Distribution and Metabolism in Man, *J. Pharm. Sci. 54*, 1126 (1965).

15. H. B. Kostenbauder, J. B. Portnoff, and J. V. Swintosky, Control of Urine pH and Its Effect on Sulfaethidole Excretion in Humans, *J. Pharm. Sci. 51*, 1084 (1962).

16. R. H. Reuning and L. S. Schanker, Effect of Carbon Tetrachloride-induced Liver Damage on Hepatic Transport of Ouabain in the Rat, *J. Pharmacol. Exp. Therap. 78*, 589 (1971).

17. H. Remmer, The Role of the Liver in Drug Metabolism, *Am. J. Med. 49*, 617 (1970).

18. R. L. Smith, The Biliary Excretion and Enterohepatic Circulation of Drugs and Other Organic Compounds, *Fortschr, Arzneim.-Forsch. 9*, 299 (1966).

19. L. S. Schanker, Secretion of Organic Compounds in Bile, in *Handbook of Physiology-Alimentary Canal*, American Physiological Society, Washington, D.C., 1968, pp. 2433-2449.

20. R. R. Scheline, Drug Metabolism by Intestinal Microorganisms, *J. Pharm. Sci. 57*, 2021 (1968).

21. D. A. P. Evans, Individual Variations of Drug Metabolism as a Factor in Drug Toxicity, *Ann N. Y. Acad. Sci. 123*, 178 (1965).

22. C. Capellos and B. H. J. Bielski, *Kinetic Systems, Mathematical Description of Chemical Kinetics in Solution,* Wiley-Interscience, New York, 1972, pp. 69-71, 73-75.
23. G. Levy, Dose Dependent Effects in Pharmacokinetics, in *Importance of Fundamental Principles in Drug Evaluation* (D. H. Tedeschi and R. E. Tedeschi, eds.), Raven Press, New York, 1968, pp. 141-172.
24. G. Levy, Possibility of Simultaneous Zero- and First-order Kinetics in the In Vivo Formation of a Single Drug Metabolite, *J. Pharm. Sci.* 55, 989 (1966).
25. G. Levy, Pharmacokinetics of Salicylate Elimination in Man. *J. Pharm. Sci.* 54, 959 (1965).
26. G. Levy, Evidence for Nonfirst-order Kinetics of Salicylate Elimination—A Rebuttal, *J. Pharm. Sci.* 56, 1044 (1967).
27. R. Nagashima, G. Levy, and R. A. O'Reilly, Comparative Pharmacokinetics of Coumarin Anticoagulants IV. Application of a Three-Compartmental Model to the Analysis of the Dose-dependent Kinetics of Bishydroxycourmarin Elimination, *J. Pharm. Sci.* 57, 1888 (1968).
28. P. G. Dayton, S. A. Cucinell, M. Weiss, and J. M. Perel, Dose Dependence of Drug Plasma Level Decline in Dogs, *J. Pharmacol. Exp. Therap.* 158, 305 (1967).
29. G. Levy, Hydroxylated Metabolites as Inhibitors of Drug Biotransformation and Their Possible Role in Dose Dependent Elimination Kinetics, Abstracts, A.Ph.A. Academy of Pharmaceutical Sciences 13th National Meeting, Chicago, Ill., 2, 179 (1972).
30. R. Nagashima, G. Levy, and E. J. Sarcione, Comparative Pharmacokinetics of Coumarin Anticoagulants III. Factors Affecting the Distribution and Elimination of Bishydroxycoumarin (BHC) in Isolated Liver Perfusion Studies, *J. Pharm. Sci.* 57, 1881 (1968).
31. J. G. Wagner, Design of Clinical Studies to Assess Physiological Availability, *Drug Inf. Bull.,* Jan./June, 45 (1969).
32. J. Wagner and E. Nelson, Per Cent Absorbed Time Plots Derived from Blood Level and/or Urinary Excretion Data, *J. Pharm. Sci.* 52, 610 (1963).
33. J. C. K. Loo and S. Riegelman, New Method for Calculating the Intrinsic Absorption Rate of Drugs, *J. Pharm. Sci.* 57, 918 (1968).
34. R. Dominguez and E. Pomerene, Calculation of the Rate of Absorption of Exogenous Creatinine, *Proc. Soc. Exp. Biol. Med.* 60, 173 (1945).
35. E. Nelson and I. Schaldemose, Urinary Excretion Kinetics for Evaluation of Drug Absorption I. Solution Rate Limited and Non-solution Rate Limited Absorption, *J. Am. Pharm. Assoc. Sci. Ed.* 49, 437 (1960).
36. D. P. Vaughn and M. Dennis, Mathematical Basis of Point-Area Deconvolution Method for Determining In Vivo Input Functions, *J. Pharm. Sci.* 67, 663 (1978).
37. J. T. Doluisio, J. C. LaPiana, and L. W. Dittert, Pharmacokinetics of Ampicillin Trihydrate, Sodium Ampicillin and Sodium Dicloxacillin Following Intramuscular Injection, *J. Pharm. Sci.* 60, 715 (1971).

38. R. E. Notari, J. L. DeYoung, and R. H. Reuning, Effect of Parallel First-order Drug Loss from Site of Administration on Calculated Values for Absorption Rate Constants, *J. Pharm. Sci. 61*, 135 (1972).

39. M. Gibaldi, Estimation of the Pharmacokinetic Parameters of the Two-compartment Open Model from Post-infusion Plasma Concentration Data, *J. Pharm. Sci. 58*, 1133 (1969).

40. J. C. K. Loo and S. Riegelman, Assessment of Pharmacokinetic Constants from Postinfusion Blood Curves Obtained After I.V. Infusion, *J. Pharm. Sci. 59*, 53 (1970).

Chapter 4

BIOPHARMACEUTICS: CLINICAL APPLICATIONS OF PHARMACOKINETIC PARAMETERS

I.   INTRODUCTION   109
     A.   Biopharmaceutics and Therapy   109
     B.   The Drug and the Dosage Form   110
     C.   The Scope of the Chapter   111

II. BLOOD LEVEL CURVES   111
     A.   Compartmental Analysis   111
     B.   Comparing Different Curves for One Drug   112
     C.   Comparing Different Drugs   112
     D.   Relationship to Biological Response   114
          1.   Minimum Effective Dose   117
          2.   Onset   118
          3.   Duration   118
          4.   Maximum Safe Dose   118
          5.   Amount Absorbed   118
     E.   Caution in Comparing Curves   119

III. ABSORPTION OF DRUGS FROM THE
     GASTROINTESTINAL TRACT   119
     A.   Absorption Processes   119
          1.   Passive Diffusion Through the Gastrointestinal Wall   119
          2.   pH-Partition Theory   120
          3.   Active Transport Through the Gastrointestinal Wall   123
     B.   Absorption of Drugs from Solutions   123
          1.   Rate-Determining Step   123
          2.   pH and Gastrointestinal Absorption Sites   123
     C.   Absorption of Drugs from Solid Dosage Forms   126
          1.   Rate-Determining Step   126
          2.   Controlling Absorption Rate from Solid Dosage Forms 127
               a.   Controlling Solubility Through Stomach Buffering 128
               b.   Adjusting the pH of the Microenvironment   130

   c. Salts of Weak Acids or Weak Bases 130
    Sample Problem 1 134
    Practice Problem 1 135
    Practice Problem 2 135
    Practice Problem 3 136
    Practice Problem 4 136
    Practice Problem 5 136
   d. Physical State of the Drug 137
   e. Determining Drug Surface Area Through Control of
    Particle|Size 139
  D. Factors Decreasing Absorption from the Gastrointestinal Tract 140
   1. Stability 140
    a. Hydrolysis of Weak Acid Drugs in Gastric Juices 141
     Practice Problem 6 142
    b. Drugs Unstable in the Stomach and Absorbed in the
     Intestines 143
   2. Complexation 145
    Practice Problem 7: Decrease in G.I. Absorption Due to
    Complexation 145
   3. Formulation 146
    Practice Problem 8: Decrease in G.I. Absorption Due to
    Formulation 147

IV. CONTINUOUS BLOOD AND TISSUE LEVELS IN THERAPY 149
  A. Constant Intravenous Infusion 149
    Practice Problem 9: Calculation of Intravenous Infusion
    Rates for Typical Antibiotics 150
  B. Sustained-Release Oral Dosage Forms 152
   1. Definitions 152
    a. Repeat-Action Tablets 152
    b. Sustained-Release Dosage Forms 152
    c. Prolonged-Action Preparations 152
   2. Advantages and Disadvantages 152
   3. Sustained-Release Theory 153
    Practice Problem 10: Calculation of Specifications for
    Oral Sustained-Release Tablets 154
    Practice Problem 11 154
    Practice Problem 12 155
   4. Product Design and Typical Examples 155
    a. Slow-Erosion Core with Initial Dose 156
    b. Erosion Core Only 157
    c. Repeat-Action Tablets 157
    d. Pellets in Capsules 157
    e. Pellets in Tablets 160

    f.   Leaching   160
    g.   Ion-Exchange Resins   161
    h.   Complexation   162
    i.   Microencapsulation   162
  5.   Choice of Drugs for Sustained-Release Products and
       Evaluation of the Dosage Form   162
    a.   Candidates for Long-Acting Dosage Forms   162
    b.   Evaluating Sustained-Release Products   164
  6.   Rational Clinical Use of Sustained-Release Products   166
       Practice Problem 13   167
       Practice Problem 14   168
REFERENCES   169

I. INTRODUCTION

A. Biopharmaceutics and Therapy

In the broadest sense of the word, biopharmaceutics may be said to deal with the problem of controlling the therapeutic effect of a drug when it is being administered to the patient. The degree of success achieved by the use of a drug product may be limited by the patient's diet, the co-administration of other drugs, inert ingredients in the dosage form, the dosage regimen, the route of administration, the physical or chemical state of the drug within the dosage form, or the improper choice or use of a particular dosage form of the drug. The safe and effective use of medicinal agents is based upon their degree of predictability with regard to the overall interaction between the patient and the drug at the time of use. The partial list of variables mentioned above are potentially capable of influencing the time profile for the drug concentration at the active site. Unsatisfactory therapeutic effects may thus result from a decrease in the total amount of drug released from the depot into the bloodstream or from the rate at which the drug transfer process takes place. In order to achieve optimum results with a therapeutic agent, the factors affecting its bioavailability time profile and its distribution-elimination pattern must be defined and clinically controlled. Thus it is suggested here that the rational choice and administration of a drug product cannot be separated from the biopharmaceutical properties of a given drug. This approach to the rational use of drug products is a natural outcome of the use of pharmacokinetic parameters in the design and evaluation of dosage forms. For if the developer has indeed examined the critical factors involving the bioavailability of the drug from the dosage form, then it is an exercise in futility if the clinician ignores these principles when the product is employed in therapy.

B. The Drug and the Dosage Form

It would be wise at this point to clarify some of the terms which might at first appear disarmingly obvious to the reader. This chapter does not deal in any way with the choice of a chemotherapeutic agent. Pharmacokinetic aspects of that decision are found in Chap. 6. Information dealing with particular therapeutic considerations might best be found under the realm of pharmacology. This chapter concerns dosage-form design and the clinical use of that product once the specific drug has been chosen. Many drugs are available in a variety of products and dosage forms. Which form should be employed in a particular case and how is it best used? Biopharmaceutics addresses itself to that question. In the narrowest sense of the word, biopharmaceutics may be defined as the effect of the dosage form and its administration on the biological effects of the drug. In this case the term dosage form is not limited to such categories as capsules, tablets, elixirs, and so on. We consider the drug to be the basic chemical structure of the chemotherapeutic agent. Everything else that is done by way of modification of that chemical entity in order to put it to clinical use is included in our definition of dosage form. Thus dosage form considerations for a given drug include:

1. Particle size of the drug
2. Chemical nature of the drug, such as salt, free acid or base, ester, complex, and so on
3. Physical state of the drug, such as crystalline, amorphous, hydrate, polymorph, and so on
4. Inert ingredients, such as diluents, buffers, disintegrating agents, excipients, and so on
5. The type of dosage form in the more traditional sense, such as tablets, enteric coated tablets, suppositories, syrups, and so on

Thus there exists a rather wide spectrum of choices in order for pharmaceutical product development to arrive at a marketed dosage form of a given drug.

The clinician is faced with still greater problems in drug usage in addition to those associated with the choice of a route of administration and a particular dosage form for that route. Patients often take several drugs simultaneously. The effects of co-administration of other agents along with the possible complicating factors of diet and the influence of the disease state on the absorption and elimination of the drug all make the final predictability of biological response a monumental problem. This is not to infer, however, that this challenge should receive anything less than our utmost attention. It is only by addressing our efforts to this important phase of rational therapy that any progress can be made in that direction. That progress is discussed in Chap. 7.

C. The Scope of the Chapter

This chapter contains very little new basic material. It is primarily composed of applications of the principles covered in Chaps. 2 and 3. In that respect it is an applied presentation. The application of pharmacokinetics to dosage-form design, evaluation, and use should be of interest to those involved in product development as well as to those involved in clinical pharmacy. The examples chosen for this section are taken from the literature, and the pertinent references are given. However, it is not the objective of this presentation to review the literature in the field. The cases chosen were used merely as illustrations. The number of examples is by no means exhaustive, and many other samples could have been used to illustrate the same points. The primary goal of this chapter is to place the principles of pharmacokinetics in a framework of practicality or utility with respect to those involved in the use, design, or testing of dosage forms.

II. BLOOD LEVEL CURVES

A. Compartmental Analysis

Compartmental schemes are generally made by fitting kinetic models to blood and urine time courses. The concentration-time profile for drug in the blood and tissues is thus illustrated as the net result of several rate processes which are influenced by many physiochemical *in vivo* factors. The control of these factors and the resultant pharmacokinetic pattern is of ultimate importance if one is to control clinical results.

An alteration is any one of the rate processes shown in Scheme I will be reflected in the blood level curve. Thus, the plasma concentration-time profile for a drug described by this compartmental model can vary in shape because of

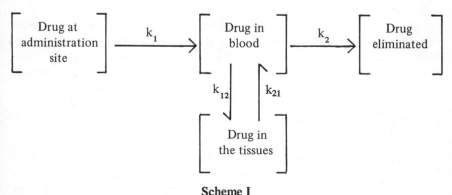

Scheme I

112 4. Biopharmaceutics: Clinical Applications

variations in: (1) absorption rate constant (k_1), (b) rate of metabolism (c) rate or urinary excretion, (d) amount available from the site of administration, (e) the distribution of drug between blood and tissues. Each of these variables will show a unique effect on the blood level pattern. These patterns will be considered individually in the following sections.

B. Comparing Different Curves for One Drug

First, let us consider how one might obtain different blood level patterns from administration of the same drug. As noted in Chap. 3, either k_1 or the bioavailable dose (or both) may vary. This case may be illustrated by using different routes of administration or by administering different forms of the same drug by one route (e.g., salt, free acid or base, amorphous, crystalline, etc.). Since we are considering one given drug, the rate constants for elimination, k_2, and distribution, k_{12} and k_{21}, will remain constant. As the rate constant for supply is increased for a given drug, the peak value is increased and the time to achieve this value is decreased. See Fig. 6, Chap. 3 for an example.

In spite of the dramatic differences in the shapes of such curves, the area under each curve from t_0 to t_∞ is identical provided that equal amounts of the drug were released into the bloodstream and only the rate of release varied. The identical areas under the curves can be used to demonstrate that equal doses of the drug were supplied from the depot. When the rate constant for supply of drug from the depot to the blood is the only rate constant subject to change, then the area under the plasma concentration-vs-time curves is proportional to the total amount available to the blood. Thus, increasing the rate of supply of a given drug increases the peak height and the speed with which the peak height is attained while decreasing the total time during which there is drug in the blood. It does not affect the area under the curve.

The amount which arrives in the bloodstream from the depot may vary due to some physical or chemical interaction of the drug at the site of administration or due to variation in the dose administered. Figure 8 of Chap. 3 is a typical pattern for five different doses of the same drug. In this example absorption rate constants have been kept constant. Since we are considering a single drug with fixed rate constants, the areas under the curves are proportional to the dose. That is, the ratio of the areas under those curves is in direct proportion to the bioavailable dose.

C. Comparing Different Drugs

By way of contrast, let us now examine the blood level curves when only the rate constant for elimination is changed. Figure 1 illustrates four examples where the absorption rate constant and the distribution constants k_{12} and k_{21} are held constant. The rate constant for total elimination by all routes, k_2, has been set

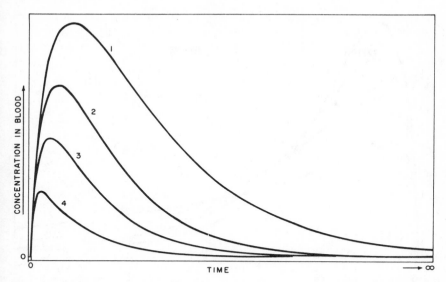

Fig. 1 Effect of increasing the elimination rate constant. The values for k_2 in Scheme I (from top to bottom) are 1 (curve 1), 2 (curve 2), 4 (curve 3), and 10 (curve 4). Other rate constants are held constant at $k_1 = 1$ and $k_{12} = k_{21} = 2$.

at 1 in curve 1, 2 in curve 2, 4 in curve 3, and 10 in curve 4. Thus, the rate constant for elimination has been varied through a factor of ten. Since the rate of output of drug from the body is increased in going from curve 1 to curve 4, the blood level peak decreases. Also, the time required to clear the blood of drug content decreases with increasing k_2, as would be expected. This set of curves could reflect four different drugs with the same distribution constants or the same drug in four different subjects with some variation in the ability of the biological system to dispose of the drug (e.g., kidney damage or enzyme deficiency). In either case, the bioavailable dose delivered to the bloodstream was kept the same in all four cases. It is therefore obvious that the areas under the curves are not proportional to the dose released when the elimination rate constant is not held constant. Thus, the areas under the curves can be used only as in indication of bioavailability when blood levels for one drug are being compared and the elimination rate constant is not undergoing change.

Figure 2 shows the resulting blood level curves where the values for k_{12} and k_{21} were varied. The higher the ratio of k_{21}/k_{12}, the higher the observed peak height. Since elimination occurs from the blood rather than the tissues (Scheme I) a higher blood level results in a shorter overall lifetime of drug in the blood. The areas under all four curves remain the same, since the rate constants for input, k_1, and output, k_2, are held constant for all four cases. The area is

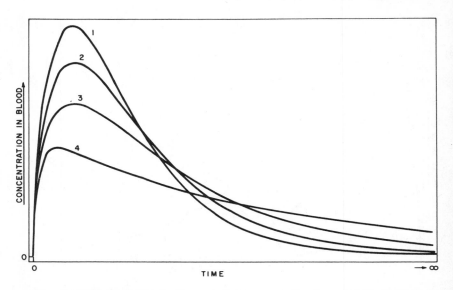

Fig. 2 Effect of distribution on time course for drug in blood. The rate
constants k_{12} and k_{21} have been given the values (from top to bottom): 1, 4
(curve 1); 2, 3 (curve 2); 3, 2 (curve 3); and 4, 1 (curve 4). Other rate constants
are held constant at $k_1 = k_2 = 1$.

therefore proportional to the total amount of drug released from the depot. No
simple trend describing the time for reaching the peak height is evident, since
curves 1, 2, and 3 are about equal, whereas curve 4 reaches its peak in roughly
one-half the time of the others. In comparison to k_1 and k_2, the time to reach
the peak is relatively insensitive to changes in the values of k_{12} and k_{21}.

D. Relationship to Biological Response

The previous section has described the effect of changing several rate processes
in Scheme I upon the shape of blood level curves. We are concerned with blood
level patterns because generally only the blood and urine compartments are
accessible, and the concentration of intact drug and metabolites are therefore
determined in these compartments. Figure 3 illustrates the fraction of the initial
dose in each compartment in Scheme I following an extravascular administration
of drug. A figure such as this could be constructed from actual biological data
representing assays for blood and urine. By fitting these data to the model in
Scheme I, one can then generate curves for the tissue and the fraction remaining
at the site of administration. This represents the general approach of
pharmacokinetics, where the concern is to account for the drug within the body

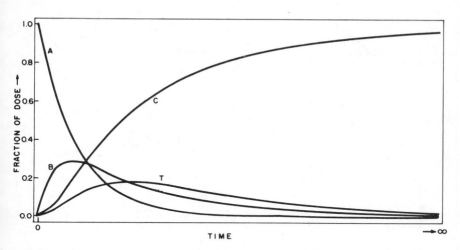

Fig. 3 The fraction of the dose in each compartment of Scheme I as a function of time. In this illustration the rate constants have the values $k_1 = k_2 = 3$ and $k_{12} = k_{21} = 2$.

at all times and to relate this distribution to the pharmacological responses. The approach, therefore, allows one to distinguish between differences in intrinsic activities of drugs and differences in their ability to reach the site of action.

Let us begin with the assumption that the intensity of the pharmacological activity is a function of the concentration of drug at the site of action. We will also be realistic in our assumption and state that the site of action is either unknown or, if known, inaccessible to the analyst except by sacrifice of the subject. That is, we cannot directly determine a dose-response curve based upon the concentration of drug which is actually at the site of action. Assuming that this site of action is not in the blood itself, Scheme I shows that drug in the blood diffuses reversibly into the tissues where the site is located. This is not to say that the site is assumed to be in a particular tissue, but only that it is somewhere outside of the bloodstream. It follows, then, that the concentration at the site corresponds to some concentration in the blood. This is illustrated in Figs. 4 and 5. These figures serve to illustrate how the distribution of a drug can affect its tissue concentration and thus its concentration at the site. A pharmacological test without the knowledge of this difference might attribute the increased biological activity of the drug in Fig. 4 to its receptor site interaction. Recognizing that it is not the concentration in the blood per se that is responsible for the pharmacological activity, it may still be possible to define dose responses based on blood levels which have some relationship to the concentration at the site of action.

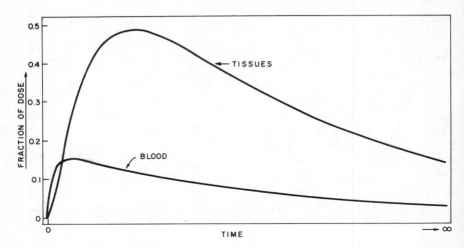

Fig. 4 The fraction of the dose in the blood and tissue compartments of Scheme I as a function of time. This corresponds to curve 4 in Fig. 2, where $k_1 = k_2 = k_{21} = 1$ and $k_{12} = 4$.

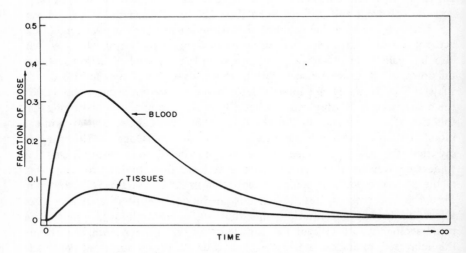

Fig. 5 The fraction of the dose in the blood and tissue compartments of Scheme I as a function of time. This corresponds to curve 1 in Fig. 2, where $k_1 = k_2 = k_{12} = 1$ and $k_{21} = 4$.

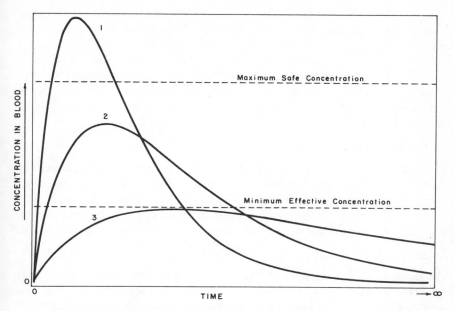

Fig. 6 Three time profiles for drug in blood following equal extravascular doses where elimination (k_2) is identical in all three cases.

Since the concentration in the blood is readily accessible, it is often convenient as well as appropriate to relate blood concentration and response. These criteria being satisfied, one can define a number of characteristics related to the dosage regimen. Consider, as an example, the three blood level curves given in Fig. 6, all of which have been constructed based on Scheme I, using the same dosage and elimination rate constant for all three cases. We can thus define several parameters based on the blood concentration, which will allow us to compare these curves.

1. Minimum Effective Dose

The minimum effective dose may be defined as the minimum dose required to achieve the desired therapeutic effect. Assuming that this represents a minimum effective concentration at the site of the action, the corresponding blood concentration can be determined by appropriate dose-response experiments. In this way a *minimum effective blood concentration* can be defined as that concentration corresponding to the desired therapeutic effect. In Fig. 6 the minimum effective concentration is indicated by a dashed line. Thus, we can observe that curves 1 and 2 achieve therapeutic results, while curve 3 does not. Since the bioavailable doses and elimination rate constants are equal in all three cases, either the absorption rate constant or the distribution of the drugs (or both) have been altered. Thus, curves 1, 2, and 3 might represent administration of three forms of the same drug or the same forms from three administration sites where the absorption rate has affected the blood level pattern. Once the minimum effective concentration has been defined, it is possible to define additional parameters on this basis.

2. Onset

The onset may now be defined as the amount of time required to achieve the minimum effective concentration following administration of the dosage form. Thus, we can observe in Fig. 6 that the onset of curve 1 is less than curve 2 and that the onset of curve 3 is nonexistent as it never achieves an effective level. The onset of curve 2 is approximately three times longer than that of curve 1.

3. Duration

The duration of action may be defined as the length of time that the blood level remains above the therapeutic level. In Fig. 6 the duration of curve 2 is 30% more than that of curve 1, and curve 3 has no duration since it never achieves an effective level.

4. Maximum Safe Dose

That dose which, if exceeded, results in side effects or untoward effects may be called the *maximum safe dose*. The blood level associated with that dose may then be defined as the maximum safe concentration. This is indicated by a dashed line in Fig. 6. Thus, it can be observed that of the three blood level curves illustrated in Fig. 6, curve 1 is not desirable since it exceeds the maximum safe concentration.

5. Amount Absorbed

The amount absorbed may be defined as the total amount that enters the bloodstream from the site of administration. If one is considering a single drug, in which case the value for the elimination rate constant shown in Scheme I is fixed, then the area under the curve is a function of the amount absorbed. If the amount absorbed in each case is equal and the absorption rate constant varies, then the areas under the curves will be equal. In this case the shape of the curves would be a reflection of the differences between the absorption rate constants rather than the amount absorbed.

Although it may not be readily apparent in Fig. 6 (because all of curves 2 and 3 are now shown), each curve has the same area. Each dose of the drug was absorbed 100% in creating this figure and k_2 was held constant. Thus, a drug may be absorbed 100% and still be inactive as in the case of curve 3. Alternatively, it may show complete absorption and fast onset but decreased duration and increased side effects such as in curve 1. Figure 6 is hypothetical, but it could easily apply to three different formulations of tablets taken orally by humans. A striking similarity to this figure has been shown by Breimer [1], who administered 600 mg of hexobarbital to humans (in order of reference to curves 1, 2, and 3 in Fig. 6) as: sodium salt orally in capsules, free acid orally in tablets, and the sodium salt in rectal suppositories.

E. Caution in Comparing Curves

While plots such as Fig. 6 can be used to compare the relative availability of a given drug from several dosage forms, such plots cannot be indiscriminately used to compare different drugs. One has only to consider Scheme I to realize the many factors which can affect the blood pattern when more than one drug is considered. For example, we can list the following parameters which can result in alteration of the appearances of blood level curves from two drugs:

1. Difference in supply rate or amount
2. Different rates of metabolism
3. Different rates of excretion
4. Different rates of distribution
5. Different distribution pattern or differences in their relative volumes of distribution
6. Differences in binding phenomena

In this chapter we will consider the first factor. All of the remaining factors in the above list will be considered in Chap. 6. Indeed, the study of these factors and of their significance in the design and evaluation of drugs and drug products serves as one justification for studying pharmacokinetics.

III. ABSORPTION OF DRUGS FROM THE GASTROINTESTINAL TRACT

A. Absorption Processes

1. Passive Diffusion Through the Gastrointestinal Wall

Drugs pass from the gastrointestinal (g.i.) tract into the bloodstream primarily by passive diffusion. Few drugs are actively absorbed, and these will be discussed later. The absorption of drugs by passive transport will thus be a function of the concentration gradient between the gastrointestinal tract and the blood. A drug moves from the gastrointestinal tract into the bloodstream because diffusion occurs from a region of high concentration to that of a lower concentration. This point has been dramatically illustrated by the demonstration that drugs administered parenterally are secreted into the gastric juice [2]. Although we are accustomed to thinking about drugs passing from the stomach into the blood, that experiment reminds us that passive transport is described by the principles of physical chemistry and that the rate and direction of mass transport from one side of a membrane to the other is due entirely to the concentration gradient of the diffusing species.

Since this gradient refers to the diffusing species only, we must define what kind of chemical entities can in fact permeate this membrane. The gastrointestinal membrane is composed of a lipoidal sheet covered on both sides by protein, oriented perpendicularly to the cell surface and having frequent water-filled pores of about 4 Å in radius. There are relatively few substances capable of passing from the g.i. tract into the blood by the pore route. Small atoms such as K^+ and Cl^- will fit through these openings, and they may be carried through the membrane by water passing through the pores—creating what is sometimes called solvent drag. Drugs, however, are generally large molecules with molecular weights in excess of 100. They are therefore too large to permeate these pores. Since the membrane is lipoidal in nature, it is believed that drugs undergo a partitioning process from the aqueous gastrointestinal fluids into the oleaginous membrane. After diffusion through the membrane, they then partition from the membrane into the aqueous blood and tissue fluids. This concept of absorption by an oil/water partitioning process is generally attributed to Hogben et al. [3] about 1957. In general we will assume that drugs are passively absorbed and that their absorption is related to their ability to leave the aqueous fluids of the gastrointestinal tract, partition into the g.i. membrane, and finally into the blood. For the purpose of our discussions we will use the following model for the g.i. membrane. We shall think of the membrane as being composed of a continuous layer of mineral oil with a number of small water-filled channels of a size much smaller than the drugs themselves. This is not meant to be a physiological model, but rather an oversimplified reference state that will prove helpful in making predictions regarding the permeability of organic molecules.

2. pH-Partition Theory

Figures 1, 4, and 5 in Chap. 2 are actually illustrations of drug transfer by passive diffusion in agreement with the pH-partition theory. It might be helpful to the reader to reread those sections in Chap. 2 before proceeding with the present chapter.

In its simplest terms this theory can be described as follows. Keeping our model of the g.i. membrane in mind, one would predict that uncharged drug molecules would permeate this membrane with more facility than charged species. That is, neutral species would be expected to be more soluble in mineral oil than ionic species. If a drug can exist in two forms, such as HA and A⁻ or RNH_2 and RNH_3^+, one would expect the absorption process to occur predominantly through the neutral form. Although the pH-partition theory is generally attributed to Schanker [4], there has been evidence for such behavior in the literature for some time [5]. An intriguing demonstration of this principle was carried out by Travell in 1940 [6]. When the pH of the stomach of experimental animals was kept low, there were no toxic effects from large doses of alkaloids. However, when the stomach contents were made alkaline, the animals died rapidly. Thus gastrointestinal membrane was shown to be permeable to the neutral form of the alkaloid and relatively impermeable to the ionic species.

$$\underset{\text{Not absorbed}}{RNH_3^+} \quad \underset{H^+}{\overset{OH^-}{\rightleftharpoons}} \quad \underset{\text{absorbed}}{RNH_2} \tag{1}$$

There is probably general agreement that a drug will be absorbed primarily as the neutral form if it is capable of existing as two species. There is another facet to the pH-partition theory, however, that seems to be qualitatively correct although not always quantitatively accurate. This principle is concerned with the prediction of relative rates or amounts of absorption by comparing the partition coefficients of the drugs in question. The apparent partition coefficient, K_{app}, may be expressed as the ratio of the equilibrium concentration of drug that is distributed between two immiscible solvents.

$$K_{app} = \left(\frac{\text{concentration in solvent 1}}{\text{concentration in solvent 2}} \right)_{equil} \tag{2}$$

There is no convention regarding which solvent appears in the numerator or the denominator. In considering drug absorption, the partition coefficient is often expressed in terms of the ratio of the concentration in the nonaqueous phase to that in the aqueous phase. For our model membrane the coefficient K_{app} might be expressed as the ratio of the drug concentration in mineral oil to the drug concentration in water, where the system involving an oil-water interface has been allowed to achieve equilibrium. Equation (2) would adequately describe a system where the drug exists as a monomer in both the aqueous and the oleaginous phase. It is important to realize that the partition coefficient will be constant only when it truly reflects the species that is in equilibrium between the phases. This is similar to our considerations regarding Fick's law and the concentration gradient of the species common to both sides of the barrier. The true partition coefficient, then, is the ratio of the concentration of the species common to both solvents. For example, if the drug undergoes dimerization in the oil phase so that

$$D_{H_2O} \rightleftharpoons D_{oil} + D_{oil} \rightleftharpoons (D_{oil})_2 \tag{3}$$

the partition coefficient reflecting the equilibrium concentration ratios of the monomeric species,

$$K = \frac{D_{oil}}{D_{H_2O}} \tag{4}$$

would be a constant whereas the apparent partition coefficient, K_{app}, defined in Eq. (2) would vary with total drug concentration since the association constant, K_a, is defined by

$$K_a = \frac{(D_{oil})_2}{(D_{oil})^2} \tag{5}$$

and therefore the apparent partition coefficient becomes

$$K_{app} = K(1 + 2K_a D_{oil}) \tag{6}$$

There have been a significant number of attempts to correlate the relative partition coefficients between nonaqueous solvents and water with the relative absorbability from the gastrointestinal tract for certain series of drugs such as barbituates, sulfonamides, and so on. Although there is an apparent relationship between g.i. absorption and partition coefficients of drugs in such solvent systems as n-octanol/water, it is by no means a completely reliable concept from a quantitative standpoint. For the purpose of the present chapter we will accept the premise that increasing the oil/water partition coefficient of a given drug will increase its gastrointestinal absorption, although we will not presume that there is necessarily a linear relationship between the absorption values and the K values.

Earlier the problem of establishing a meaningful number for the partition coefficient of a drug relative to its actual distributive behavior between the g.i. membrane and the aqueous g.i. fluids was discussed. This may not be the only obstacle to establishing a dependable method for predicting absorption of drugs based on their partition coefficients. One problem may reside in the fact that the partition coefficient is an equilibrium value and the membrane concentration of drug may never be in an equilibrium state but rather in a steady state due to loss of drug at the systemic side. We cannot even be entirely predictive regarding the types of organic molecules which are capable of being absorbed. Although one may predict that a molecule existing as both an ion and a neutral species will be primarily absorbed in the noncharged form, there are many quaternary drugs which exist only as cations that are still absorbed. In spite of the limitations outlined here we can still make some practical use of the pH-partition theory, as will be demonstrated throughout this chapter.

3. Active Transport Through the Gastrointestinal Wall

Most drugs are absorbed by passive diffusion and their transport is therefore characterized by the factors outlined in Chap. 2. However, some drugs are absorbed by active transport mechanisms. The characteristics of such a transport system were also described in Chap. 2. The carrier system may be an enzyme or some other component of the g.i. wall, and each carrier is generally concentrated in a specific segment of the g.i. tract. The substrate for that carrier will be preferentially absorbed in the location of highest carrier density. For example, more riboflavin is absorbed from the prosimal portion of the small intestine than from the large intestine or upper intestine. Some studies have indicated better vitamin B_{12} absorption in the lower small intestine. Drugs such as 5-fluorouracil and 5-bromouracil are actively absorbed—presumably in the same manner as uracil itself, which is absorbed by the pyrimidine transport system. Several substances which are essential to the body, such as vitamins, minerals such as iron, bile salts, amino acids, and monosaccharides, are actively absorbed. In some cases the level of activity of the carrier system has been thought to directly reflect the body's immediate need for the particular substrate. Drugs absorbed by active mechanisms most likely compete with the natural substrates for the active site in the transport system.

B. Absorption of Drugs from Solutions

1. Rate-Determining Step

The fastest rate of absorption by the oral route can generally be achieved by administering a solution of the drug. Thus if one is concerned primarily with onset of action, the drug would best be administered in the form of an elixir, syrup, or aqueous solution. For a neutral drug the rate-determining step would simply be the passive transfer of drug from the g.i. fluids through the g.i. wall to the systemic circulation. In this case the process should be relatively independent of the position in the g.i. tract, since we have limited the example to passive absorption of a neutral drug. Many drugs are either general acids or general bases and are therefore influenced by the environment or the g.i. fluids. This is discussed next.

2. pH and Gastrointestinal Absorption Sites

Figure 7 is a schematic representation of part of the digestive tract. As noted in the figure, there is a gradual decrease in acidity in moving from the stomach to the lower intestine. The stomach varies in pH from 1 to 3.5, but pH 1 to 2.5 is

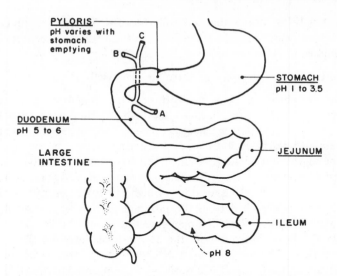

Fig. 7   Diagram illustrating the pH of various regions in the gastrointestinal tract.

probably the most common range. Stomach pH is affected by foods and can be clinically altered by administration of antacids. By comparison, the intestinal pH is relatively independent of such foreign influences. The duodenum has a pH of 5 to 6 and the lower ileum approaches a pH of 8.

This difference in pH of the g.i. fluids can be a key factor in determining the primary site of absorption of a drug from an orally administered solution. We have already discussed the absorption of a drug that can exist in both a charged and an uncharged form. According to the pH-partition theory the primary mode of absorption will be by passive diffusion of the neutral species. If we consider all drugs as acids (in the protonated form), we can generalize their dissociation by considering two groups. The groups may be represented

$$\underset{\text{Absorbable form}}{HA} \quad \rightleftharpoons H^+ + \underset{\text{nonabsorbable form}}{A^-} \tag{7a}$$

and

$$\underset{\text{Nonabsorbable form}}{R_3NH^+} \quad \rightleftharpoons \underset{\text{absorbable form}}{R_3N} \quad + H^+ \tag{7b}$$

where HA represents carboxylic acids, sulfonamides, imides, phenols, and so on, and R_3NH^+ represents all amines such as alkyl amines, phenylalkylamines, alkanolamines, pyridines, quinolines, imidazoles, piperidines, indoles, and phenothiazines. The only word of caution is to remember that the protonated form is *neutral for acidic compounds* (HA) and *charged for basic amines*. Thus the Henderson-Hasselbalch equation can be employed to calculate the relative amount of the charged form from the pK_a of the drug (HA or RNH_3^+) and the pH of the environment.

Since the rate determining step in g.i. absorption of drugs that are orally administered in solution is partitioning of the neutral species, the preferred site for absorption would be expected to be that area of the g.i. tract where the neutral species is at its maximum. If we consider the ingestion of a weak acid, HA, of pK_a in the range 4 to 5 for example, we would expect this drug to exist primarily in the neutral form in the stomach at pH 1 to 3.5. Thus we would predict that the drug would be absorbed primarily from the stomach. It is likely that we will be correct in this case at least in a semiquantitative sense. When the solution of drug is ingested, it will first arrive in the stomach. Since the neutral species will predominate, absorption would be expected to occur. This is not to say that absorption from the intestines cannot take place. If the drug solution passes into the intestines, its absorption may not be limited by pH considerations alone. Absorption may still occur in spite of the fact that a drug of type HA with a pK_a of 4 would be predominantly charged throughout the intestines. The reason for this behavior lies in the anatomy of the intestinal tract. The intestinal tract is extremely long. In addition to its length, it is composed of large numbers of villi which serve to increase the overall surface area of the intestines. When drug is exposed to this long tract of great area, it becomes relatively easy for absorption to occur across the thin, 25-μm epithelial layer which also has 6,000 ml/min of blood plasma circulating on the systemic side—thus maintaining a high concentration gradient. Thus the intestine is anatomically well adapted for absorption of drugs and other substances.

Our predictions for R_3N types of drugs will be a little more successful. Since the stomach is relatively small, a drug that exists in the charged form, R_3NH^+, will probably not be well absorbed from the stomach. Using the same pK_a value of 4 for the protonated amine, we would predict that absorption from the stomach would be poor since the drug would exist almost entirely in the protonated (and in this case charged) form in the stomach. Once the drug passed into the intestines, it would be in the neutral form and would be expected to show good absorption by the intestinal route.

It should be recognized here that we have referred to absorption in a rather undefined manner. That is, we have not differentiated between absorption rate and amount absorbed. The large intestinal surface may in certain cases result in complete absorption at a rather slow rate. As previously discussed, the time profile may be all important clinically. We will discuss this aspect further under the section on solid dosage forms. It might also be mentioned here that a drug absorbed primarily from the intestines could have stomach emptying time as its rate-determining step. Since this would be more pronounced with a solid dosage form, it will also be discussed in that section.

C. Absorption of Drugs from Solid Dosage Forms

1. Rate-Determining Step

In the previous discussions the absorption process began the instant the drug arrived at the site for absorption. This is not the case when a drug is administered in a solid dosage form. In order for a drug to be absorbed, it must first be in solution. Let us consider the absorption of an acidic drug, HA, from a tablet. The usual steps involved in the absorption process are represented in Fig. 8. Once the tablet is swallowed, it normally undergoes disintegration, dissolution, and finally absorption as illustrated in the figure.

It is important to realize the difference between disintegration and dissolution. Disintegration is simply the coming apart of the compressed tablet into primary particles. By including certain disintegrating agents in the formula, one can produce a tablet that will literally explode when simply dropped into a glass of water. While disintegration is a prerequisite for absorption and fast disintegration certainly enhances a speedy onset, it does not ensure that absorption will occur. If the drug particles do not dissolve after disintegration takes place, then the drug will never reach the bloodstream. This would be no

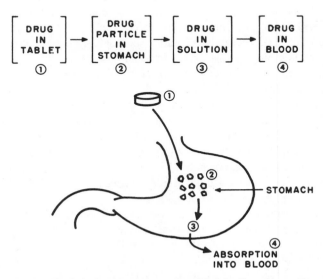

Fig. 8 Illustration of the usual steps involved in the absorption of a drug after the oral administration of a tablet.

different from swallowing the ancient "perpetual pill" of gold which was retrieved for continuous use throughout a man's lifetime and passed along with the family inheritance. It is easily recognized that such treatment never resulted in blood levels of gold. Yet people are often prone to accept a disintegration test as evidence for a fast onset of the drug. A negative disintegration test is certainly evidence of a poor tablet, for if the first step does not occur, dissolution will be difficult and absorption may never take place. Fast disintegration will certainly aid in predicting uniform behavior from the tablets, but it will not, in itself, ensure efficacy.

We will assume that the proper technology has been employed to allow rapid disintegration of the tablet on ingestion. This brings us to the second step in Fig. 8, that of dissolution. It is likely that this will represent the rate-determining step in the absorption of a drug from a tablet. We are considering the rate of appearance of drug in the blood for a well-absorbed general acid, HA, taken orally in a tablet. In our scheme we have represented this process as having three major steps. (Diffusion has not been included for simplicity.) The drug can appear in the bloodstream at a rate no faster than the slowest step. This may be likened to a bucket brigade, in which the rate of arrival of buckets at the delivery end will be no faster than the rate of the slowest person in the line. Thus if disintegration has been adequately designed and the drug is readily absorbed from solution, then the rate-limiting step will be dissolution. We may expect dissolution to be generally rate-determining in the absorption of drugs from tablets and especially when the drug is poorly soluble.

2. Controlling Absorption Rate from Solid Dosage Forms

Under conditions of fast disintegration and well-absorbed drug, the dissolution rate of the drug particles themselves will limit the rate of appearance of drug in the blood. These conditions may be considered as generally applicable. That is, one can usually increase absorption rate by increasing the rate of dissolution. Since dissolution rate is the limiting factor, it follows that to control dissolution rate is to control absorption. This is the ultimate goal in any product development: to control the behavior of that product when it is in use in the clinic. In the case of solid dosage forms it is therefore necessary to examine the methods of controlling dissolution rate. Let us begin by examining the factors that influence the dissolution rate of a drug. By choosing those factors that can be controlled either by the design or use of the product, we should be able to control the dissolution rate of drug and ultimately absorption.

For the purpose of this discussion it is convenient to examine a modified form of the Noyes-Whitney dissolution rate law given as

$$\frac{dC}{dt} = \frac{kDS}{Vh}(C_s - C) \tag{8}$$

Although this expression appears complex, we will make it extremely simple in just a moment. First let us define the terms. The rate we are considering, dC/dt, is the rate of increase in C, the concentration of drug in a bulk solution in which dissolution of the solid particles is taking place. The constants are defined as follows: k ≡ proportionality constant; D ≡ diffusion coefficient of the drug in the solvent; S ≡ surface area of undissolved solid; V ≡ volume of the solution; h ≡ thickness of the diffusion layer around a particle; and C_s ≡ solubility of the drug in the solvent. The rate-controlling step in this process can be a function of agitation in that dissolution rate into the diffusion layer may be slower than diffusion to the bulk solution under high rates of stirring and vice versa. However, it is not necessary to examine the mechanism at a molecular level in order to understand the application of these principles to the design and use of solid dosage forms. If we consider a given drug under well-defined conditions of use (such as controlled liquid intake), we may assume that D, V, and h are relatively constant values that are not conveniently altered to any dramatic degree by the product formulation. Thus we can easily reduce Eq. (8) to:

$$\frac{dC}{dt} = k'S(C_s - C) \tag{9}$$

If we further assume that dissolution is rate-limiting to the point that the accumulation of drug in the g.i. fluids is negligible relative to the solubility of the drug itself, or $C_s \gg C$, then

(Dissolution rate) ∝ (surface area) (solubility)   (10)

and we are now in a position to examine some clinical applications of this law.

Equation (10) states that the variables to be controlled by the formulation are the surface area and the solubility of the drug. These two variables can be altered by the following techniques:

1. Control solubility of a weak acid or base by buffering the entire dissolution medium, the "microenvironment" or the diffusion layer surrounding a particle.
2. Control the solubility of the drug through choice of the physical state such as crystal form, its hydrate, its amorphous form, and so on.
3. Determine the surface area of the drug through control of particle size.

We shall consider each of these factors individually with examples.

   a. Controlling Solubility Through Stomach Buffering. It would be well to keep in mind that we are dealing with *solubility* as a means of increasing or decreasing *dissolution rate*. The difference between these terms should be clear in the reader's mind before proceeding. Equation (10) illustrates the fact that they are different although related. (It should be noted here that there are exceptions to the generality that dissolution rate is proportional to solubility, but they are sufficiently rare that we will assume there is generally a relationship.) Solubility is a thermodynamic parameter; that is, it represents the concentration of a solution of drug at equilibrium with undissolved solute. Dissolution rate is a kinetic term that describes how fast the drug dissolves in the medium. We are now considering increasing or decreasing the total solubility, C_s, of a drug in the g.i. fluids in order to affect the rate of dissolution and thus the rate of absorption.

The total solubility, S_T, of a weak acid increases with pH according to the equation

$$S_T = S_0 (1 + 10^{pH - pK_a})$$ (11)

where S_0 is the intrinsic solubility of the undissociated form and is therefore a constant that is independent of pH. This equation is valid at pH values below that pH at which the solution becomes saturated by the ionic species [7]. Thus, in the region where Eq. (11) applies, as the pH of the solvent is increased the total solubility of a weak acid will increase due to increased formation of the anion, A⁻. An obvious approach to the problem of increasing dissolution rate would be to co-administer an antacid with a weak acid drug, HA. It was previously pointed out that the stomach pH can be buffered toward alkalinity. Thus the total solubility of the drug would increase in accordance with Eq. (11), and the dissolution rate would be enhanced as described in Eq. (10). The alert reader may immediately question the wisdom of converting a weakly acidic drug to its charged form in order to enhance absorption. However, the principle can be documented by considering some studies done on aspirin [8]. When aspirin was dissolved in water in the presence of buffers and administered orally, the onset for salicylate blood levels was found to be faster than those obtained by swallowing plain and buffered aspirin tablets in spite of the fact that the pH of the stomach was raised to 7 in the case of the solution. One must keep in mind that two different rate-limiting steps are being compared here. In the case of the buffered solution the dissolution step has already taken place before swallowing. Absorption occurs primarily through the uncharged form of aspirin, but this is in rapid equilibrium with a reserve of the charged form. In the case of the tablets, the rate-limiting factor is that of dissolution. One explanation for the difference in absorption rates is that dissolution of aspirin at pH 1 to 3.5 is slower than partitioning of aspirin from a solution of pH 7 into the g.i. membrane. This is partially due to the fact that the total amount of aspirin in solution is much greater at pH 7 than at pH 1 to 3.5, as can be seen from Eq. (11). In general, we will assume that speeding up dissolution rate will result in increased absorption in spite of the problem associated with the effect of pH on the concentration of absorbable species. Adjusting the pH of the entire gastric fluid content will not often be the approach used for increasing dissolution rate.

  b. *Adjusting the pH of the Microenvironment.* A method more frequently employed is that of controlling the pH in the solution surrounding the undissolved particles of drug. In the case of an acidic drug this may be accomplished by including such agents as sodium bicarbonate, sodium citrate, magnesium oxide, magnesium carbonate, and so on. The amount of these agents in a typical buffered tablet is by no means sufficient to alter the pH of the stomach contents. For example, a typical buffered aspirin tablet contains magnesium carbonate 0.1 g and aluminum dihydroxyaminoacetate 0.05 g. Another contains 0.15 g of magnesium and aluminum hydroxide. A typical antacid dose of magnesium carbonate is 0.6 g, aluminum dihydroxyaminoacetate is 1 g and magnesium and aluminum hydroxide (combined) is 0.8 to 1.6 g. It is obvious that these agents are not included with the intent of raising the pH of the stomach. In fact, it has been determined that the pH of the stomach remains unchanged by buffered aspirin. Yet it has been demonstrated that the dissolution rate and the absorption rate of aspirin is increased in buffered tablets as compared to plain aspirin [8-10].

  This might be thought of as raising the pH of the microenvironment, since the pH of the bulk solution is not changed but dissolution rate is increased. Thus the area immediately surrounding the aspiring particles may be elevated in pH due to the proximity of the buffer components of the dosage form itself.

  c. *Salts of Weak Acids or Weak Bases.* When a weak acid is dissolved in water, the pH may be approximated from

$$pH = \frac{1}{2} (pK_a - \log C) \qquad\qquad (12)$$

where C is the total concentration of the acid in the solution [7]. If a salt of a strong base and a weak acid is dissolved in water, the pH may be approximated from

$$pH = \frac{1}{2} (pK_w + pK_a + \log C) \qquad\qquad (13)$$

Thus for moderately concentrated solutions, the pH of a solution of the salt of a weak acid and a strong base will be higher than that of a solution of the same weak acid. Consider 1 M solutions using an acid of pK_a 4 as a convenient example. Since the log of 1 is zero and the pK_w for water is 14, we can easily calculate that the pH of a 1 M solution of the acid will be 2 and the pH of a 1 M solution of its sodium or potassium salt will be 9.0. We can now easily understand why salts are more soluble than the free acids. They are not more soluble in the literal sense of the word, since the solubility in both cases is described by Eq. (11). We can expect a higher total solubility in the case of a salt due to the buffering of the solvent to a higher pH by the strong base cation. In the example just discussed the pH was estimated as 7.0 units higher for the salt than for the acid.

Consider what difference in dissolution rate might be observed in the preparation of two solutions, an acid and its sodium salt, each in a beaker of water. As the free acid dissolves, the pH of the water would be lowered and the total solubility would approach the value of S_0 in Eq. (11). However, as its sodium salt dissolves, the pH would be increased and the total solubility, S_T, would also increase. If we were to measure the rate of dissolution, we would find that the sodium salt is dissolving at a much faster rate. This is easily understood by examinining Eq. (10) for the case where the surface area for the acid and its salt are equal so that

$$\frac{dC}{dt} \propto C_s \propto S_T \tag{14}$$

Since we are speaking of one acid, the value for S_0 is constant in both beakers. The ratio of the dissolution rates will be equal to the ratio of the total solubilities as indicated in Eq. (14). This ratio may be expressed as

$$\frac{S_T}{S'_T} = \frac{(1 + 10^{pH - pK_a})}{(1 + 10^{pH' - pK_a})} \tag{15}$$

where S'_T and pH$'$ are the values for the free acid, and S_T and pH are the values for the sodium salt. For the sake of illustration let us assume that an acid of pK_a 3 had a pH of 2 at saturation while its salt produced a pH of 6. The ratio S_T/S'_T would thus be 910. If all the other variables are held constant, then Eq. (14) would predict that the dissolution rate for the salt of the acid would be 910 times faster than the free acid.

So far we have discussed dissolution rates in beakers of water. How significant are these calculations in vivo? Certainly the salt form of an acidic drug would not be expected to buffer the pH of the gastric fluids. We have already examined the large difference between an average dose of an antacid and the dosage contained in a typical buffered aspirin tablet. The salt form of the active ingredient would generally be even smaller than the amounts of antacids in a buffered tablet. It is easily recognized that this salt would not affect the pH of gastric juice.

There are a large number of examples illustrating the fact that the sodium or potassium salts of weak acid drugs are more rapidly absorbed than the free acid itself when each is administered orally in tablets. A few examples are sodium and potassium salts of penicillins and sodium salts of barbiturates, sulfonamides, and salicylates [11]. If the pH of the stomach is unchanged by these salts, how can the increase in absorption rate be rationalized?

We can assume that each particle of undissolved drug is surrounded by a thin zone of saturated solution which may be called the diffusion layer. The thought here is that dissolved drug diffuses from this zone into the bulk solution and thus leaves a nonsaturated space in the diffusion layer. As this occurs, more drug is dissolved from the particle into the layer. Thus the diffusion layer remains at a steady-state concentration that would approach the saturation solubility of the drug in the area immediately adjacent to the solid. We might diagram this as

$$\begin{bmatrix} \text{Drug in} \\ \text{solid state} \end{bmatrix} \underset{\longleftarrow}{\longrightarrow} \begin{bmatrix} \text{Drug in} \\ \text{diffusion layer} \end{bmatrix} - - - - - \xrightarrow{\text{Diffusion}} \begin{bmatrix} \text{Drug in} \\ \text{bulk solution} \end{bmatrix} \quad (16)$$

The migration of drug from the layer surrounding the particle into the bulk solution would take place due to the concentration gradient in a manner similar to that illustrated in Fig. 1, Chap. 2 and the discussion on Fick's law. However, the g.i. fluids are poorly represented by a beaker of solvent at rest. Agitation would occur constantly, and the movement of drug into the bulk solution would be due primarily to this mixing rather than the diffusibility of the drug itself, which would achieve relatively slow distribution in the example shown in Fig. 1.

The model shown in Eq. (16) has two areas where drug exists in solution. This, of course, is diagrammatic, since a continuous concentration gradient would exist between the solution near the particle and that in the bulk. In terms of the model, we have assumed that the diffusion layer is in the steady state and that it is a saturated solution of the drug. If the pH of this layer were increased, then one would expect the solubility of a weak acid to increase. A sodium or potassium salt of a weak acid would be expected to have a diffusion layer of higher pH than that of the free acid. In spite of the fact that the bulk solution will have the same pH in both cases, the salt will have a faster dissolution rate. If we consider the dissolution rate of an acidic drug in the stomach at pH 1 to 3, it is immediately obvious that the total solubility in the bulk solution is rather limited. The question is then reduced simply to which form will saturate this gastric fluid first, the acid or the salt. Since the salt form has a higher pH in the diffusion layer, the dissolution of the particle will take place faster. If absorption is fast, we may assume that the bulk solution will also be in a near steady state and that the particle which dissolves faster into its diffusion layer will result in faster absorption. Thus it is a general observation that the sodium or potassium salts of acidic drugs are absorbed faster. It should be apparent here that one might expect reprecipitation of the free acid to occur in the bulk solution if the pH is several units lower than that surrounding the particle, since total solubility is described by Eq. (11). Several writers have expressed the opinion that this precipitation would result in very fine crystals with a resultant increase in surface area as compared to the free acid form itself. While this may or may not represent an additional advantage of the salt form, it does not negate the fact that a saturated solution of free acid in stomach fluids occurs faster beginning with the salt form.

The discussions to this point have centered around increasing the rate of absorption of weak acids. There are somewhat analogous examples for weak base drugs, R_3N. As we have previously discussed, these drugs would be expected to be absorbed from the intestines. Since they must first pass through the stomach, there is an opportunity for rapid dissolution in acidic medium as the total solubility of a base increases when it is protonated to form the charged species. However, the variability in stomach emptying time precludes any dependability in predicting that dissolution will take place in the stomach before the tablet is passed into the intestines. For this reason several basic drugs are administered in the protonated forms as chloride or other salts. This approach generally ensures that stomach emptying and not dissolution rate will be rate-determining. A few examples of such drugs are tetracyclines, antihistamines, phenylalkylamines such as amphetamine and ephedrine, and most alkaloids [12].

Thus the absorption rate of both acidic and basic drugs from solid dosage forms may be increased by administration of their salts. As shown in Fig. 6, increasing the absorption rate would decrease onset, increase peak blood level but decrease the duration. For example, the shortest duration for a given dosage would result from an I.V. injection. If onset and peak height are the most significant parameters for a given drug therapy, then rapid absorption should be the goal in the development of that solid dosage form. However, it may be a therapeutic advantage to have a lower peak level and a longer duration. To be more specific, we might consider the hypothetical problem of developing an oral tablet for control of blood sugar level or an oral hypoglycemic agent. If the drug is quickly absorbed, a fast dissolution rate would result in a high blood level and a possible temporary state of hypoglycemia to the patient. The very short duration would result in frequent dosing in order to control blood sugar. The onset of the action would not be so critical here, since the treatment would be a chronic one and not subject to the same considerations as treating a systemic infection with an antibiotic where onset and peak height might be paramount. Since the patient will continue to take the hypoglycemic agent, a more constant blood level of longer duration may be deemed more ideal. A case in point may be that of tolbutamide and tolbutamide sodium. It has been reported that the sodium salt gives a very fast, strong, but short-acting effect on the lowering of blood sugar levels, whereas the control with the free acid was more suitable for therapy [13]. The commercial tablets are in the free acid form. Thus the control of dissolution rate can be tailored to the specific needs of the disease under treatment. From the standpoint of optimum clinical effectiveness, there is an ideal dosage regimen for every drug.

Sample Problem 1

Three formulations for aspirin tablets were prepared and their bioavailability was tested in ten subjects. The formulations were described as: (A) tablets, (B) buffered tablets, and (C) buffered tablets of micronized aspirin. Results are given in Fig. 9. Assuming that tablets A and B give similar results (the difference being due to biological variation), what is the percent increase of aspirin absorbed from product C?

Solution: A rough estimate can be obtained from the peak heights which occur at about 2 hr. It would appear that approximately 50% more is absorbed from product C. However, in such an evaluation of products it is necessary to know the dose. Product C contains 7.5 grains of aspirin per tablet while products A and B contain 5 grains.

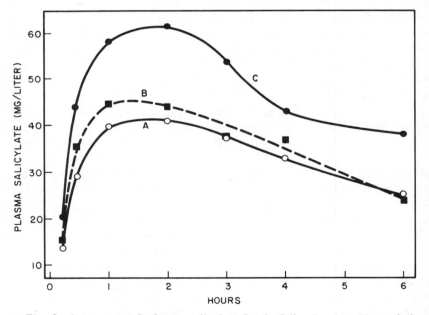

Fig. 9   Average total plasma salicylate levels following ingestion of three commercial types of aspirin tablets by ten patients. Curve A represents aspirin tablets, B is buffered aspirin tablets, and C is buffered tablets of micronized aspirin.

If this comparison was made with equal numbers of tablets (rather than equal doses), the 50% increase would be attributed to 50% more aspirin administered. The time course for aspirin per se is also masked by the fact that this figure represents total salicylate in blood. Unfortunately, it is not difficult to observe such presentations in the advertising media.

Practice Problem 1

(a) What is the concentration in moles per liter of the diffusion layer surrounding penicillin G potassium if the pH of the layer equals 8? (The pK_a of penicillin G is 2.76.)
Answer: 0.174 mol/liter

(b) What is the *solubility* of penicillin G (not the potassium salt) at a pH sufficiently low to allow only the nondissociated form? [Hint: Use your answer from part (a) and Eq. (11). Consider the diffusion layer to be saturated.]
Answer: 1×10^{-6} mol/liter

(c) Consider the initial rates of absorption of penicillin G potassium and penicillin G from identical solid dosage forms. Calculate the value which you would predict for the ratio of the rates where Ratio = R_1/R_2 and R_1 = Rate of absorption from penicillin G potassium, R_2 = Rate of absorption from penicillin G. [Assume the solubilities that you calculated in parts (a) and (b).]
Answer: 1.74×10^5

Practice Problem 2

(a) Calculate the pH of a 4×10^{-3} M solution of sodium sulfathiazole. (The pK_a of sulfathiazole is 7.1.)
Answer: 9.35

(b) Calculate the pH of 4×10^{-3} M solution of sulfathiazole.
Answer: 4.75

(c) Assuming that the diffusion layer in the case of (a) has the pH which you calculated and that of (b) has the pH which you calculated, calculate the *total* solubility of sodium sulfathiazole and of sulfathiazole in their respective stagnant layers. The intrinsic solubility is given above, 4×10^{-3} M.
Answer: Sodium sulf = 0.716 mol/liter; sulfathiazole = 0.004 mol/liter

(d) Given in similar tablets (e.g., same binders, disintegration, etc.), which would be absorbed faster? Explain your choice.
Answer: The sodium salt

Practice Problem 3

(a) Explain, using equations, why the rate of dissolution of sodium phenobarbital is faster than that of phenobarbital.

(b) Why would you expect to find a difference in absorption between sodium phenobarbital tablets and phenobarbital tablets but not between enteric-coated sodium phenobarbital tablets and enteric-coated phenobarbital tablets?
Answer: See discussion in text regarding absorption from tablets.

Practice Problem 4

(a) Consider the absorption following oral administration of an elixir containing two drugs: Drug A = RCOOH and Drug B = RNH_2. *Given:* the pH of the stomach is 2. Which would you expect to be better absorbed from the stomach, and why?
Answer: Drug A; see text for discussion.

(b) Write the rate expression for the absorption of each.
Answer: (Rate absorption of Drug A) = k_1 [RCOOH]; (rate absorption of drug B) = k'_1 [RNH_2]

(c) What kinetic order are these rates?
Answer: First order

(d) *Given:* The pK_a of drug A is 2; the pK_a of protonated drug B is 3; the dose of each drug is 1 g; the volume of gastric juice is 100 ml. Write the expression for *initial* rate of absorption substituting the concentration of the absorbable species in grams per 100 milliliters for each case.
Answer: (Rate absorption of drug A)$_0$ = k_1 (0.5 g/100 ml); (Rate absorption of drug B)$_0$ = k'_1 (0.09 g/100 ml)

Practice Problem 5

(a) Consider transport from blood (pH 7.4) to stomach (pH 2.0) following I.V. injection. Which would appear to a larger extent in the stomach, phenobarbital (pK_a = 7.4) or morphine (pK_a = 7.9, aminium) and why?
Answer: Morphine (consider uncharged form in blood and stomach)

(b) Explain why the rate of absorption of prednisone, prednisolone, testosterone, and androsterone esters given orally in sesame oil solutions was greater than the corresponding aqueous suspensions.
Answer: Change in rate-limiting step

(c) Explain why the absorption rate of tetracyclines was increased by reducing the particle size, but the absorption rate of tetracycline hydrochloride was not affected by the same treatment.
Answer: Dissolution was not rate-limiting for the hydrochloride. Why?

(d) Consider this data:

	Percent absorbed by oral route
Hesamethonium chloride	5
Pentolinium tartrate	4
Mecamylamine hydrochloride	50

Why are hexamethonium chloride and pentolinium tartrate poorly absorbed compared with mecamylamine hydrochloride? Why is the apparent volume of distribution of drugs such as hexamethonium chloride and pentolinium tartrate only about 7 to 21%? Why are drugs such as hexamethonium chloride and pentolinium tartrate particularly dangerous by oral administration? Would you expect to find any difference in absorption from tablets of mecamylamine and mecamylamine hydrochloride and why?
Answer: Hint: Mecamylamine hydrochloride is not a quaternary, but the others are.

(e) A commercial for buffered aspirin states that two of the buffered tablets deliver almost twice as much acetylsalicylic acid as two of the plain aspirin tablets. If the aspirin is completely absorbed in both cases, what is the meaning of the statement?

(f) It has been stated by Hogben et al. that acids with a pK_a below 2 and bases with a pK_a above 9 are poorly absorbed when taken orally. Do you agree or disagree and why?

(g) Heparin is marketed only as an injection (heparin sodium injection, Panheprin, Abbott; etc.) because the weak acid, heparin, is not absorbed at a pH above 4, thus limiting oral availability. Esterification has been shown to result in absorption at pH 5, 6, and 7. Offer an explanation for this difference in g.i. absorption.

d. Physical State of the Drug. Polymorphism is the ability of a drug to crystallize as more than one distinct crystal species [14]. These forms can differ in such properties as melting point, density, X-ray diffraction, hardness, infrared spectra and, most important to this discussion, solubility. Thus while the solution phase will have only one form of the dissolved drug, the solid phase can contain two or more forms. Only one form will ultimately be stable, and if the solution is allowed to stand it will approach an equilibrium containing a single type of solid. If this transformation is sufficiently slow, the thermodynamically unstable polymorph is called *metastable*. The most stable polymorph usually has the highest melting point and the lowest solubility. The amorphous form is always more soluble than the crystalline form. Since the dissolution rate is proportional to the solubility and the drug must be dissolved in order to be absorbed, the conversion from a metastable to a stable form can represent a real problem in bioavailability.

A well-publicized example of this phenomenon is that of novobiocin in suspension [14]. The amorphous form of novobiocin is readily absorbed and therefore therapeutically effective, whereas the crystalline form is not. At 25°C in 0.1 N HCl, the amorphous form was found to be ten times more soluble than the crystalline form. In novobiocin aqueous suspensions the following equilibrium,

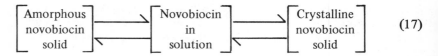

$$\begin{bmatrix} \text{Amorphous} \\ \text{novobiocin} \\ \text{solid} \end{bmatrix} \rightleftharpoons \begin{bmatrix} \text{Novobiocin} \\ \text{in} \\ \text{solution} \end{bmatrix} \rightleftharpoons \begin{bmatrix} \text{Crystalline} \\ \text{novobiocin} \\ \text{solid} \end{bmatrix} \qquad (17)$$

will slowly convert to the more stable crystalline precipitate, with decreasing oral effectiveness to the point where the therapeutic effect is finally lost entirely. Aqueous suspensions of amorphous novobiocin can be stabilized against conversion to the inactive crystalline form for sufficient periods of time to be clinically useful by including such agents as methylcellulose, PVP, sodium alginate, or propylene glycol algin.

Novobiocin represents only one example. There are many drugs which could have been chosen to document the importance of this principle, among them chloramphenicol palmitate, cortisone acetate, sulfathiazole, methylprednisolone, hydrocortisone, prednisolone, and perhaps even aspirin (where a 50% difference in dissolution rate between two polymorphs has been reported). Poole et al. [15] have demonstrated that the solubility of anhydrous ampicillin is 20% higher than the trihydrate, and this resulted in both an increased rate and amount of drug absorbed after oral administration of suspensions and capsules to humans.

The above examples should serve to illustrate that the bioavailability of a drug from a solid dosage form can be increased by proper control of the physical state of the drug. It should also serve to point out the fact that a product can assay for 100% potency yet be clinically inactive due to the use of the wrong polymorphic form of the drug.

e. Determining Drug Surface Area Through Control of Particle Size.
Equation (10) contains two variables that can be controlled in the development
of solid dosage forms: surface and solubility. We have not yet discussed any
examples of surface effects on therapy. One might immediately consider the
advantages of presenting a large surface area by using very finely powdered drug
in order to enhance the dissolution rate. While we are prone to think in terms of
fast absorption, we tend to overlook the fact that controlled absorption or an
ideal absorption pattern for each individual drug should be the goal of modern
product development. Two examples have been chosen to illustrate this point
further. In one case we will review the rationale behind a microcrystalline
product and in the other case a macrocrystalline product.

Griseofulvin is a white, thermostable powder or needlelike crystals with a
solubility in water between 1 and 10 μg/ml. When given orally, griseofulvin often
exhibits irregular absorption due to its limited solubility [16]. Once absorbed,
however, griseofulvin is distributed into tissues, fat, skeletal muscle, and keratin
and is also bound to protein in the bloodstream. Tissue levels parallel blood
levels, and the apparent biological half-life is of the order of 18 to 24 hr
following oral administration. The most common reason for clinical failure with
griseofulvin therapy is poor absorption. Since absorption is the limiting factor
for effective griseofulvin therapy, several methods for increasing dissolution rate
were examined. Sodium lauryl sulfate was deemed insignificant in multiple-dose
therapy. Marvel et al. [16] and Kraml et al. [17] demonstrated that 0.5 g of
microcrystalline griseofulvin produced blood levels equal to or higher than 1.0-g
doses of regular griseofulvin. Since griseofulvin is fat-soluble, high-fat diets were
also examined. It was shown by Crounse [18] that 1 g of microcrystalline
griseofulvin gave blood levels roughly twice as high as those from regular
griseofulvin in fasting patients and that a high-fat diet more than doubled the
levels from the microcrystalline material. The average serum levels from
microcrystalline griseofulvin doses of 0.5 g can be expected to be equal to or
better than those obtained from 1.0 g of the regular form. It should be kept in
mind that the potential danger from administration of a drug increases as the
percent absorption decreases. If a drug is only 5% absorbed, for example, the
patient is swallowing 20 doses. If for some reason erratically high absorption
takes place, there is a chance for toxic symptoms. The advantage of microcrystalline griseofulvin seems to be quite clear. Evidence has led Blank [19] to
conclude that there is no apparent reason to employ any form of griseofulvin
other than the microcrystalline form since it produces higher blood levels and,
weight for weight, is more effective than the original form. We might also add
that high-fat diet would seem to be a rational adjunct.

There are other examples of micronized drugs, such as sulfadiazine,
sulfaethylthiadiazole, aspirin, tetracycline, and so on. However, this does not
imply that micropulverization of drugs for solid dosage forms is a general

panacea. Let us examine the rationale behind at least one exception, nitrofurantoin.

Nitrofurantoin has a solubility of about 200 mg/liter at a pH of 7. The usual dose is about 50-100 mg taken four times a day. Since it is a weak acid and the volume of stomach fluid is about 100 ml, one would not expect an entire dose to dissolve easily. However, it would appear that about 36% of the amount ingested in the form of fine crystals (10 μm/range) is absorbed [20]. An unspecified percent incidence of nausea and vomiting has been reported in patients taking nitrofurantoin. It was thought that these side effects might be linked to the rate of absorption. As illustrated in Fig. 6, rapid absorption can result in peak blood levels approaching those associated with side effects. In the present case unabsorbed drug in solution in contact with the surface of the gastrointestinal tract might also cause some irritation, contributing to the nausea and vomiting. In either case the proper control of dissolution rate would be expected to decrease the untoward response. Graphs representing excretion of nitrofurantoin for various particle sizes were similar in appearance to those in Fig. 6 in Chap. 3, indicating that the rate constant for release from the depot was a function of particle size. The effect of crystal size on the rate and amount absorbed was studied by determining the percent excreted as a function of time. Data indicate that the blood level peak height as well as total amount absorbed decreased with increasing crystal size. However, it was possible to choose a large crystal size (80-200 mesh) that represented about 31% absorption, which was considered to be roughly equivalent to the originally marketed crystals (10 μm) which are 35% absorbed. The macrocrystals gave lower peak blood levels as reflected by the maximum amount excreted in a fixed time interval, which was 20% for the fine crystals and about 15% for the macrocrystals. Capsules of macrocrystals were used clinically in 112 patients who experienced nausea and vomiting with the tablets (fine crystals), and 89 (79%) tolerated the macrocrystals. Twenty-two of these were rechallenged with the tablets and 86% of these again experienced nausea and/or vomiting. Thus the use of large crystals, in this case, reduced the side effects without significant reduction in the percentage of absorption. It should be noted here that total absorption is not a valid criterion for therapeutic equivalency. Nitrofurantoin is indicated for the treatment of genitourinary tract infections. The therapeutic equivalency claimed for Macrodantin is based on equivalent urinary concentrations [21] and effectiveness in treating urinary tract infections as measured by clinical and biological criteria [22].

D. Factors Decreasing Absorption from the Gastrointestinal Tract

1. Stability

Drugs may be unstable to gastric acid or enzymes present in the g.i. tract. Hydrolysis in the stomach fluids is a rather common occurrence. If a drug undergoes hydrolysis in the g.i. tract, it becomes involved in parallel rate processes as discussed in Chap. 3. This may be represented by

$$
\begin{bmatrix} \text{Drug} \\ \text{in blood} \end{bmatrix} \xleftarrow{\quad k_1 \quad} \begin{bmatrix} \text{Drug in} \\ \text{g.i. fluids} \end{bmatrix} \xrightarrow{\quad k_1' \quad} \begin{bmatrix} \text{Drug} \\ \text{degradation} \\ \text{products} \end{bmatrix} \quad (18)
$$

and the apparent first-order rate constant, k_{app}, may be defined by

$$
k_{app} = k_1 + k_1' \tag{19}
$$

It should be recalled that the ratio of the rate constants will define the ratio of the competing rate processes so that

$$
\frac{k_1'}{k_1} = \frac{P'}{P} \tag{20}
$$

where P' is the degradation product and P is the drug in the blood. What does this mean in terms of absorption? Let us suppose that k_1'/k_1 was 2. That is, the rate of degradation of the drug was twice as fast as its absorption. For every molecule of drug absorbed, two molecules would undergo degradation. Thus the maximum absorption would be 33%.

We will consider the problem of hydrolysis in the gastric fluids under two categories: drugs absorbed in the stomach and drugs absorbed in the intestines. The second category will be considered separately, since it presents the problem of getting the drug through the stomach without degradation.

   a. Hydrolysis of Weak Acid Drugs in Gastric Juices. A good example of this problem is that of penicillins. The carboxylic acid group of the basic structure, named 6-aminopenicillanic acid, has a pK_a in the range 2-3. As would be expected, absorption from the stomach is significant. The primary difference in the structure of the penicillins is in the substituent group on the amide. This group is largely responsible for the observed differences in gastric stability, enzyme stability, Vd, and protein binding [23,24] (see Chap. 6).

   Instability to gastric acid represents the major limitation in oral effectiveness. One of the major limitations in systemic activity is instability to penicillinase, an enzyme produced by microorganisms (especially staphylococci). The β-lactam ring is extremely susceptible to hydrolysis with resultant loss in activity.

   Schwartz [23] has reviewed the stability of various penicillins at pH 1.3, 35°C. The half-lives for hydrolysis are summarized in Table 1.

Table 1

Half-Lives for Hydrolysis of Various Penicillins—pH 1.3, 35°C

Penicillin	$t_{1/2}$ (min)
Methicillin	2.3
Penicillin G	3.5
Phenethicillin	68
a-Methoxybenzyl	77
Oxacillin	160
Penicillin V	160
a-Chlorobenzyl	300
Ampicillin	660

It is obvious from this table why methicillin is available only in injectable form. It is perhaps less obvious why the same is not true for penicillin G. As an injectable, methicillin has the advantage of being the most stable to penicillinase along with oxacillin and cloxacillin. Penicillin G is the least stable, and the rest lie between these extremes.

In order to calculate the percent hydrolysis of a penicillin relative to its absorption, it is necessary to have a value for the absorption rate constant. Methods for calculating the values of the absorption constant from blood level data were presented in Chap. 3. One can easily estimate the hydrolysis which would be expected to occur in the absence of parallel absorption, and it is significant. The following problem serves to illustrate this point.

Practice Problem 6

For the purpose of solving this problem we will approximate the $t_{1/2}$ for hydrolysis by using those given in the above table. These estimates will serve to compare the stability of penicillin G to V under conditions of pH 1.3, 35°C, which is closer to that of the stomach than to orange juice. The present example is meant to simplify the calculations by eliminating absorption from the problem.

(a) A mother wishes to crush penicillin G tablets in orange juice and administer them to a child. If the process takes 2 min, how much penicillin will the child swallow? (Answer in percent of dose.) What if the process takes 5 min?
Answer: 67% (2 min); 37% (5 min)

(b) What answers would you get for part (a) if penicillin V were employed?
Answer: 99% (2 min); 98% (5 min)

(c) Consider the case where the tablets are mixed with juice at 8 a.m. and used throughout the day. For each penicillin listed, how much active drug would remain at 6 p.m.?
Answer: Meth (0); G (0); Pheneth (0.2%); α-methoxy (0.5%); oxa (7.6%); V (7.6%); α-chlorobenzyl (25%); and amp (53%)

(d) Why is it recommended that all penicillin G oral tablets (including buffered) be taken on an empty stomach at least 2 hr after meals, yet no such statement is found in prescribing information for penicillin V?
Answer: Penicillin G should be taken when stomach is least acidic.

b. Drugs Unstable in the Stomach and Absorbed in the Intestines. Weakly basic drugs would be expected to be absorbed primarily in the intestines, while neutral drugs would be absorbed throughout the g.i. tract. If such drugs are not stable in stomach fluids, they may be protected from degradation by preventing their dissolution in the stomach. This approach is opposite to the mechanisms that might be employed for a weak acid, which would not be expected to show good absorption from the intestines. An acid-labile, weakly basic, or neutral drug can exhibit increased oral absorption when its dissolution takes place in the intestines but not in the stomach. Some specific examples of drug products that serve to illustrate methods for accomplishing delayed behavior are discussed below.

The antibiotic, erythromycin, provides a good example of an acid unstable drug that is available in a number of different tablet and capsule formulations. Erythromycin is most stable at pH 6-8 and is rapidly destroyed at pH values less than 4. The protonated form of the erythromycin base has a pK_a of approximately 8.9. Thus erythromycin would be primarily in the protonated form throughout the g.i. tract. (Figure 7 illustrates the pH range involved.) One would therefore expect the oral absorption of erythromycin to be poor or perhaps irregular at best. Intestinal absorption should be better than absorption from the stomach. Thus the g.i. absorption may be increased if erythromycin can be protected from the gastric fluids. Three different approaches have been employed in this case. The most obvious solution is to use enteric coating. This simple approach is not without its problems, however. In addition to the fact that certain types of enteric coatings become unacceptable upon aging [25], Wagner [26] has discussed the "all-or-none effect" in using enteric-coated tablets. The average time for passing an enteric-coated tablet from the stomach to the intestines has been reported as 3.61 hr and 2.63 hr [25]. However, a time average obtained from a group of individuals can be a misleading figure when one is considering a single tablet swallowed by one patient. In the latter case the tablet may leave the stomach right away, or it may remain in the stomach for anywhere from 0 to 12 hr [26]. This presents the potential for a patient experiencing periods of no medication or receiving a double dose on an intermittent dosage regimen. However, if the drug is divided into many small particles, then the passing of the particles within a given patient will be randomized and the effect will be a gradual and more predictable emptying. In the case of erythromycin, this effect has been achieved by development of prodrugs.

Three types of erythromycin in common usage are ethylsuccinate, stearate, and estolate. These forms are available in addition to enteric-coated tablets of erythromycin free base. The erythromycin stearate is a salt of the tertiary aliphatic amine of erythromycin and stearic acid. Although the coated tablet of the stearate disintegrates rapidly in the stomach, the salt does not dissolve readily and its degradation is thus retarded. Once in the intestine, however, the salt dissociates, yielding free erythromycin base to be absorbed at a pH more favorable to its stability. Since disintegration occurs in the stomach, the passing of the drug is more predictable as a divided powder.

One prodrug of erythromycin is represented by the lauryl sulfate salt of erythromycin propionate ester. These modifications promote oral absorption in two ways. Salts of weak carboxylic acids and erythromycin base tend to dissolve in human gastric juice and lose antibiotic activity quickly. Lauryl sulfuric acid is a sufficiently strong acid to resist displacement by gastric juice. Thus the estolate remains undissolved and retains its potency in acid for long periods of time [27]. In addition to protection from stomach acids by the lauryl sulfate salt, the intestinal absorption of the propionyl ester is enhanced by its solubility in oil and its pK_a of 6.9, which is two units below that of the free base—thus allowing more uncharged drug in the intestines [27,28]. Once in the bood, the propionyl ester would hydrolyze to yield the free erythromycin. The half-life for hydrolysis in human serum at pH 7.5-7.8 has been reported to be 93 min [29].

There have been conflicting opinions with regard to the advantages of obtaining high blood levels of the propionyl ester prodrug as opposed to the lower levels of drug obtained by administration of the stearate salt. Stephens [30] has reported that the levels in humans after the fifth dose contained 20-35% free base and 65-80% ester, which gives a higher net average of free base than that obtained from the salt. Part of the confusion regarding the advantage of the ester can be attributed to assay procedures and the question of bioactivity of the prodrug itself. Since the in vitro half-life for hydrolysis of the ester is 0.5 hr at pH 8, increasing to 5.0 hr at pH 5 [31], it has been suggested that hydrolysis would occur in buffered culture media during microbial assays with a resultant increase in activity due to a free form. (See Chap. 6.)

Thus the estolate has shown higher blood levels than the stearate in fasting patients and with controlled food intake, and the sulfonate ester appears to be more stable and better absorbed as a prodrug [32]. It should also be noted that the estolate (and not the free base, stearate, or ethylsuccinate) can infrequently result in a reversible cholestatic hepatitis that may be idiosyncratic in nature and has been found to subside upon switching to an alternate form of erythromycin [33].

Methenamine represents an example of a prodrug that is converted to ammonia plus the antibacterial agent formaldehyde in acidic media at pH 5.5 or less. The formaldehyde that is released in this manner in the urine provides the basis for the utility of methenamine in treating urinary tract infections. However, this same mechanism can act to destroy methenamine in the stomach. It has been stated that approximately 10-30% of orally administered methenamine is prematurely converted in the stomach but that enteric-coated preparations will avoid this problem [34]. An interesting approach to the combined problem of instability in gastric juice coupled with the necessity for acidic urine is that of enteric-coated methenamine mandelate. This is a salt of the methanamine base and mandelic acid. The mandelic acid aids in acidification of the urine, while the enteric coating protects the methenamine from conversion in the stomach. It should be remembered that foods or other substances, such as $NaHCO_3$, which would buffer the urine toward alkaline pH would result in decreased effectiveness of methenamine.

2. Complexation

The problem of decreasing the absorption of drugs by complexation with other agents in the gastrointestinal tract has been widely publicized through the examples of tetracyclines and heavy metals [35,36]. Aluminum hydroxide gels, milk, and milk products have been co-administered with tetracyclines to decrease nausea and vomiting. The complexation of tetracyclines by aluminum, calcium, and so on, might decrease such symptoms since the complex becomes inactive and unable to penetrate biological membranes. Since tetracyclines sometimes upset the normal g.i. flora, complexation might result in decreased g.i. distress, but the same results would be obtained by not administering the tetracyclines. The following example will illustrate that this is not a facetious remark.

Practice Problem 7:   Decrease in G.I. Absorption Due to Complexation

In Chap. 3 it was stated that the total amount of drug absorbed was proportional to the area under the blood level-time profile. Methods for comparing the relative areas were described in Sec. II.E. of Chap. 3. Examine the data in Table 2 and then answer the questions.

(a) What percent absorption takes place when declomycin is taken orally with 8 oz of milk as compared with an equal dose taken after 8 hr of fasting?
Answer: 13% (by the cut-and-weigh method)

Table 2

Effect of Heavy Metal Complexation on Absorption of
Declomycin in Human Subjects[a] Following 300 mg Taken Orally

| Time (hr) | 8 hr fasting | Average[b] Serum Concentrations Declomycin (μg/ml) | | |
		Meal without dairy products	With 8 oz. of whole milk	With 20 ml Amphojel
0	0.0	0.0	0.0	0.0
1	0.7	1.0	0.1	0.2
2	1.1	1.2	0.3	0.3
3	1.4	1.7	0.4	0.4
4	2.1	2.0	0.4	0.5
5	2.0	–	0.4	0.5
6	1.8	2.1	0.4	0.5
12	1.4	1.8	0.3	0.4
18	–	–	0.2	0.3
24	0.8	1.1	0.1	0.2
48	0.4	0.7	0.0	0.1
72	0.2	0.3		0.0
96	0.1	0.2		

[a] Data taken from figures in Ref. 36.
[b] Six volunteers in fasting group and four in others.

(b) What percent absorption occurs when coadministered with aluminum hydroxide gel, 20 ml?
Answer: 22%

(c) What is the effect of taking declomycin during a meal that contains no dairy products?
Answer: Appears to have increased (140%); see discussion in Ref. 36.

3. Formulation

It is common knowledge that factors such as inert ingredients, manufacturing processes, the form of the drug, and many other formulation variables can markedly influence both bioavailability and the time release pattern from the dosage form. Several reviews have summarized observed differences in bioavailability [37]. In the earlier discussion (Fig. 8) it was suggested that tablet disintegration should not limit bioavailability, since competent technology would normally ensure fast disintegration. This remark should not be misconstrued to imply that disintegration can never be a problem. In order to illustrate formulation effects as well as to emphasize the importance of dependable technology, an example has been chosen in which one might not expect disintegration to be a problem. The example is one of a capsule, and the disintegration of the capsule mass might better be termed deaggregation or dispersion. This would be analogous to the processes outlined for a tablet, since absorption from a capsule would proceed according to

$$\begin{bmatrix} \text{Drug in} \\ \text{capsule} \end{bmatrix} \xrightarrow{\text{Deaggregation}} \begin{bmatrix} \text{Solid} \\ \text{drug} \\ \text{particles} \end{bmatrix} \xrightarrow{\text{Dissolution}} \begin{bmatrix} \text{Drug in} \\ \text{solution} \end{bmatrix} \rightarrow \begin{bmatrix} \text{Absorbed} \\ \text{drug} \end{bmatrix}$$

(21)

The problem of slow deaggregation limiting the absorption of a drug from a capsule can be well illustrated by the antibiotic chloramphenicol. Four commercial lots of chloramphenicol capsules produced by different manufacturers were compared with respect to their deaggregation rates, dissolution rates, particle size, analysis of fill, labeled strength, and absorption profiles in human subjects [38]. These studies emphasize the importance of pharmaceutical formulation in controlling the bioavailability of chloramphenicol from capsules. Although all four products contained equivalent quantities of chloramphenicol, their blood level curves were dramatically different. A qualitative correlation was found to exist between the absorption of chloramphenicol and the deaggregation rates of the capsules. In one case the deaggregation rate was so slow that the capsule mass still maintained its capsulelike shape after 3 hr in simulated gastric fluid even though the gelatin capsule had dissolved. The dramatic differences in the absorption rates are demonstrated in Practice Problem 8. In a later study, 14 oral preparations of chloramphenicol were compared [39].

Practice Problem 8: Decrease in G.I. Absorption Due to Formulation

In Practice Problem 7 the relative amounts of drug absorbed were compared by comparing the weights of the curves. Another method for determining the relative areas under a series of curves was illustrated in Fig. 7 of Chap. 3. The area under a curve may be estimated by the trapezoidal rule. The individual areas of the trapezoids, $a(c + d)/2$, and the triangles, $ab/2$, are summed to obtain the area under the curve. It is necessary to have the same units of concentration and time in order to compare different curves. However, it is not necessary to have the same scale. In fact, one of the advantages of the trapezoidal method is that the curves can be drawn to occupy the maximum amount of space on the graph paper, and the estimates of the length of the sides involved in the calculations are therefore improved. In the method involving cutting

148   4. Biopharmaceutics: Clinical Application

Table 3

Average Plasma Levels for Groups of Ten Human Subjects
Receiving 0.5-g Oral Doses of Chloramphenicol in Capsules[a]

| Time (hr) | Mean plasma levels (μg/ml) | | | |
	Capsule A	Capsule B	Capsule C	Capsule D
0.0	0.0	0.0	0.0	0.0
0.5	5.8	1.1	1.4	0.6
1.0	9.4	2.4	3.9	1.3
2.0	9.1	4.5	5.7	2.2
4.0	6.7	4.7	5.2	2.2
6.0	5.2	3.4	3.6	2.1
8.0	3.8	2.5	2.6	1.8
12.0	2.3	1.1	1.4	1.0
24.0	0.6	0.2	0.2	0.3

[a]Data taken from Table V in Ref. 38b.

and weighing, a small blood level profile would be less accurate than
the larger one that might be used for comparison. The data in Table
3 illustrate the chloromycetin case just discussed. Use the trapezoidal method for estimating areas under the curves, as illustrated in
Fig. 7 of Chap. 3. Then answer the questions regarding chloromycetin absorption.

(a) If capsule A is used as the standard of reference, what is the
    percent of chloromycetin absorbed from capsule D?
    Answer: 35%

(b) What relative percent absorption takes place from capsules B
    and C as compared with capsule A?
    Answer: 52% (B); 61% (C)

(c) Why is it not possible to calculate the absolute percent
    absorption rather than the relative percent absorption from this
    table, and what type of data would be required to calculate the
    absolute percent absorption?
    Answer: An intravenous dose is required.

Bioavailability from capsules has been erroneously taken for granted. The
data in the Practice Problem 8 illustrate the hazard in assuming that untested
products are all bioequivalent. Over 200 million chloramphenicol capsules which
passed the usual federal regulations were recalled from eight different sources
due to poor absorption and decreased bioavailability [40]. Barr et al. [40]
demonstrated significant differences in the absorption characteristics of three

commercially available tetracyclines during both single- and multiple-dose administration. Wagner et al. [41] demonstrated that a commercially available enteric-coated tablet of aminosalicylic acid gave "zero" plasma levels in eight subjects following oral administration. Whole tablets and tablet fragments were recovered in the feces. Wagner [42] has cautioned against the falacious assumption that products are all bioequivalent until shown otherwise. There is no basis to assume that every lot untested in man is bioequivalent.

IV. CONTINUOUS BLOOD AND TISSUE LEVELS IN THERAPY

A. Constant Intravenous Infusion

The use of constant intravenous infusion in pharmacokinetic analyses has been discussed in Chap. 3. The same approach can be used to maintain constant therapeutic levels of drugs in a hospitalized patient. This type of administration is most commonly employed with anti-infective agents, such as antibiotics, although heparin, lidocaine, procaine, pentobarbital, thiamylal, methoxyhexital, nutrients, electrolytes, vitamins, anticancer agents, steroids, and several other drugs are administered by intravenous infusion. Examples of steady-state blood and tissue levels achieved through constant intravenous infusion of a drug distributed according to a two-compartment open model were shown in Chap. 3, Fig. 15. Similar curves would be obtained for the one-compartment case. That figure illustrates how the infusion rate determines the steady-state blood level for a given drug. If a constant rate of infusion is used for several different drugs, the resulting steady-state blood levels may be influenced by the biological half-life, volume of distribution, protein binding, and so on. Standiford et al. [43] have examined the steady-state blood levels for several antibiotics using fixed infusion rates. Of the seven antibiotics examined, carbenicillin gave the highest blood levels. The high concentrations of carbenicillin in the blood were attributed to its long biological half-life and small volume of distribution.

In the case of a one-compartment model drug it is rather simple to calculate the rate of infusion necessary to maintain a given therapeutic level. The first, and most obvious, parameter needed is that of the desired steady-state blood level. The minimum desired blood level for an antibiotic is often referred to as the minimum inhibitory concentration (M.I.C.). Once the desired steady-state plasma level has been chosen, one can calculate the amount of drug in the body under steady-state conditions from

$$D_{inf} = (\text{amount in body})_{ss} = P_{inf} Vd \qquad (22)$$

where P_{inf} is the steady-state plasma level and Vd is the apparent volume of distribution. When the plasma level is constant, its rate of change is zero and therefore

$$(\text{Rate of drug input to plasma}) = (\text{rate of drug output}) \qquad (23)$$

or the rate in equals the rate out. Thus if we calculate the rate out of the body under steady-state conditions, we will have defined the rate that must be used for the intravenous infusion, k_0:

$$k_0 = \beta P_{inf}\ Vd = k_2\ P_{inf}\ Vp \qquad (24)$$

Practice Problem 9: Calculation of Intravenous Infusion Rates for Typical Antibiotics

The data in Table 4 are to be used to answer the questions by assuming a one-compartment model.

(a) A physician wishes to maintain a carbenicillin plasma level of 15 mg% for a 10-hr period. If a liter of intravenous solution is to be constantly infused over this time period, how much carbenicillin must be dissolved in the solution?
Answer: 9.35 g

(b) If the calibration of the intravenous injection delivers 10 drops/ml, how many drops per minute must be infused into the patient?
Answer: 17 drops/min

(c) How much more oxacillin would have to be dissolved in a liter to be used for intravenous infusion in order to accomplish the

Table 4

Mean Values of Pharmacokinetic Parameters for
Several Antibiotics in Human Subjects[a]

Pharmacokinetic Parameters: Antibiotics	$t_{1/2}$ (hr) Normal	Uremic	Vd (liters)	C_R (ml/min)
Carbenicillin	1.0	15.0	9.0	86
Ampicillin	0.8	8.0	25[b]	210
Dicloxacillin	0.7	1.0	9.4	114
Cloxacillin	0.6	0.8	10.8	162
Nafcillin	0.55	1.2	27.0	160
Penicillin G	0.5	3.0	24[b]	386
Oxacillin	0.4	1.0	13.0	190

[a]Data taken from Ref. 43.
[b]Corrected for difference in the reported infusion rates.

same result as defined in part (a)? How would you explain this difference?

Answer: 24.4 g more

(d) Assuming that nonrenal mechanisms are solely responsible for elimination in uremic patients, calculate the fraction of β due to urinary excretion for carbenicillin, dicloxacillin, and cloxacillin. How would you explain why the normal half-life of carbenicillin is longer than dicloxacillin or cloxacillin?

Answer: Carbenicillin (0.93); dicloxacillin (0.30); cloxacillin (0.25)

(e) Using the renal clearance values, what estimates might be made regarding the mechanism by which the kidneys eliminate carbenicillin and penicillin G? Which one would you expect to be most affected by probenicid and why?

Answer: Penicillin G is actively secreted, since $C_R \gg 130$.

(f) How much carbenicillin should be administered in an I.V. "stat" dose to achieve an immediate onset?

Answer: 1.35 g

A point which is sometimes a source of confusion to the student centers about the question of how any plasma level can be achieved if the output rate is equal to the input rate. It must be remembered that this equality is true only at the steady-state blood level. Our input rate (the infusion) is zero-order. The elimination of drug from the body is a first-order process. Equation (24) describes a single rate at the steady-state, but the rate is less than this at all times prior to the steady state. At time zero, for example, the elimination rate is zero but the infusion rate remains the same. Thus input is faster than output at all times preceding the steady state.

A rapid intravenous injection (or "loading dose") may be used to eliminate the onset period. This will be more important as the $t_{1/2}$ of the drug increases, since the calculated input rate will also decrease. For example, the time for carbenicillin to reach the steady state will be greater than 1.4 hr, since it will take 1.4 hr for the intravenous infusion to release 1.35 g and the body will delay onset further due to simultaneous elimination. The time to reach steady state is roughly four to five times the $t_{1/2}$. If a drug had a $t_{1/2}$ of 7 hr, it would require 28 to 35 hr to reach the desired blood level. In Practice Problem 9 it would not reach that level, since we were dealing with a 10-hr infusion. Except for drugs that have very short half-lives, it might be considered a general rule that an initial I.V. dose is advantageous. One can estimate the onset time in the manner just discussed to decide whether or not the initial dose is appropriate. It should be re-emphasized here that the actual onset time is always longer than the time it takes for the infusion to release the steady-state amount in the body, since elimination is occurring simultaneously with infusion.

B. Sustained-Release Oral Dosage Forms

1. Definitions

There are several types of oral dosage forms that are designed to increase the duration of therapeutic action of the drug contained therein. In many cases these products are similar in appearance to the sustained-release preparations. Often the descriptive phrases accompanying the products do not accurately define the mechanism controlling the release pattern. General terms such as timed release, time release, extended action, or long-acting may or may not be meant to indicate that the formulation is a sustained release preparation. Unfortunately, there are no standard definitions or classifications. The following distinction will be used as a starting point, and later more precise terminology and definitions will be given to sustained release dosage forms. In general, oral long-acting solid dosage forms may be divided into three major groups:

a. Repeat-Action Tablets. Repeat-action tablets are designed to release one dose immediately and a second dose after some period of time has elapsed. Some products contain a third dose, which is released some time after the second dose. The release of a subsequent dose is delayed by use of either a time barrier or an enteric coating. Basically these products save the patient a swallow or perhaps two. They can mean the difference between a continuous night of sleep and having to arise for medication. However, they are not designed for steady-state therapy. This dosage form results in the usual "peak-and-valley" type of blood level pattern, as illustrated later in Fig. 1 of Chap. 5. The primary advantage is that additional doses are provided without the necessity of further administration of another tablet. Blood levels are the same as obtained with intermittent therapy rather than continuous.

b. Sustained-Release Dosage Forms. Sustained-release dosage forms provide an initial therapeutic dose that is available upon administration of the product followed by a gradual release of medication over a prolonged period of time. The goal of this type of dosage form is to achieve a therapeutic blood level quickly and then maintain that level with the prolonged-release dose. Ideally, the resultant blood levels would be continuously maintained in the therapeutic range without the intermittent "peak-and-valley" effect of a normal dosage regimen.

c. Prolonged-Action Preparations. Prolonged-action preparations provide slow release of a drug at a rate which will provide a longer duration of action in comparison to the normal single dose. They may differ from sustained-release products only in that no initial dose is included in the prolonged-action formulation.

2. Advantages and Disadvantages

The advantages generally claimed for sustained-action products may include improved therapy, patient convenience, and/or economy. Improved therapy claims are based upon the advantage of continuous therapeutic blood levels as opposed to an intermittent or "peak-and-valley" pattern. While continuous blood levels are not necessarily ideal for all drugs and disease states, there are certainly conditions in which clinical or therapeutic advantage can be realized. Typical examples are those cases where depletion of the drug from the body or low blood levels would result in symptom breakthrough, such as might be encountered with antihistamines, tranquilizers, sedatives, anorectic agents, antitussives, ataractics, antispasmodics, and so on. It is possible under certain conditions to obtain definitive therapeutic advantage from sustained-release products.

Patient convenience may represent a common reason for using a sustained-release product, although perhaps it will not always represent the most rational reason for the choice. It has also been argued that sustained-release forms help to eliminate the possibility of forgotten doses, since the patient may take one morning and night rather than three or four times a day during what may be a busy schedule. We have already mentioned the advantage of not waking a sick person during sleeping periods.

Economy may be involved from one of two points of view. Sometimes the sustained-release form may provide a less expensive approach to equivalent therapy even though the dosage form is more expensive than the normal one. That is, a daily treatment may cost less. Economy may also be the result of decreased cost of nursing time for the administration of drugs in institutions.

The primary disadvantage is probably the loss of flexibility in dosage. One dose is designed to last 8-12 hr, and the release pattern cannot be altered to accommodate individual needs of the patient. In addition, if the patient experiences some undesirable effect, such as drowsiness from an antihistamine, he cannot adjust his regimen as readily as with a dosage regimen of every 3 or 4 hr, where he could skip a dose intentionally. Although it may be more economical to take a drug in a sustained-release dosage form, there are many examples where it is more costly due to the technology involved in producing the formulation. Because these products are rather sophisticated and complex, one might suggest that it would be unwise to employ sustained-release forms of rather toxic or potent drugs because of the increased hazard involved in administering the large doses used in a long-acting preparation. However, this should be considered by pharmacy research and development, and it will therefore be mentioned again in Sec. IV.5.a regarding appropriate candidates for sustained-release dosage forms.

3. Sustained-Release Theory

There are several models that could be employed in considering the theory governing the design of a sustained-release oral dosage form. The simplest model will be discussed here, and exceptions to it will be delineated as they arise in the next section. This model is analogous to the I.V. infusion with an initial rapid I.V. injection or "loading dose." The only difference here is that both the initial and sustained dose have an absorption step before entering the blood. Thus the model may be written

$$
\begin{array}{c}
I \searrow \ ^{k_I} \\
\\
S \nearrow \ _{k_0} \quad B \xrightarrow{\ k_2\ } C \\
\quad\quad k_{12} \Big\downarrow\Big\uparrow k_{21} \\
\quad\quad\quad T
\end{array}
\qquad (25)
$$

where I is the immediate dose; S is the sustained-release dose; and B, T, and C represent the blood, tissues, and elimination. It is assumed that the I dose is rapidly absorbed following oral administration, with a first-order rate constant, k_1, being the absorption constant, and that the zero-order release from the S compartment is rate-determining and equal to k_0. Thus the I compartment is designed to achieve a rapid therapeutic blood level, and the S compartment is meant to maintain it in accordance with Eq. (23). The rate of elimination is calculated in the same way it was done in the I.V. infusion case by using Eq. (24).

Practice Problem 10:   Calculation of Specifications for Oral
Sustained-Release Tablets

A sustained-release tablet having an outer dose of immediately available drug and an inner slow-release core is to be formulated. The desired blood level is 0.4 mg%, and the distribution volume in a 70-kg man is 50 liters. It is found that the drug is quickly and completely absorbed upon oral administration and that 200 mg is sufficient to provide a therapeutic blood level. The biological half-life is 4 hr. If 200 mg is placed into the outer shell, how much drug must be placed in the sustained-release core to maintain a therapeutic blood level for 12 hr?
Answer: 415 mg.

Practice Problem 11

A prolonged-action formulation of sulfaethidole is to be designed. The optimum blood level range is 8-16 mg%. The average biological half-life is 8 hr. A 1.5-g dose administered to a 90-kg man yeilds a blood level of 6 mg% after 3 hr; the total amount eliminated during this time is 300 mg. At what rate must the drug be supplied in order to maintain a 12 mg% blood level, and how much must be placed in the tablet to result in a 12-hr duration?
Answer: Rate = k_0 = 208 mg/hr; 2.5 g

Practice Problem 12

A first-order plot for plasma levels of drug as a function of time in hours gave slopes of –2.8 and –0.18. How much drug must be placed in the S compartment to maintain the blood level for 8 hr, if the I compartment contains 0.40 g, and this amount produces a therapeutic level without significant loss of drug?

Answer: 576 mg

4. Product Design and Typical Examples

One assumption that has been stated is that the sustained-release portion of the dosage form must have a release rate that is slower than absorption. That is, it must be the rate-limiting step in absorption. Earlier, the slowest step in the absorption from tablets has been generalized as being dissolution. If the sustained-release form is to control the absorption, then it must limit the dissolution rate. Thus the normal absorption pattern,

$$A \xrightarrow[\text{Dissolution}]{\text{RDS}} \quad\Vert\quad \longrightarrow B \tag{26}$$

G.I. wall

must be altered by the design of some physical barrier, which may be represented as

$$\left(A\right) \xrightarrow[\text{barrier}]{\text{Release from}} \quad\Vert\quad \longrightarrow B \tag{27}$$

Physical barrier　　　　G.I. wall

There are many methods by which the physical barrier is built into the oral dosage form. Included among them are coatings, embedding in a wax-fat matrix, incorporating into a porous plastic base, binding to ion-exchange resins, complexing with colloidal material, microencapsulation, and so on. The details of the manufacturing processes are not of concern for this discussion. However, the type of mechanism employed for the sustained-release products is important, since it governs the rational use of the products. For that reason we will attempt to survey the commonly used structures for sustained-release oral dosage forms. The titles used here are by no means standard and, in some cases may not be found outside of this text. It is believed, however, that these descriptive categories will be very helpful in providing a "handle" to aid those involved in clinical practice in remembering the types of sustained-release dosage forms and in classifying newer products as they are introduced into practice.

a. Slow-Erosion Core with Initial Dose. The drug is incorporated into a tablet with insoluble materials usually of high-molecular-weight fats and waxes. This tablet *does not* disintegrate, but instead maintains its geometric shape throughout the g.i. tract. The drug release is due to surface erosion from the intact tablet. The initial dose may be in a pan-coated or press-coated outer shell or in another layer in the case of a laminated tablet. These may be illustrated as

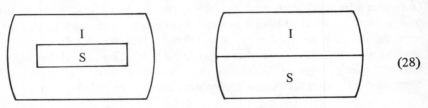

(28)

Tablet in a tablet   Laminated tablet

The principle of this dosage form can be explained using Eq. (10). As demonstrated in Eq. (23), the sustained release rate must be zero-order, which is, of course, a constant rate. Since the solubility term in Eq. (10) may be considered constant for a given drug, the overall rate may be made constant by maintaining a constant surface area. Naturally, the surface cannot be constant in the absolute sense, since the dosage form will become smaller on erosion. However, the tablets are designed to approach a constant value as closely as possible. Thus the geometric shape of the S compartment is chosen so as to give the least possible decrease in surface area as the core undergoes erosion. For example, a cylinder having a large diameter/height ratio would present a constant surface as it dissolved, providing that the diameter remained relatively constant. The slow dissolution of a silver dollar, for example, might be expected to proceed with relatively constant surface since the area would remain constant at $2\pi r^2$ (neglecting the edge), whereas a sphere would undergo a vast change in surface since its area is $4\pi r^2$ and the radius would decrease with dissolution.

A typical example of a compressed tablet surrounding an erosion core is the Pyribenzamine Lontab. The core contains carnauba wax and stearyl alcohol, which are melted together with Pyribenzamine, granulated, and compressed to form the core. The 100-mg Lontab is taken every 8-12 hr in place of two or three separate tablet or elixir doses.

Donnatal Extentab has an outer colored pan coating containing the I dose. The core is enteric-coated and slowly dissolves in the intestines, releasing the equivalent of two additional doses. The total of three doses provides sustained effects for 10-12 hr.

Typical examples of laminated erosion-core tablets are Tedral SA and Peritrate SA. The 80-mg Peritrate SA contains 20 mg in the I layer and 60 mg in the S core. The core releases drug over an 8-hr period. and the overall duration is given as 12 hr since therapeutic blood levels are maintained for 4 hr after the core is expended. Tedral SA contains 90 mg of theophylline in each of the I and S, ephedrine HCl (16 mg in I, 32 mg in S) and 25 mg of phenobarbital in I only.

A number of manufacturers produce sustained-release tablets based on the erosion-core mechanism coupled with an initial dose. Some of these are listed in the summary given in Table 5.

b. Erosion Core Only. Many drugs may not require an initial dose. That is, the onset may not be important if the patient is primarily interested in maintaining blood levels. In such cases a prolonged-action dosage form may be more appropriate than a sustained-release form. Typical examples are erosion-core tablets of an anorexic agent such as Tenuate Dospan and Tepanil Tentabs. The equivalent of three normal doses of the drug are contained within a uniform-release erosion core. Table 5 lists additional examples of prolonged-action tablets that are of the erosion-core type.

Another aspect of prolonged-action medication involves the fact that an initial dose may be required only when the patient first begins therapy and not accompanying every dose. One method previously used to deal with this problem was an erosion core without an initial-dose compartment. The dosage regimen was adjusted to include several tablets to initiate therapy followed by a maintenance dose every 12 hr.

c. Repeat-Action Tablets. As previously defined, repeat-action tablets are not forms of continuous therapy but represent intermittent dosing by the administration of a single dosage form. They are discussed here primarily to avoid the possibility of confusing them with sustained-release tablets. When a repeat-action tablet is cut in two, the cross-sectional appearance will often be similar to that of the tablet in a tablet shown in Eq. (28). However, the labeling (Timed-Release, Repetabs, R-A, Repeat Action) and the description of the release pattern should indicate the difference. Several examples of such products and the manufacturers are given in Table 5.

d. Pellets in Capsules. The original sustained-release product was introduced on the market in October 1952 by Smith, Kline and French Laboratories. The Spansule (SK & F) consists of medicated pellets in a hard gelatin capsule. An average Spansule contains two to four times the normal single dose. The drug is contained within small pellets. There may be three to four different groups, each containing 100 pellets per group. One group of pellets is left uncoated to act as the initial dose. A slowly permeable lipid membrane is used to coat the remaining groups, and the rate of permeability is controlled by the thickness of this layer along with its composition. The second

Table 5

Partial Listing of Marketed Long-Acting Oral Dosage Forms
and Their Probable Categories[a]

Designation	Manufacturer	Typical Product
(a) Slow-erosion core with initial dose		
Chronotab	Schering	Disophrol Chronotab
(Note: Chronotab is also used to designate repeat action in "Disomer Chronotab")		
Enduret	Boehringer Ingelheim	Preludin Enduret
Extentab	Robins	Donnatal Extentab
		Dimetane Extentab
Lontab	Ciba	Forhistal Lontab
		Priscoline Lontab
Lontab	Geigy	PBZ Lontab
SA	Warner/Chilcott	Peritrate SA
		Tedral SA
Sustained-Action	Schering	Drixoral
(b) Erosion core only		
Dospan	Merrell	Tenuate Dospan
Tempotrol	Philips Roxane	Geroniazol TT
		Guaiahist TT
Ten-Tab	Riker	Tepanil Ten-Tab
Timespan	Roche	Mestinon Timespan
		Roniacol Timespan
(c) Repeat-action tablets		
Chronotab	Schering	Disomer Chronotab
(Note: Chronotab is also used to designate sustained-action in "Disophrol Chronotab")		
R-A	McNeil	Clistin R-A
Repetab	Schering	Chlortrimeton Repetab
		Demazin Repetab
		Polaramine Repetab
Timed-Release	Dorsey	Triaminic Tablets
		Triaminic Juvelets
(d) Pellets in capsules		
Continuous Action	Menley James	Contac
Controlled Release	Dow	Novafed Capsules
S.A.	Burroughs Wellcome	Sudafed S.A.
Sequels	Lederle	Artane Sequels
		Diamox Sequels
		Pathilon Sequels

Table 5 (Continued)

Designation	Manufacturer	Typical Product
Spansules	Smith, Kline and French	Combid Spansules Ornade Spansules Prydon Spansules Teldrin Spansules (many others)
—span	Key	Nico-Span
—span	Wallace	Meprospan
Tembids	Ives	Isordil Tembids Capsules
Tempules	Armour	Nicobid
Timesule	Arnar-Stone	Isoclor Capsule
(e) Pellets in Tablets (or mixed granulations)		
(None)	Bristol	Naldecon
P.A.	Searle & Co.	Pro-Banthine P.A.
—S	Dorsey	Bellergal-S
—S	Sandoz	Belladenal-S
Sustained Action	Key	Nitroglyn Theo-Dur
Tembids	Ives	Isordil Tembids Tablets
(f) Leaching		
Gradumets	Abbott	Desoxyn Gradument Fero-Gradumet Tral Gradumet
(g) Ion-exchange		
Pennkinetic	Pennwalt	Biphetamine Ionamin Omni-Tuss (liquid) Tussionex (liquid)
(h) Complexation		
—tan	Wallace	Rynatan (tablets and suspension)
(i) Microencapsulation		
Plateau Caps	Marion	Duotrate Nico-400
—span	USV	Cerespan Histaspan Nitrospan
(None)	Breon	Measurin

[a]Estimated from product descriptions in *Physician's Desk Reference,* 33rd ed., Medical Economics, Oradell, N.J., 1979.

group of pellets may be thinly coated, the third coated medium, and the fourth coated to a thickness sufficient to last about 9 hr.

If each pellet in a group behaved exactly alike, then the spansule would release its drug like a repeat-action tablet; but this is not the case. The drug-release pattern approaches a normal type of distribution within each group. For example, the mean value for a group may be 3 hr, but the pellets may be distributed over a range of, say, ±30%. It is this distribution pattern that results in a sustained-release effect. As the pellets in subsequent groups begin to overlap somewhat, the sum total of the release patterns approaches a constant. Thus release of drug is nearly continuous and dependent only on the rate of permeation of the pellets by moisture from the g.i. fluids. See Table 5 for examples.

It should be noted here that the Spansule does not really fit our model. One might picture the mechanism involved in these capsules by imagining a rubber stamp which will print a curve similar to those commonly seen for a normal distribution. If the stamp is used to print a series of such curves along the x axis of a piece of graph paper, it is possible to choose a constant time interval between the starting points so that the sum of the curves is a constant. Let us examine this analogy in the case of a spansule. If there are four groups of pellets, we will need to stamp four times. Since the total blood level will be the sum of the effects of all the pellets, all of the overlapped lines must be added. Thus with proper spacing of the individual curves, the overall sum can be made to approach a constant value as function of time. Table 5 lists additional products using this principle.

e. Pellets in Tablets. The same principle used in the Spansules can be employed in tablets. Pellets are prepared in the manner previously described, mixed with appropriate tabletting agents, and compressed into tablets. Bellergal S may be considered as one example of this approach. See Table 5.

f. Leaching. Leaching is rather unusual in that the tablet shell excreted in the feces differs very little in appearance from the original tablet ingested by the patient. The shell is actually a plastic matrix that passes through the entire body intact. It may be thought of as a plastic sponge which contains drug within the pores. As the tablet passes through the g.i. tract the drug is leached out by the g.i. fluids at a rate that is relatively independent of pH, g.i. motility, and enzymes. Thus the shell that is excreted intact has been depleted of its drug content.

Gradumets represent one application of this principle. The initial dose is controlled by the geometry of the tablet. Since the channels open to the surface of the tablet, there is a certain amount of drug that comes into immediate contact with g.i. fluids. This drug dissolves at once and supplies an initial dose. The amount in this dose is thus dependent on surface area, which is controlled by the geometry of the tablet.

The design of a Gradumet is obviously tailored to the specific drug to be used. The size of the channels, the ratio of drug to soluble and insoluble ingredients, the tablet geometry, and so on, must all be made compatible with the physical-chemical properties of the drug as well as its pharmacokinetic properties. This means that combining two drugs into a Gradumet presents a technological problem. One interesting solution to this problem can be found in the example of a laminated Gradumet which is actually two independent Gradumets with a common interface [Eq. (28)]. Thus a pair of agents can be administered in combination, yet the release mechanism can be tailored to the individual drugs.

g. Ion-Exchange Resins. The ion-exchange principle involves administration of capsules containing salts of drugs with a polystyrene sulfonic acid resin. This resin salt exchanges drug for ions as it passes through the g.i. tract. For example, an amine drug might be exchanged as

$$[RSO_3^- \cdots {}^+ H_3N - R'] \overset{X^+}{\rightleftharpoons} RSO_3^- \ X^+ + R'NH_3^+ \qquad (29)$$
Amine drug resinate

where $X^+ = H^+, Na^+, K^+$ or

$$[RSO_3^- \cdots {}^+ H_3N - R'] \overset{Y^-}{\rightleftharpoons} RSO_3^- + RNH_2 + HY \qquad (30)$$
Amine drug resinate

where $Y^- = OH^-, Cl^-$, and so on. The rate of release is thus proportional to the concentration of the ions present in the g.i. tract. The contributions by H^+ and OH^- are negligible in g.i. fluids. We can estimate the total concentrations of Na^+, K^+, and Cl^- from published data as given here in Table 6 [44]. Although some ions, such as bicarbonate, are not included in this table, it can be seen that the sum of the ions listed remains fairly constant throughout the g.i. tract. These

Table 6

Concentration of Ions in G.I. Tract

Ion	Concentration (mg%)			
	Gastric juice	Small intestine	Large intestine	Bile
Na^+	115	322	347	340
K^+	40	17	34	28
Cl^-	500	313	310	338
Sum	655	652	691	706

concentrations would obviously vary with changes in volume of g.i. fluids due to liquid intake. However, the constant-release principle is based upon a relatively constant exchange rate.

h. Complexation. Pharmacists who still remember their dispensing lectures no doubt recall the warning regarding the preparation of solutions of alkaloids in vehicles such as wild cherry syrup. Syrups that are high in tannins (wild cherry syrup was made from the bark) can result in precipitation of the drug-tannin complex in the case of amine drugs. This principle is employed by Mallinckrodt to produce long-acting oral dosage forms. These tablets contain a complex of the amine drug with tannic acid, $RCOO^- {}^+H_3N-R$. The clinician will have no problem remembering these forms, since they are conveniently named Ryna*tan*, Obo*tan*, and Naler*tan*.

i. Microencapsulation. Microencapsulation is perhaps the most recent addition to oral prolonged-release mechanisms. Drug powders (or in some cases particles) are covered with a thin coating that behaves like a dialysis membrane. The drug is released by diffusing through the membrane rather than by disintegration and dissolution. Gastrointestinal fluids diffuse through the membrane to form a saturated solution of drug within the sac or cell. Then the drug undergoes passive diffusion from this highly concentrated solution within the cell through the membrane to the less concentrated g.i. fluids. The rate of release is thus governed by the diffusion properties of the drug with respect to the membrane. The microencapsulated drug can be incorporated into tablets or capsules. Release rate can be controlled by the size of the drug particles that are encapsulated, the surface area of the cells, and the permeability of porosity of the membrane coating. Several manufacturers employ this technique; examples are given in Table 5.

5. Choice of Drugs for Sustained-Release Products and
    Evaluation of the Dosage Form

a. Candidates for Long-Acting Dosage Forms. We might begin this discussion by giving nine reasons why a drug would not be a wise choice for a sustained-release type of product:

1. Very short half-life
2. Long half-life
3. Large dose
4. Very potent drug
5. Poorly absorbed drug
6. Poorly soluble drug
7. Blood levels do not mirror biological activity
8. Actively absorbed drug
9. Large first-pass metabolism

This list is by no means complete, but it should serve to stimulate the reader's thoughts with regard to criteria. A drug with a very short half-life will require too much in the sustained-release pool relative to a normal dose. If a drug has a long half-life, say greater than 8 hr, there is no need to have a sustained form. A large dose, 1-2 g, for example, becomes impossible. Imagine a drug with a 1-hr half-life and a 1-g dose. The initial dose, I, would be 1 g and the S portion could easily be 4 g for a grand total of 5 g. "Now open wide, Johnny, and get ready for a big swallow!"

The question of a potent drug in a long-acting form may be more controversial. In my opinion it is not good practice to swallow five doses of a potent agent, especially if the margin of safety is relatively small. In spite of the fact that a well-designed, long-acting formulation should behave in a predictable manner, there is always that chance of an unexpected event in biological systems, and the potential for increased absorption is there. My reasoning behind eliminating poorly absorbed drugs as candidates is somewhat the same. Consider drugs such as hexamethonium or pentolinium, which are discussed in Practice Problem 5. These are fairly potent agents. They are extremely variable in their response upon oral administration, and this is easily understood when you consider that a patient is really swallowing 20 doses if a drug is only 5% absorbed. If, by some quirk of biological fate, the patient is able to absorb more on a given day, the potential for overdose is there. Now put such a drug in a sustained-release form. How much will be administered—80 doses? If the drug is poorly absorbed because it cannot pass the g.i. wall, then it must remain in the g.i. tract. That means a continuous-release dosage form is resulting in a pool of available but unabsorbed drug in solution in the g.i. tract.

What about the drug that is poorly absorbed because it is poorly soluble? Release from the dosage form must be the rate-limiting step. If the drug is poorly soluble and thus poorly absorbed, then it is likely that dissolution of the drug itself is rate-determining. The dosage form is therefore not governing the absorption pattern but may be superfluous, as undissolved drug particles in the g.i. tract would behave independently of the formulation.

If the therapeutic activity of a drug is independent of its concentration, it would seem to be irrational to expend time, effort, and money in an attempt to maintain constant blood levels. Reserpine has a 15-min half-life, yet its activity persists for as long as 48 hr [45]. Since reserpine may act by irreversibly inhibiting monamine oxidase, the duration may be related to the time of formation of new enzymes by the body. Thus the pharmacological activity occurs independently of the time course for drug in the blood, and pharmacokinetic parameters calculated from blood level data would not be therapeutically meaningful when applied to development of a prolonged-release product.

An actively absorbed drug generally exhibits a preferential area of the g.i. tract for its absorption. If this is an enzyme-transport process, that area will be located where the enzymes exist in greatest density. Producing a prolonged-release pattern before reaching that site makes little sense, since all of the drug that arrives in solution will behave in the same manner as it would in the case of a normal dosage form. Releasing drug after the formulation has passed by the site will give decreased absorption compared to the normal case. The overall problem makes the chances for success very slim for a drug that is primarily absorbed actively.

Retarding the rate of absorption can increase the fraction metabolized for drugs susceptible to first-pass metabolism. Sustained release aspirin has been shown to reduce the bioavailability of unmetabolized aspirin while total salicylate absorption is unchanged [9]. This is discussed further in the following section and in Sec. III.A of Chap. 6.

   b.   *Evaluating Sustained-Release Products.* Naturally the clinical evaluation of sustained-release products should include all of the statistical parameters normally encountered in a good experimental design. It is not the intent here to review biomedical statistics and experimental design. However, it is considered appropriate to examine some of the components of a good clinical evaluation and to emphasize those aspects unique to long-acting products. This becomes especially apparent when one begins examining the literature in this area, since it is exceedingly easy to locate studies with conclusions that cannot be readily accepted in light of the experimental design.

Obviously, the study should be designed to remove bias. In spite of the fact that double-blind techniques are commonly employed, many such studies do not include a placebo or make any attempt to disguise the dosage forms. Sustained-release formulations are generally unique in appearance. The value of a double-blind study based on information collected by clinicians interviewing patients becomes rather questionable when the dosage forms have such distinguishing characteristics that a brief mention of it by the patient removes the blind. An interesting study was carried out to test the efficacy of the double-blind. One hundred patients were given a drug by a group of interns and the results were determined subjectively. Excellent results were obtained in 61% of the cases. A known placebo was introduced and 56% response obtained. When the same tests were carried out using a double-blind technique with unknown placebo, only 38% excellent results were reported. How common is the problem of experimental design affecting interpretation? An analysis of 100 consecutive articles in a group of medical journals revealed that 45 did not compare the treatment with a control and an additional 18 had inadequate control for a total of 63%.

It does not seem unreasonable that a manufacturer could produce a placebo which would appear like the real thing. Sometimes it is not possible to use a placebo, as patients should not go untreated. Comparison with standard forms or other sustained-release products then becomes the only alternative. While a

Latin square design involving placebo, standard, and new product is ideal, the elimination of placebo should result in at least a crossover approach. Yet it is a common occurrence to find a group divided in two and treated with two drugs without any attempt at crossover. It goes without saying that the normal unbiased methods for random selection of patients should be employed in all tests.

A problem that is unique to sustained-release forms is proving that they are indeed sustained-release. This may not be as easy as it appears at first. Certainly the release pattern for a sustained-release preparation should be independent of pH, enzymes, agitation, and any other variables that might be encountered in the g.i. tract. This type of behavior can be tested in vitro, but negative results are more meaningful than positive ones. That is, if the dosage form is unpredictable in vitro, then the in vivo behavior will certainly not be more reliable. However, good results in vitro do not ensure success in the clinic. There is no substitute for clinical proof. At best, in vitro tests can be correlated with blood level data for use in quality control, but studies done in a beaker do not prove therapeutic utility. In fact, clinical proof that sustained-release dosage forms produce the desired release patterns within the g.i. tract itself does not demonstrate that they will provide sustained therapeutic responses. The release of drug in the g.i. tract is not the final test for a constant absorption rate. Absorption of a given drug may vary as the dosage form travels down the g.i. tract. Thus X-ray studies commonly employed to follow the behavior of an ingested long-acting formulation can document only the release pattern. While this is certainly important, the absorption pattern must be determined by other methods.

The most obvious criterion for sustained release is the appearance of the time course for the drug in the blood. The formulation is designed to produce steady-state blood levels, and the level of success can be determined directly from blood or urine assays as a function of time. While this seems simple enough, there are some problems associated with the choice of a reference standard in addition to the problems encountered in developing suitable analytical methods. It is common practice to compare the sustained-release form of the drug to the normal dosage regimen of the same drug. While this is a necessary part of a good study, it has been criticized as being incomplete. It does not prove that the sustained-release form works, because there is no comparison made with a single but equal dose of the same drug. Hollister [46] has suggested that a study should include a single normal dose, the normal dosage regimen, the sustained-release form, and a single dose of drug equal to the amount in the sustained-release form. In his commentary, "Measuring Measurin: Problems of Oral Prolonged-action Medications" [9], he demonstrated similar results from tablets and sustained-release tablets based on *salicylate* time course in blood following equal doses. The rank order for peak *acetylsalicylic acid* plasma levels (at 30 min) was roughly 7/4.5/3 (in μg/ml) for (buffered tablets/plain tablets/

sustained-release tablets). The beta phase (which begins at approximately 1 hr) appeared similar for all three products with respect to acetylsalicylic acid. Furthermore, using this approach he demonstrated several cases where essentially equivalent blood level patterns were obtained with a single dose of drug equal to that contained in the "long-acting" form [46]. Obviously, it will not always be possible to administer such a large dose, but Hollister's point appears to be well conceived for those cases where it is possible.

Even if the sustained-release form does indeed work, it does not follow automatically that this results in a proven clinical advantage. The results must be compared to the current "standard" of therapy and the advantage demonstrated. This is best done by objective studies. Some real clinical manifestation of the disease should be measured quantitatively as a function of time. Such tests have been developed for adrenergics, cholinergics, sympathomimetics, parasympathomimetics, ganglionic blockers, vasodilators, antitussives, antacids, and countless others [47]. It is becoming increasingly difficult to accept the argument that no clinical test exists as a justification for a purely subjective study. However, when subjective tests are conducted, the credibility of the resultant data is completely dependent on the experimental design.

6. Rational Clinical Use of Sustained-Release Products

The rational use of sustained-release products is based upon an understanding of their construction and the principle by which they are meant to function. Those employing the erosion-core principle, for example, contain several doses and depend on the geometry of the intact core for their continuous release pattern. Anything that would destroy this structure could result in an overdose. While this seems obvious enough, it cannot be taken for granted that this is common knowledge. In one report a markedly greater response was observed when tablets of the slow-release type were chewed by the patient before swallowing [48]. The workers concurred with other investigators who recommended chewing of the tablets as a routine procedure. In making use of sustained-release forms, it is good practice to avoid the introduction of new variables that may not have been present in the original evaluation studies. Thus beverages such as hot drinks that might soften fats or waxes, alcoholic beverages that might dissolve coatings, and so on, should be avoided. A worthwhile precaution would be to warn patients against the simultaneous ingestion of any foods or drugs that might affect the integrity of the dosage form with resultant increase in drug release rate.

It is not an uncommon practice to administer sustained-release preparations or fractions of them to children. There are several factors that would raise doubt regarding the wisdom of this procedure. Children are not little adults. The dosage regimen for a child should be one that is specifically developed for that purpose independently of the adult regimen and not calculated by applying some arbitrary equation to adjust the adult dose. It should be obvious that a given fraction arrived at by any formula cannot be considered optimum for every drug known to man when administered to a given child. However, this is a problem associated with pediatric posology in general, and there are some more specific problems with respect to the present subject of long-acting products.

We might first begin with the potential biological differences. The release pattern and the amount of drug in the slow-release compartment is directly related to the desired blood level and biological half-life in adults. Of course, these will be average values for an adult population. It is reasonable to expect that the distribution volume, biological half-life, and perhaps desired blood level would all be different for children. The Vd will be a function of the child's weight. The $t_{1/2}$ may be longer due to undeveloped enzyme systems with resultant decrease in metabolic rate. There may also be differences in urinary clearance values, protein binding, absorption, and so on. In short, it does not seem rational to administer either the whole or a part of long-acting adult dosage form to a child, especially since these forms will contain several doses.

There are additional problems associated with the administration of a fraction of a sustained-release dosage form. These are related to the physical make-up of the formulations themselves. For example, how can one take one-half the contents of a Spansule? Some physicians direct the parents to open the gelatin capsule and pour out one-half of the pellets. But which half do they obtain? Stratification of pellets in a mixture is a well-known "unmixing" problem to the pharmaceutical industry. A drum of granulation may have to be remixed before tabletting if it has been moved or stored long enough to result in different analyses at the top and bottom of the mixture. A Spansule may contain four groups of pellets. One cannot expect to pour one-half of each group out on a spoon and get one-half of the release pattern on ingestion.

Erosion-type products may be broken or cut in half, but this is not without its problems. Obviously, if an enteric coating is involved in the time-lapse mechanism it will be destroyed. Less obvious is the fact that one-half of the tablet has more than one-half the surface area. How much more will vary with the geometry of the original tablet. The surface will be greater than half, and thus the release rate will also be greater than half. The result would be blood levels that are greater than half and shorter duration than the original tablet. The relative blood levels and duration can be calculated rather simply.

Practice Problem 13

The relative dimensions as estimated with a ruler and the druation of action estimated from the manufacturer's product information are listed in Table 7 for several products. Choose from the list of categories the appropriate descriptive phrase that best describes each product. Then calculate what you would expect to be relative blood level (%) and duration (hr) following administration of one-half of the

Table 7

Duration of Action and Relative Dimensions
for Several Products

Product	Duration (hr)	Relative dimensions[a]
Mestinon Timespan	ca. 6	1 X 1 X 3
PBZ Lontab	8	core diameter = 2 thickness = 1
Tenuate Dospan	12	3 X 5 X 12
Triaminic Timed Release Tablets	8	core diameter = 4 thickness = 1
Rynatan	12	1 X 2 X 5

[a]Geometric formulae for areas: circle = πr^2; sphere = $4\pi r^2$; rectangle = length X width.

dosage form. (Hint: Use the relative release rate and dosage form lifetime to estimate the answers.)

List of Types of Dosage Forms

1. Erosion core only
2. Pan-coated erosion core
3. Press-coated erosion core
4. Repeat action
5. Laminated tablet/core
6. Spansule pellets in capsule
7. Enteric pellets in capsule
8. Spansule pellets in tablet
9. Leaching from plastic matrix
10. Polystyrene sulfonic acid resin
11. Tannic acid complex
12. Microencapsulation

Practice Problem 14

(a) Why are Gradumets containing two drugs formulated as 2-layer tablets?

(b) A patient has complained to his physician that undisintegrated tablets (Gradumets) are appearing in his feces. The physician, in turn, asks the pharmacist if he is using "old stock." What should he answer?

(c) What objection might be offered to the simultaneous ingestion of a Spansule along with: hot tea or coffee; a saline cathartic?

(d) What objection can be raised to reducing an Extentab to a powder and administering it as a suspension in milk to a patient who has difficulty swallowing the tablet?

An excellent comprehensive review of the considerations regarding drug candidates and the theory and practice of sustaining mechanisms has been edited by Robinson [49]. This extensive multi-authored text includes detailed discussions on physical, chemical, and bioengineering approaches, the biological and drug-related constraints as well as the pharmacokinetic theory for dosage regimens.

REFERENCES

1. D. D. Breimer, On the Biological Availability of Drugs, *Pharmaceutisch Weekblad 108,*309 (1973).
2. P. A. Shore, B. B. Brodie, and C. A. M. Hogben, The Gastric Secretion of Drugs, *J. Pharmacol. Exp. Therap. 119,* 361 (1957).
3. C. A. M. Hogben, L. S. Schanker, D. J. Tocco, and B. B. Brodie, Absorption of Drugs from the Stomach, II, The Human, *J. Pharmacol. Exp. Therap. 120,*540 (1957).
4. L. S. Schanker, Absorption of Drugs from the Rat Colon, *J. Pharmacol. Exp. Therap. 126,*283 (1959) and leading references.
5. E. Overton, *Arch. Ges. Physiol. 92,* 115 (1902).
6. J. Travell, Influence of Hydrogen Ion Concentration on Absorption of Alkaloids from Stomach, *J. Pharmacol. Exp. Therap. 69,* 21 (1940).
7. T. D. Sokoloski, Solutions and Phase Equilibria, in *Remington's Pharmaceutical Sciences,* 15th ed., Mack Publishing Co., Easton, Pa., 1975.
8. J. R. Leonards, The Influence on Solubility on the Rate of Gastrointestinal Absorption of Aspirin, *Clin. Pharmacol. Ther. 4,* 476 (1963) and references therein.
9. L. E. Hollister, Measuring Measurin: Problems of Oral Prolonged-action Medications, *Clin. Pharmacol. Ther. 13,* 1 (1972) (Note: See Fig. 4 for previously unpublished data.)
10. E. B. Truitt and A. M. Morgan, Gastrointestinal Factors in Aspirin Absorption, *J. Pharm. Sci. 53,* 129 (1964), and Evaluation of Acetylsalicylic Acid Esterase in Aspirin Metabolism, *J. Pharm. Sci. 54,* 1640 (1965).
11. Examples of sodium or potassium salts of weak acid drugs showing increased absorption rates may be found in H. Juncher and F. Raaschou, *Antibiotic Med. Clin. Ther. 4,* 497 (1957); C. C. Lee, R. C. Anderson, F. G. Henderson, H. M. Worth, and P. N. Harris, *Antibiotic Chemother 8,* 354 (1958); and E. Nelson, *J. Pharm. Sci. 47,* 297 (1958).
12. Examples of salts of weakly basic drugs showing increased absorption rates may be found in B. B. Brodie and C. A. M. Hogben, *J. Pharm. Pharmacol.*

9, 345 (1957); E. Nelson, *J. Pharm. Sci. 48*, 96 (1959); and W. Morozowich, T. Chulski, W. E. Hamlin, P. M. Jones, J. I. Northram, A. Purmalis, and J. G. Wagner, *J. Pharm. Sci. 51*, 993 (1962).

13. E. Nelson, E. L. Knoechel, W. E. Hamlin, and J. G. Wagner, Influence of the Absorption Rate of Tolbutamide on the Rate of Decline of Blood Sugar Levels in Normal Humans, *J. Pharm. Sci. 51*, 509 (1961).

14. J. Haleblian and W. McCrone, Pharmaceutical Applications of Polymorphism, *J. Pharm. Sci. 58*, 911 (1969).

15. J. W. Poole, G. Owen, J. Silverio, J. N. Freyhof, and S. B. Rosenman, Physicochemical Factors Influencing the Absorption of the Anhydrous and Trihydrate Forms of Ampicillin, *Current Therap. Res. 10*, 292 (1968).

16. J. R. Marvel, D. A. Schichting, and C. Denten, The Effect of a Surfactant and Particle Size on Griseofulvin Plasma Levels, *J. Invest. Dermat. 42*, 197 (1964).

17. M. Kraml, J. Dubuc, R. Gaudrey, and D. Beall, Gastrointestinal Absorption of Griseofulvin, II, *Antibiot. Chemother. 12*, 239 (1962), and Gastrointestinal Absorption of Griseofulvin, I, *Arch Dermat. 87*, 179 (1963).

18. R. G. Crounse, Effect of Use of Griseofulvin, *Arch. Dermat. 87*, 176 (1963).

19. H. Blank, Antifungal and Other Effects of Griseofulvin, *Am. J. Med. 39*, 831 (1965).

20. H. E. Paul, K. J. Hayes, M. F. Paul, and A. R. Borgmann, Laboratory Studies with Nitrofurantoin, *J. Pharm. Sci. 56*, 882 (1967).

21. J. D. Conklin and F. J. Hailey, Urinary Drug Excretion in Man During Oral Dosage of Different Nitrofurantoin Formulations, *Clin. Pharmacol. Ther. 10*, 534 (1969).

22. F. J. Hailey and H. W. Glascock, Gastrointestinal Tolerance to a New Macrocystalline Form of Nitrofurantoin: A Collaborative Study, *Current Therap. Res. 9*, 600 (1967).

23. M. A. Schwartz and F. H. Buckwalter, Pharmaceutics of Penicillin, *J. Pharm. Sci. 51*, 1119 (1962).

24. J. P. Hou and J. W. Poole, β-Lactam Antibiotics: Their Physicochemical Properties and Biological Activities in Relation to Structure, *J. Pharm. Sci. 60*, 503 (1971).

25. J. G. Wagner, W. Veldkamp, and S. Long, Enteric Coatings, IV, *J. Pharm. Sci. 49*, 128 (1960).

26. J. G. Wagner, Biopharmaceutics: Absorption Aspects, *J. Pharm Sci. 50*, 359 (1961).

27. V. C. Stephens, J. W. Conine, and H. W. Murphy, Esters of Erythromycin, IV, *J. Pharm. Sci. 48*, 620 (1959).

28. R. S. Griffith and H. R. Black, A Comparison of Blood Levels After Oral Administrations of Erythromycin and Erythromycin Estolate, *Antibiotic Chemother. 12*, 398 (1962).

29. P. H. Tardrew, J. C. H. Mao, and D. Kenny, Antibacterial Activity of 2'-Esters of Erythromycin, *Appl. Microbiol. 18*, 159 (1969).

30. V. C. Stephens, C. T. Pugh, and N. E. Davis, A Study of the Behavior of Propionyl Erythromycin in Blood by a New Chromatographic Method, *J. Antibiot. (Tokyo) 22*, 551 (1969).

31. W. E. Wick and G. E. Malitt, New Analysis for the Therapeutic Efficacy of Propionyl Erythromycin and Erythromycin Base, *Antimicrob. Ag. and Chemother.*, p. 410 (1968).

32. R. S. Griffith and H. R. Black, Comparison of the Blood Levels Obtained After Single and Multiple Doses of Erythromycin Estolate and Erythromycin Stearate, *Am. J. Med. Sci. 247*, 69 (1964).

33. J. A. Gronroos, H. A. Saarimaa, and J. L. Kalliomaki, A Study of Liver Function During Erythromycin Estolate Treatment, *Current Therap. Res. 9*, 589 (1967) and leading references.

34. L. S. Goodman and A. Gilman, *The Pharmacological Basis of Therapeutics*, 4th ed., The Macmillan Co., New York, 1970, p. 1040.

35. R. G. Remmers, G. M. Sieger, N. Anagnostakos, J. C. Corbett, and A. P. Doerschuk, Metal-acid Complexes with Members of the Tetracycline Family, III, *J. Pharm. Sci. 54*, 49 (1965) and references therein.

36. J. Scheiner and W. A. Altemeier, Experimental Study of Factors Inhibiting Absorption and Effective Therapeutic Levels of Declomycin, *Surgery 114*, 9 (1962).

37. The following reviews have summarized observed differences in bioavailability of products: (a) J. G. Wagner, Generic Equivalence and Inequivalence of Oral Products, *Drug Intell. and Clin. Pharmacol. 5*, 115 (1971); (b) Symposium on Formulation Factors Affecting Therapeutic Performance of Drug Products, *Drug Information Bull. 3*, No. 1, Jan.-June (1969); (c) *Bioavailability of Drugs* (B. B. Brodie and W. M. Heller, eds.), S. Karger, New York, 1972; and (d) (Anon.), Biological Availability, A Statement by the Pharmaceutical Society of Great Britain, *Drug Intell. and Clin. Pharm. 7*, 117 (1973).

38. (a) A. J. Aguiar, L. M. Wheeler, S. Fusari, and J. E. Zelmer, Evaluation of Physical and Pharmaceutical Factors Involved in Drug Release and Availability from chloramphenicol Capsules, *J. Pharm. Sci. 57*, 1844 (1968); (b) A.J. Glazko, A. W. Kinkel, W. C. Alegnani, and E. L. Holmes, An Evaluation of the Absorption Characteristics of Different Chloramphenicol Preparations in Normal Human Subjects, *Clin. Pharmacol. Therap. 9*, 472 (1968).

39. H. Bell, H. Johansen, P. K. M. Lunde, H. A. Andersgaard, P. Sinholt, T. Midtvedt, E. Hollum, Absorption and Dissolution Characteristics of 14 Different Oral Chloramphenicol Preparations Tested in Healthy Human Male Subjects, *Pharmacology 5*, 108 (1971).

40. W. H. Barr, J. Adir, and L. Garrettson, Decrease of Tetracycline Absorption in Man by Sodium Bicarbonate, *Clin. Pharmacol. Therap. 12*, 779 (1971).

41. J. G. Wagner, P. K. Wilkinson, H. J. Sedman, and R. G. Stoll, Failure of USP Tablet Disintegration Test to Predict Performance in Man, *J. Pharm. Sci. 62*, 859 (1973).

42. J. G. Wagner, Estimation of Defect Rate, *J. Pharm. Sci. 62*, Open Forum Page VI, (1973).

43. H. C. Standiford, M. C. Jordan, and W. M. Kirby, Clinical Pharmacology of Carbenicillin Compared with Other Penicillins, *J. Infect. Dis. 122*, 9 (Sup.), 1970.
44. G. J. Martin, *Ion Exchange and Adsorptive Agents*, Little, Brown & Co., 1955.
45. For a discussion of this and other subjects related to this chapter, see Chap. 2, by G. Levy, in *Prescription Pharmacy* (J. B. Sprouls, Jr., ed.), J. B. Lippincott Co., Philadelphia, 1963.
46. L. E. Hollister, Studies of Delayed-action Medications, *New Eng. J. Med. 266*, 281 (1962); *Current Therap. Res. 4*, 471 (1962); *Clin. Pharmacol. Therap. 4*, 612 (1963).
47. *Animal and Clinical Pharmacologic Techniques in Drug Evaluation*, Vol. I (1964) (J. H. Nodine and P. E. Siegler, ed.), and Vol. II (1967) (P. E. Siegler and J. H. Moyer, eds.), Year Book Medical Publishers, Chicago.
48. J. C. King, Clinical Experience with a New Long-acting Antacid-Anticholinergic Preparation, *Am. J. Gastroenterol. 32*, 509 (1959).
49. J. R. Robinson (ed.), *Sustained and Controlled Release Drug Delivery Systems*, Marcel Dekker, Inc., New York, 1978, 773 pp.

Chapter 5

DOSAGE REGIMENS

I. INTRODUCTION   174

II. ACCUMULATION DURING REPETITIVE DOSING   176
  A. Rapid I.V. Injections   176
     Practice Problem 1   178
  B. Prediction of Multiple-Dose Blood Levels from a
     Single-Dose Curve   179
    1. Steady-State Blood Levels: Rapid I.V.   179
       Practice Problem 2   180
       Practice Problem 3   183
    2. Steady-State Blood Levels: Oral   184
       Practice Problem 4   188
    3. Predictions of Blood Levels After the n-th Dose   188
       Practice Problem 5   189
       Practice Problem 6   189
    4. Degree of Accumulation   190
       Practice Problem 7   192
  C. Average Steady-State Levels for Any Route and Model   192
     Practice Problem 8   193
  D. Repetitive Dosing for Minimum Effective Concentrations   194
    1. Predictions of P^{∞}_{min} from Single-Dose Plots   194
    2. Calculating Dosage Regimens to Maintain Minimum
       Plasma Levels   195
     Practice Problem 9: Calculation of the Dosage Interval to
     Maintain M.I.C. with 500-mg Capsules of Tetracycline   196
     Practice Problem 10: Calculation of the Oral Dose of
     Tetracycline to Maintain M.I.C. with a 12-hr Dosage Interval   197
     Practice Problem 11   198
    3. Calculating the Minimum Dosage Interval (τ_{min}) to Use the
       Monoexponential Approximation   198
  E. Calculation of Loading Dose   199
     Practice Problem 12: Calculating Loading Dose   200

III. ADJUSTMENT OF DOSAGE REGIMEN IN RENAL FAILURE   202
    A. Minimum and Maximum Desired Blood Levels   202
    B. Kinetic Basis for Renal Effects   204
    C. Individualization of Dosage Regimens   206
        Practice Problem 13   207
    D. A Method of Approximation by Dettli   208
        Practice Problem 14   208
        Practice Problem 15   209

REFERENCES   211

I. INTRODUCTION

The development of an optimum dosage regimen, which balances patient convenience with proper body content of drug, is an essential consideration for rational therapy with a drug product. The concept of achieving a certain desirable blood level following administration of a single oral dose of drug was considered in a previous section. However, few drugs are used in a single dose. Some examples of single-dose drugs are headache remedies, digestive aids, antinauseants, laxatives, anthelmintics, and antacids, all of which may be used in one or two doses as the occasion arises. The large majority of drugs are administered repetitively on either a maintenance regimen (as in cardiovascular diseases) or to the end of prescribed course of therapy (as in treatment with an antibiotic). This type of therapy is illustrated in Fig. 1, which shows a blood level curve for a fixed oral dose repeated every 4 hr.

For many drugs a desirable minimum plasma concentration can be established. Kruger-Thiemer [1-3] has stressed the clinical significance of maintaining constant minimum inhibitory blood concentrations for certain antimicrobial agents. For other agents, such as digoxin, theophylline, procainamide, and gentamicin, a rather narrow range of minimum and maximum blood concentrations can be defined. A multiple-dosage regimen can be calculated for either type of drug, i.e., those which simply require a minimum or those which have a narrow margin of safety. The primary prerequisite for such calculations is that the desired therapeutic response must be related to a corresponding concentration of drug in blood.

The complexity of the equations employed for dosage regimen calculations is dependent upon the complexity of the pharmacokinetic model describing the situation. For example, a dosage regimen for a one-compartment model drug, administered by repetitive rapid I.V. injections of equal doses, is easily calculated. But a multicompartment model drug administered orally may become quite complex, and accurate assessments may require a value for the absorption rate constant, k_1. Since values for k_1 are often not readily obtainable,

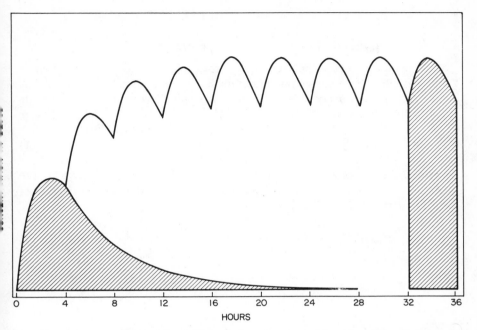

HOURS

Fig. 1 An equal dose is administered orally every 4 hr. The absorption rate constant and bioavailable fraction (F) have been held constant. The total area under the curve (AUC) from t = 0 to ∞ following a single dose is equal to the AUC value between successive doses during the steady state.

approximate methods have been devised for estimating dosage regimens. The present treatment will deal with the one-compartment I.V. case, the two-compartment I.V. case, the biexponential oral administration and model-independent estimates for drug administered by intra- or extravascular routes. Literature references for more complex treatments will be cited.

Regardless of the route of administration or the pharmacokinetic model, there are only two parameters which can be adjusted in developing a regimen for a given drug: size of dose and frequency of administration. The amount of a drug in the body at any given time will be a function of how much drug is administered and how often it is administered. If we know the mathematical relationship between the body content and the dose and frequency, we can estimate a regimen to maintain any desired body level. If a desirable therapeutic body content can be clinically defined, the optimum regimen can then be calculated to provide that level during repetitive multiple-dose therapy. The following sections are designed to illustrate this statement.

II. ACCUMULATION DURING REPETITIVE DOSING

A. Rapid I.V. Injections

Accumulation is most simply considered for rapid I.V. injections of a dose of drug described by a one-compartment model and administered at a fixed time interval, τ. An ordinary first-order equation will describe the loss from the body following a rapid I.V. injection:

$$\ln D = \ln D_0 - \beta t \tag{1}$$

where D_0 is the dose and D is the total amount remaining in the body. The equation may be rearranged to define the natural logarithm of the fraction of the dose remaining, $f = D/D_0$, as

$$\ln f = \ln \left[\frac{D}{D_0}\right] = -\beta t \tag{2}$$

which can be rearranged to this form:

$$t_f = \frac{\ln f}{-\beta} \tag{3}$$

which includes the well-known half-life expression when $f = 0.5$. Thus, the time for the body content to reach any fraction of the administered dose (t_f) is the natural logarithm of that fraction divided by the negative value for β.

Consider the case where rapid equal I.V. doses of this drug are administered repetitively at a fixed time interval, τ. For example, let us say that the dose was administered every time a half-life had elapsed. Then $\tau = t_{0.5}$. Just prior to the second injection, one-half of the dose would remain in the body. Upon injection the body would contain 1.5 doses. Before the third dose, 0.75 dose remains. After the third dose, 1.75 doses are present. The drug is accumulating within the patient. What does accumulation mean? After each subsequent dose there is more drug within the patient than after the previous dose. Therefore the administered dose is greater than the dose eliminated. But there is a limit. When the rate of drug supply becomes equal to its rate of loss, a steady state will be achieved. The time required to achieve the steady state will depend upon the $t_{0.5}$ value of the drug. The difference between the repetitive dosing and that of a zero-order constant rate I.V. infusion is that the repetitive dose steady state will fluctuate between a minimum and a maximum value as a function of time. This pattern (illustrated in Figs. 1 and 2) is shown quantitatively in Table 1 for the dosage intervals where $\tau = t_{0.5}$ and $\tau = t_{0.75}$. Once the body has reached the steady state, it is a necessary condition that the equivalent of a single dose must be eliminated during each

Table 1
Fraction of Dose in the Body Immediately Before and After Rapid I.V.
Administration Where $\tau = t_f$ for a One-Compartment Drug

Number of doses	f = 0.50		f = 0.75	
	Before dose	After dose	Before dose	After dose
1	0	1.00	0	1.00
2	0.50	1.50	0.75	1.75
3	0.75	1.75	1.313	2.313
4	0.875	1.875	1.734	2.734
5	0.938	1.938	2.050	3.050
6	0.969	1.969	2.288	3.288
7	0.984	1.984	2.466	3.466
8	0.992	1.992	2.600	3.600
9	0.996	1.996	2.700	3.700
10	0.998	1.998	2.775	3.775
∞	1.000	2.000	3.000	4.000

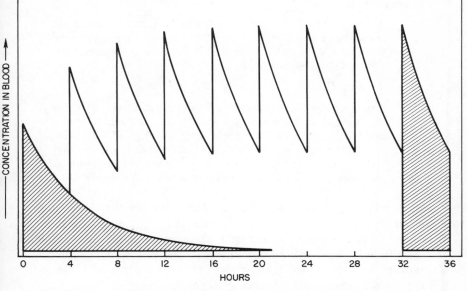

Fig. 2 An equal dose is administered by rapid I.V. injection every 4 hr.
The total area under the curve (AUC) from $t = 0$ to ∞ following a single dose is
equal to the AUC value between successive doses during the steady state.

period of time equal to τ. This is implicit in the definition of steady state, which asserts simply that the dose administered is equal to that which has been eliminated. In Table 1 it is readily apparent that the difference between the body content before and after each dose approaches a constant value that is equal to a single dose. Thus during each dosage interval, τ, a single dose is eliminated and then replaced by the injected dose. The body content (or dose remaining in the body, D) before each subsequent dose will be called the minimum, so that

$$D_{min}^n = (P_{min}^n)Vd \qquad (4)$$

and the peak or maximum value

$$D_{max}^n = (P_{max}^n)Vd \qquad (5)$$

where n = number of doses. If an infinite number of fixed doses (n → ∞) are given at constant τ, the steady-state maxima (D_{max}^∞ or P_{max}^∞) and minima (D_{min}^∞ or P_{min}^∞) will approach constant values as illustrated in Figs. 1, 2, and Table 1.

Practice Problem 1

(a)   A drug that is distributed according to a one-compartment model has a $t_{0.5}$ value of 6 hr. A 210-mg dose is administered by rapid I.V. injection every 12 hr. If the Vd is 40 liters, what value will be achieved for P_{min}^∞ and P_{max}^∞?

   Answer: P_{min}^∞ = 1.75 mg/liter; P_{max}^∞ = 7 mg/liter

(b)   Construct a single figure showing three accumulation plots for the fraction of the dose in the body vs time in hours following rapid I.V. injections of a single drug with $t_{0.5}$ of 4 hr when f = 0.5, f = 0.75 (data in Table 1), and f = 0.25 [as in part (a)] and $\tau = t_f$. Note the steady-state maximum and minimum in each case and the time required to achieve the steady state.

Practice Problem 1 was designed to familiarize you with the kinetics of drug accumulation. The equations for quickly estimating D_{max}^∞ and D_{min}^∞ are quite simple and should become obvious upon examination of the time profile in your plot for part (b) of that problem. Keep in mind that the dosage interval, τ, is defined as the time to deplete the body content to the fraction f. Replacing t_f is Eq. (3) by τ provides the equation describing this:

$$\tau = \frac{\ln f}{-\beta} \qquad (6)$$

We have observed that D_{max}^∞ is always one dose larger than D_{min}^∞. Your figure in part (b) should show that relative to a single dose: $D_{max}^\infty = 4$, $D_{min}^\infty = 3$ (f = 0.75); $D_{max}^\infty = 2$, $D_{min}^\infty = 1$ (f = 0.5); $D_{max}^\infty = 1.33$, $D_{min}^\infty = 0.33$ (f = 0.25). The difference between D_{max}^∞ and D_{min}^∞ is always *one dose*, as you would expect for the steady state where each subsequent dose replaces the one that has been lost. You should have no problem remembering this equation:

$$D_0 = D_{max}^\infty - D_{min}^\infty \tag{7}$$

It is also a simple matter to calculate either D_{max}^∞ or D_{min}^∞ directly. The time of decrease from D_{max}^∞ to D_{min}^∞ is equal to the dosage interval, τ. Since we have defined $\tau = t_f$ [Eq. (6)], then, by definition, $D_{min}^\infty = f(D_{max}^\infty)$. We know that one dose was lost during this time interval [Eq. (7)]. Therefore, $D_0 = (1 - f)D_{max}^\infty$. This can also be derived by substituting $f(D_{max}^\infty)$ for D_{min}^∞ in Eq. (7) and rearranging to obtain

$$D_{max}^\infty = \frac{D_0}{1 - f} \tag{8}$$

The previous examples (Table 1 and Practice Problem 1) set f = 0.75, 0.50, and 0.25, and $\tau = t_f$. Equations (7) and (8) will provide the same steady-state approximations. Try them. (A mathematical derivation for Eqs. (7) and (8) is provided in Appendix D.)

The estimation of P_{min}^∞ and P_{max}^∞ may be a practical problem in therapy or in a research problem. Equation (8) may be written in terms of the plasma concentration using the relationship $P = (D/Vd)$ to give

$$P_{max}^\infty = \frac{B}{1 - f} \tag{9}$$

and

$$P_{min}^\infty = \frac{B(f)}{1 - f} = f(P_{max}^\infty) \tag{10}$$

where $B = D_0/Vd$ is the intercept value of the semilog plot following a single rapid I.V. injection of a one-compartment model drug.

B. Prediction of Multiple-Dose Blood Levels from a Single-Dose Curve

1. Steady-State Blood Levels: Rapid I.V.

If a fixed dose is repetitively administered at a constant dosage interval and all rate processes remain first-order, then the results are additive, as illustrated in Practice Problem 1. Under these conditions a single-dose equation may be converted to its corresponding multiple-dose equation by multiplying each term containing t in the exponent by the factor X, defined as

$$X = \frac{(1 - e^{-nk_i\tau})}{(1 - e^{-k_i\tau})} \tag{11}$$

where k_i is the rate constant in the exponential term and n is the number of doses [4]. This is Eq. (71a) derived in Appendix D. In the case of a rapid I.V. injection of a one-compartment open-model drug where the single dose is described by

$$P = Be^{-\beta t} \tag{12}$$

where P is the plasma concentration at time, t, the multiple-dose equation becomes

$$P^n = \frac{B(1 - e^{-n\beta\tau})(e^{-\beta t})}{(1 - e^{-\beta\tau})} \tag{13}$$

where the limits of time are $0 \leqslant t \leqslant \tau$. After $n \rightarrow \infty$ the equation approaches

$$P^\infty = \frac{Be^{-\beta t}}{(1 - e^{-\beta\tau})} \tag{14}$$

From the antilog of Eq. (3) we see that f, the fraction remaining, equals $e^{-\beta\tau}$ so that $(1 - e^{-\beta\tau}) = (1 - f) =$ fraction eliminated. The numerator of Eq. (14), $Be^{-\beta t}$, is the single-dose curve described by Eq. (12). Thus, Eq. (14) states that the plasma steady-state concentration at a given time equals the single-dose concentration at the same time divided by $(1 - f)$. In these equations, the measurement of time begins anew with each dose so that time falls within the limits $0 \leqslant t \leqslant \tau$.

Practice Problem 2

Figure 3 is an example of the plasma concentration time course for a one-compartment model drug following a single I.V. bolus injection. Assume that this dose is to be repeated every 12 hr. What steady-state time course would result?

Answer: At t = 12 hr, n = 1, the concentration in plasma is 2.8 mg%. Since the initial concentration is 8 mg%, f = 2.8/8 = 0.35. Therefore $P^\infty = P/(1 - f) = 1.54P$. The steady-state plasma level curve may be predicted by multiplying each of the data points in Fig. 3(a) or (b) by the factor 1.54. Figure 4 shows the results where $0 \leqslant t \leqslant \tau$.

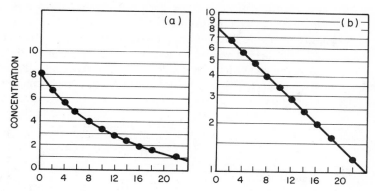

Fig. 3 (a) Concentration of drug in blood as a function of time (in hours) following a single rapid I.V. injection of a one-compartment model drug. (b) Semilog plot for the data in (a).

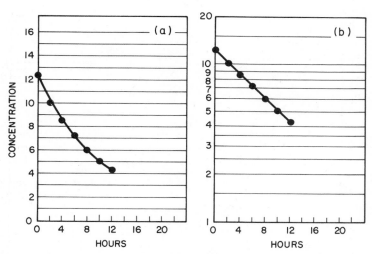

Fig. 4 (a) Predicted steady-state time course for the drug in Fig. 3 administered at equal doses every 12 hr by rapid I.V. injection. This plasma profiled would be repeated following each steady-state dose as illustrated in Fig. 2. (b) Semilog plot for the data in (a).

Any monoexponential curve may be converted to its steady-state time course by multiplying the data points or the line of best fit by the factor $1/(1 - f)$. The value for f, the fraction remaining, is based on the initial value or zero-time intercept for the curve. If a curve is made up of more than one exponential, each component may be converted individiually and the results summed for the overall curve. This is illustrated using a two-compartment model drug in Practice Problem 3.

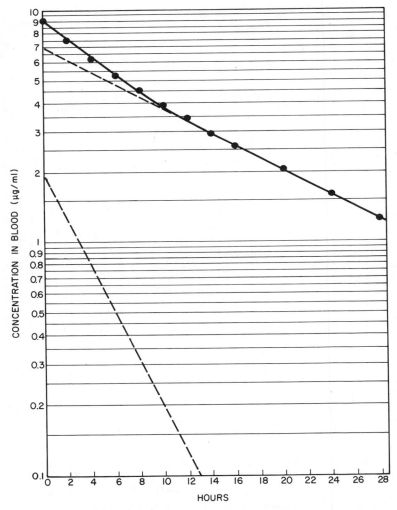

Fig. 5 Feathered semilog plot of data for concentration of drug in blood as a function of time following a rapid I.V. injection.

Practice Problem 3

Figure 5 shows the feathered semilog plot for an I.V. bolus injection of a two-compartment model drug. Compare the steady-state time course that would result from repetitive equal doses administered

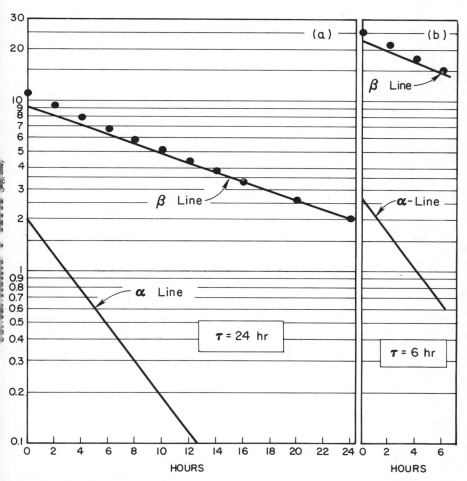

Fig 6 (a) Semilog plots of the predicted steady-state α line, β line, and data points for the drug in Fig. 5 administered at equal doses every 24 hr by rapid I.V. injection. This plasma profile would be repeated after each steady-state dose given at $\tau = 24$ hr. (b) Semilog plots of the predicted steady-state α line, β line, and data points for the drug in Fig. 5 administered at equal doses every 6 hr by rapid I.V. injection. This plasma profile would be repeated after each steady-state dose given at $\tau = 6$ hr.

every 24 hr to that which would result from administration every 6 hr.
Answer: The results are compared in Fig. 6(a) and (b). The methods are discussed below.

Since it is a two-compartment model drug, two exponential functions must be added. When τ = 24 hr the value of f for the β line can be estimated in the figure as f = 1.6/7 = 0.23. Thus the steady-state β line will be 1/(1 – f) = 1/0.77 = 1.30 times the single-dose β line. The steady-state β intercept will be (1.30)(7) = 9.10 and the value at τ will be 2.08 as shown in Fig. 6(a). The value of the α line at 24 hr cannot be read from Fig. 5. A rough estimate may be made by observing that the α line passes through an entire log cycle (from P = 2 to P = 0.2) in 10 hr. Therefore in 24 hr P will be less than one-tenth of the value at 13 hr or P < 0.01. Thus f < (0.01/2) = 0.005 and 1/(1 – f) < 1.005 $\approx$ 1. Since the conversion factor approaches 1, the α line will be the same in the steady state as it was following a single dose. The resulting steady-state blood level will be the sum of these two lines as shown in Fig. 6(a).

When τ = 6 hr, the β-line value for f = 4.8/7 = 0.69 and 1/(1 – f) = 3.2. The steady-state β line will be 3.2 times higher than the single-dose line. The α-line value for f is now significant as the α value at 6 hr is 0.5, making f = 0.5/2 = 0.25. Thus the steady-state α line is obtained by multiplying the single-dose α line by 1/(1 – f) = 1/0.75 = 1.33. The overall steady-state blood level curve will be the sum of these individual steady-state lines as shown in Fig. 6(b).

2. Steady-State Blood Levels: Oral

This process may be extended to any time profile that can be described by one or more exponentials. For example, blood level curves following oral administration can often be described by an equation for the difference between two monoexponential terms. The equation describing this is of the form

$$P = B_{app}e^{-S_1 t} - B_{app}e^{-S_2 t} \tag{15}$$

where S_1 and S_2 are the negative slopes of the first-order plots for the terminal slope (S_1) and the feathered data (S_2). The smaller slope (S_1) represents the rate-limiting step. This equation for a one-compartment model with first-order absorption often fits a two-compartment model with first-order absorption since the distribution phase is not easily seen unless absorption is extremely rapid. If the blood level curve following oral administration can be described by Eq. (15), the data may be feathered as shown in Fig. 7 provided $S_1 \neq S_2$. It is not necessary to assign any physical meaning to the slopes in order to predict the steady state. It is only necessary that the plasma level time course can be described by the difference between a slow monoexponential term (the terminal

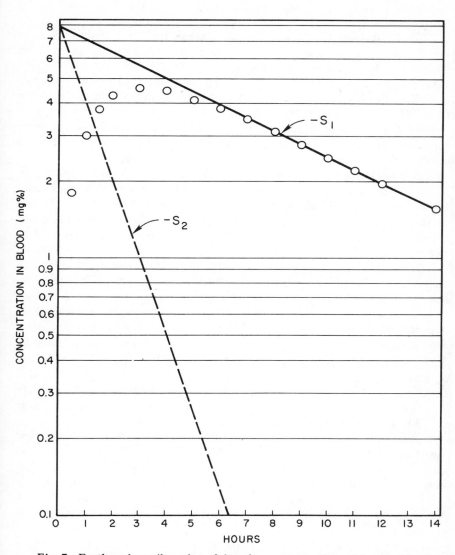

Fig. 7 Feathered semilog plot of data for concentration of drug in blood as a function of time following oral administration when Eq. (15) describes the time course. Data such as this can result from first-order absorption of a one-compartment model drug or a two-compartment model drug with distribution being too rapid to observe by this route of administration. It is not necessary to know what the slow (S_1) and fast (S_2) slopes represent in order to predict the steady state.

slope) and a fast one (the feathered slope) as shown in Fig. 7 and described by Eq. (15).

Let us compare the steady-state blood level for the oral dose given in Fig. 7 repetitively dosed at $\tau = 12$ hr to the results when $\tau = 3$ hr. At $\tau = 12$ hr, f associated with the slower exponential (S_1) is f = 2/8 = 0.25 and 1/(1 − f) = 1.33. For the faster exponential X will approach 1/(1 − f) $\approx$ 1 as f becomes insignificant in Fig. 7. The actual f value may be calculated from $-\ln f = S_2 t = (0.693)(12)$ to give f = 0.00024. Therefore the line associated with S_1 must be multiplied by 1.33 to obtain the steady-state line and the S_2 line remains constant. The actual blood level curve during each 12-hr dosage interval in the steady state will be the S_1 steady-state line minus the S_2 line.

At $\tau = 3$ hr the S_1 value for f = 5.6/8 = 0.7 and 1/(1 − f) = 3.33. The f value for the S_2 line is f = 1/8 = 0.125 and 1/(1 − f) = 1.14. Therefore at steady state the S_1 line will be 3.33 times its single-dose line, the S_2 line will be 1.14 times its single-dose line, and the blood level curve will be the S_1 steady-state line minus the S_2 steady-state line. Figure 8 illustrates these results for $\tau = 12$ hr and $\tau = 3$ hr.

One may also calculate any given data point in the steady state by this method. For example, the value for P at 3 hr in Fig. 7 appears to be the single-dose maximum value. It is simple to calculate the value at t = 3 hr in the steady state when $0 \leqslant t \leqslant \tau$. This may not be the steady-state maximum value. However, the calculation can be repeated on adjacent points to search for the steady-state maximum. For example, when $\tau = 12$ hr the factor was calculated to be 1.33 for S_1 and ~1 for S_2. Therefore at $\tau = 12$ hr, $P_{t=3\,hr}^{\infty}$ is 1.33 × (value in S_1 line) − (value in S_2 line) = (1.33)(5.6) − (1) = 6.45. The steady-state value for P^{∞} at t = 3 hr will be 6.45 when $\tau = 12$ hr. Similarly, one could calculate P_{min}^{∞} by adjusting the single-dose data point for P at t = τ. This is simple at $\tau = 12$ hr since the S_2 line is insignificant and $P_{min}^{\infty} = (2)(1.33) = 2.66$.

Consider the case where the same drug is dosed at 3-hr intervals. Now the steady-state *minimum* (P_{min}^{∞}) must occur at t = 3 hr (Fig. 8), which is the time of *maximum* concentration following a single dose (Fig. 7). This P_{min}^{∞} value may be calculated from the single-dose value of $P_{3\,hr} = 5.6$ using the factors calculated previously for the two reference lines as follows: $P_{min}^{\infty} = 3.33(5.6) - 1.14(1.0) = 17.51$. As seen in Fig. 8, the steady-state P_{min}^{∞} value at $\tau = 3$ hr is 17.51 mg%.

The above behavior is significant for deciding when to draw blood samples for monitoring steady-state drug plasma levels in dosage management in clinical pharmacokinetics. If the feathered line is significant relative to the steady-state calculations, then the time of the steady-state maximum (t_{max}^{∞}) is always less than that of a single dose (t_{max}). This can be seen by comparing the t_{max}^{∞} for $\tau = 3$ hr in Fig. 8 to t_{max} in Fig. 7. If the S_2 line is insignificant, then $t_{max}^{\infty} \approx$

t_{max} as seen when t_{max}^{∞} at $\tau = 12$ hr in Fig. 8 is compared to t_{max} in Fig. 7. Thus, the use of a single-dose t_{max} value to monitor P_{max}^{∞} in the steady state can lead to erroneous conclusions which may be avoided by examining the steady-state time course as done in Fig. 8.

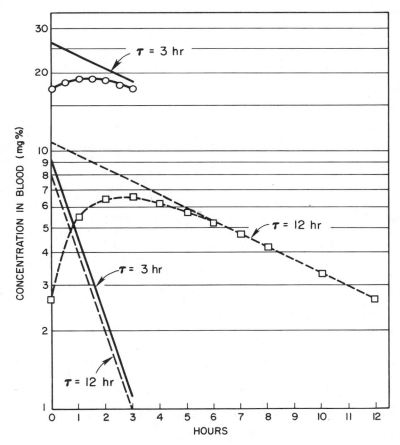

Fig. 8 Semilog plots of the two pairs of steady-state lines predicted from the S_1 and S_2 lines in Fig. 7 by assuming that equal oral doses are administered either every 3 hr (solid lines) or every 12 hr (dashed lines). Data points represent the absolute difference between the two solid lines (○) or the two dashed lines (□).

Practice Problem 4

A tablet containing 500 mg of drug was administered as a single oral dose to 10 normal adults. Blood samples were withdrawn as a function of time and the average results are given in Table 2.

Table 2
Average Concentration of Drug in Blood Following Oral Administration of a 500-mg Tablet to 10 Normal Adults

t (hr)	Conc (mg%)	t (hr)	Conc (mg%)
0.5	13.4	4.0	7.5
1.0	16.1	5.0	5.4
1.5	15.4	6.0	4.0
2.0	13.7	7.0	2.9
3.0	10.2		

(a) Predict the value for P_{min}^{∞} and the value for $P_{t=1\,hr}^{\infty}$ if a 200-mg dose is administered every 4 hr and blood levels are proportional to dose.

(b) Predict the steady-state time course for concentration of drug (P^{∞}) in the blood if a 500-mg dose is administered every 6 hr. What time course would result from 500 mg every 3 hr?

Answer: (a) The f value associated with the terminal slope (S_1) is f = 7.5/26 = 0.29. Thus $1/(1 - f) = 1.4$ is the conversion factor for the curve associated with S_1. The feathered plot for S_2 has a factor of $1/(1 - f) \approx 1$. Therefore, at a 500-mg dose $P_{1\,hr}^{\infty} = 1.4(19) - 1(3.1) = 23.5$ mg%. The P_{min}^{∞} value would not be affected by the S_2 line since its contribution is insignificant at $t = \tau = 4$ hr. Since the 4-hr data point is on the S_1 first-order plot, it can be used to calculate $P_{min}^{\infty} = 1.4(7.5) = 10.5$ mg%. At a dose of 200 mg $P_{1\,hr}^{\infty} = 9.4$ mg% and $P_{min}^{\infty} = 4.2$ mg%.

(b) At $\tau = 6$ hr, f = 0.15 (S_1 line) and $f \approx 0$ (S_2). The steady-state values are therefore $1.18 \times$ (S_1 data) – (S_2 data). For the time points in Table 2 the results are (hr, mg%): 0.5, 17.4; 1.0, 19.5; 1.5, 18.2; 2.0, 16.2; 3.0, 12.0; 4.0, 8.85; 5.0, 6.37; 6.0, 4.72.

At $\tau = 3$ hr, f = 0.39 (S_1 line) and f for S_2 remains negligible. Steady-state values are $1.65 \times$ (S_1 data) – (S_2 data). Results are (hr, mg%): 0.5, 27.9; 1.0, 28.2; 1.5, 25.9; 2.0, 22.7; 3.0, 16.8.

3. Predictions of Blood Levels After the n-th Dose

Equation (11) provided the basis for employing the factor $1/(1 - f)$ to predict steady-state blood levels. The numerator approached unity since $(1 - e^{-nk_i\tau}) \approx 1$ when $n \to \infty$. For the general case of dose n, Eq. (11) can be used in the same manner as previously employed. Since $e^{-k_i\tau} = f$ for the monoexponential curve of rate constant, k_i, Eq. (11) may be written:

$$X = \frac{(1 - f^n)}{(1 - f)} \qquad (16)$$

which is Eq. (71a) derived in Appendix D. This is employed exactly as $1/(1 - f)$ was used to predict steady-state values but n = the number of doses administered must be used to calculate $(1 - f^n)$. The factor X is used to convert a single-dose plasma concentration to the corresponding value after n doses but prior to the steady state which is achieved when the total elapsed time exceed 4-5 half-lives.

Practice Problem 5

In each of the cases for Practice Problems 2-4, predict the drug time course in blood following the third dose.
Answer: In Problem 2, the factor $(1 - f^n)/(1 - f) = (1 - 0.04)/(1 - 0.35) = 1.47$ is slightly less (4.5%) than the original value of 1.54. The points in Fig. 3 multiplied by 1.47 represent the profile following the third dose.

In Problem 3, when $\tau = 24$ hr the β-line factor becomes $(1 - 0.012)/(1 - 0.23) = 1.28$ instead of 1.30 or 1.5% less. The time course for $n = 3$ will be 1.28 times the β line plus the α line, which does not accumulate at $\tau = 24$ hr. At $\tau = 6$ hr the β line must be multiplied by $(1 - 0.33)/(1 - 0.69) = 2.16$, which is 32% less than the original 3.2 factor. The α-line factor is $(1 - 0.016)/(1 - 0.25) = 1.31$, which is nearly the same as the previous 1.33. The overall blood level curve following the third dose will be the sum $2.16 \times$ (β line) plus $1.3 \times$ (α line).

In Problem 4(a) the factor for the S_1 curve is $(1 - 0.024)/(1 - 0.29) = 1.36$ and that for S_2 remains ~ 1. Since the original S_1 factor was 1.40, the $n = 3$ value is 97% of that for the steady state; $P^3_{min} = 0.97 \ (P^\infty_{min}) = 4.1$ mg%. The value for $P^3_{1\,hr} = 1.36(7.6) - 1.24 = 9.1$ mg%.

In Problem 4(b), at $\tau = 6$ hr, the time course following $n = 3$ is the same as that given as the answer for $n = \infty$. For $\tau = 3$ hr, P^3_t values are $1.55 \times$ (S_1 data) − (S_2 data).

Practice Problem 6

Table 3 summarizes the concentration of drug in blood following a single rapid I.V. injection. Assume that only two additional doses are administered at intervals of 2 hr ($\tau = 2$ hr) for a total of $n = 3$. What is the concentration of drug in blood 8 hr after the first dose?

Table 3
Concentration of Drug in Blood Following Rapid I.V. Injection

t (hr)	Conc (mg%)	t (hr)	Conc (mg%)
1.0	0.82	6.0	0.34
2.0	0.70	7.0	0.28
3.0	0.59	8.0	0.24
4.0	0.49	10.0	0.17
5.0	0.41	12.0	0.12

Answer: 1.08 mg%.

4. Degree of Accumulation

A variety of suggestions have been published regarding the calculation of accumulation of drug in the patient during repetitive multiple dosing. A simple and practical way to approach the problem is to calculate X in Eq. (16), which becomes $1/(1 - f)$ for $n = \infty$. If the single-dose curve is monoexponential (first-order), then X will predict the increase in blood level of drug after dose n relative to the level when $n = 1$. For example, if the drug is administered at $\tau = t_{0.5}$, then $f = 0.5$ and $X = [1 - (0.5)^n]/(0.5)$. In the steady state the blood levels will be twice that of $n = 1$. The accumulation is therefore 2-fold or 200% that of the single dose. By using the value for n one can calculate the accumulation following any specific dose in the regimen.

In the cases that involve more than a single exponential this simple approach can only be employed for the terminal exponential slope where the data are not significantly influenced by the more rapid (or feathered) exponential. For example, the answer to Practice Problem 3 shows that at $\tau = 24$ hr, the blood concentration data for the single dose at any time $t > 12$ hr can be used to predict the corresponding steady-state values using $X = 1.30$. The accumulation of the terminal phase is therefore 1.3-fold or 130% of the single dose.

This approach must be modified at $\tau = 6$ hr where both the α and β lines contribute to the sum of the exponentials. The β-line values were $f = 4.8/7 = 0.69$ and $X = [1/(1 - f) = 3.2]$. Those for the α line were $f = 0.5/2 = 0.25$ and $X = [1/(1 - f) = 1.33]$. Therefore $P_{min}^{\infty} = (3.2)(4.8) + (1.33)(0.5) = 16$ mg% at $\tau = 6$ hr while $P_{6\,hr}^{1} = 4.8 + 0.5 = 5.3$ mg%. The degree of accumulation at P_{min}^{∞} is therefore three times that of a single dose. A similar treatment applied to P_{max}^{∞} results in a different value for X. The value for the single dose is $P_{max}^{1} = 7 + 2 = 9$ mg%. At $\tau = 24$ hr, $P_{max}^{\infty} = (1.30)(7) + (2) = 11.1$ mg%. At $\tau = 6$ hr, $P_{max}^{\infty} = (3.2)(7) + (1.33)(2) = 25$ mg%. Thus, at $\tau = 24$ hr, P_{min}^{∞} shows 130% accumulation and P_{max}^{∞} shows 123%. At $\tau = 6$ hr, P_{min}^{∞} shows 300% accumulation and P_{max}^{∞} shows 278%. Using this approach on a monoexponential curve allows steady-state accumulation to be described by a single ratio, $X = 1/(1 - f)$. However, if the curve is biexponential, only the terminal phase may be described by a single factor since the rapid phase becomes insignificant when the data points lie on the terminal slope. When both phases contribute to the drug time course it is necessary to specify the time at which the accumulation is considered since, as just demonstrated, the factor can vary between two points, i.e., P_{max}^{∞} and P_{min}^{∞}. The degree of accumulation may be considered following any number of doses by using $X = (1 - f^n)/(1 - f)$ as shown previously.

If we assume that the dosage interval, τ, corresponds to a time wherein the data points lie on the negative terminal slope, S, we can define the *apparent* half-life as

$$t_{0.5}^* = \frac{0.693}{S} \tag{17}$$

The $t_{0.5}^*$ value will equal the biological half-life when $S = \beta$. However, for an oral or I.M. dose, the value of S may represent rate-determining input in the case of a "flip-flop" situation [5, 6]. As shown in Table 4, one can consider the effect of τ on f and on the resultant accumulation (X) assuming that τ is on the terminal log-linear phase.

Table 4

Degree of Accumulation During Repetitive Dose Steady-State Relative to the Linear Terminal Phase Observed with a Single Dose

τ (in number of apparent half-lives)[a]	f[b]	$X = [1/(1 - f)]$	% increase from single dose
0.5	0.707	3.41	241
1.0	0.50	2.00	100
1.5	0.35	1.55	55
2.0	0.25	1.33	33
2.5	0.177	1.21	21
3.0	0.125	1.14	14
3.5	0.088	1.10	10
4.0	0.063	1.07	7
∞	0	1.00	0

[a]Eq. (17).
[b]Based on linear first-order plot of terminal phase.

As f approaches zero, the degree of accumulation, $1/(1 - f)$, approaches 1, indicating that steady-state values are similar to those following a single dose. This is the mathematical limit as $\tau \to \infty$ and is therefore not of practical value. One must therefore decide what percent increase over the single dose can be regarded as insignificant. For many drugs 10–15% increase may not be clinically significant. Table 4 shows that if $\tau \geqslant 3$ ($t_{0.5}^{*}$), then accumulation will be less than 15%. As a first approximation, a dosage interval that equals or exceeds three times the apparent half-life may be regarded as negligible accumulation of the drug relative to a single dose.

Practice Problem 7

What is the degree of accumulation at $t \geqslant 8$ hr for the drug shown in Fig. 7 if it is repetitively administered as the same dosage form, in the same dose size, and at $\tau = 12$ hr? (See Fig. 8 and discussion for steady-state curves.)
Answer: At $\tau = 12$ hr and $t \geqslant 8$ hr, $1/(1 - f) = 1.33$. The terminal phase accumulation is 133%.

In the above problem the degree of accumulation at $t \geqslant 8$ hr is constant at 133%. This is due to the fact that all of the data points at $t \geqslant 8$ hr are on the terminal log-linear phase of Fig. 7 and $\tau = 12$ hr lies on this line. If accumulation is evaluated in the biexponential portion, the degree will increase. If we compare the peak values for example ($t_{max} = 3$ hr) the steady-state value ($P_{3\,hr}^{\infty}$) is 1.44 times the single-dose value ($P_{3\,hr}^{1}$) or 144% accumulation.

If we consider $\tau = 3$ hr, both exponentials will contribute to every data point in the single-dose curve and its steady-state counterpart. The value for P_{min}^{∞} ($t = 3$ hr $= \tau$) in this case is roughly 3.9 times the $P_{3\,hr}^{1}$ value. The t_{max} has shifted from ≈ 3 hr ($n = 1$) to ≈ 1.5 hr ($n = \infty$). The steady-state maximum value (P_{max}^{∞} at $t = 1.5$ hr) is roughly four times the single dose P_{max}^{1} (at $t = 3$ hr). Thus the accumulation factor (X) is roughly 4, so that the steady-state curve is 400% of the single-dose curve when $\tau = 3$ hr.

The degree of accumulation has thus been shown to be inversely related to τ. At $\tau = 12$ hr the accumulation factor was approximately 1.4 while at $\tau = 3$ hr it was shown to be ≈ 4.

C. Average Steady-State Levels for Any Route and Model

The total area under the blood level curve following a single dose, $AUC = \int_{0}^{\infty} P\,dt$, is equal to the area between successive doses during the multiple-dose steady state wherein $AUC = \int_{0}^{\tau} P^{\infty}\,dt$ and $0 \leqslant t \leqslant \tau$. This is illustrated by the shaded areas in Figs. 1 and 2. Thus, for *any route and model* (assuming linear kinetics and elimination from the central compartment), the average steady-state plasma level $(\bar{P}_{ss})$ during repetitive dosing at fixed time intervals may be predicted from single-dose data since $\bar{P}_{ss} = AUC/\tau$. The value for $\bar{P}_{ss}$ is therefore average *area* between doses and *not* the average of $(P^{\infty}_{max} + P^{\infty}_{min})$. Since $AUC = [F(D_0)/clearance] = F(D_0)/\beta Vd$, then substitution for AUC in $\bar{P}_{ss} = AUC/\tau$ gives

$$\bar{P}_{ss} = \frac{F(D_0)}{\beta Vd\tau} = \frac{F(D_0)(1.44)(t_{0.5})}{Vd\tau} \tag{18}$$

where F is the bioavailable fraction of the administered dose (D_0). For an I.V. injection, $F = 1$. This equation was originally derived for a one-compartment model [7] and later applied to multicompartmental models [8]. For a *one-compartment model*, where the amount in the body equals $(P_t)(Vd)$, steady-state average amount may be calculated from

$$\bar{D}_{ss} = \bar{P}_{ss}(Vd) \tag{19}$$

where the volume of distribution (Vd) may be calculated by any of the standard methods. For a drug described by a model employing more than one compartment, the calculated value for Vd may vary with the method employed. Since the values $\bar{P}_{ss}$ and $\bar{D}_{ss}$ are steady-state values, one would expect the steady-state estimate (Vd_{inf}) to provide the best $\bar{P}_{ss}$ estimates. If Vd_{area} values are estimated following a single rapid I.V. dose, the resulting estimates for $\bar{D}_{ss}$ obtained from the product of $(\bar{P}_{ss})(Vd)$ will overestimate the actual amount in the body [9]. The degree of error is minimal as $[(k_{12} + k_{21})/\alpha]$ approaches unity. When this condition is not met errors can be large. For example, it has been calculated that the percent error is 70% for penicillen G, 32% for lidocaine, 23% for ethchorvynol, but negligible for warfarin [9]. Thus, for a *two-compartment model*, the steady-state infusion value, Vd_{inf}, will provide the correct relationship as follows:

$$\bar{P}_{ss} = \frac{\bar{D}_{ss}}{Vd_{inf}} \tag{20}$$

Practice Problem 8

(a) If the desired average plasma level for a drug is 0.4 mg%, what dose should be given orally on a regimen of every 6 hr around the clock? The drug is 85% absorbed and the patient weighs 70 kg. The Vd value is 140 liters and $t_{0.5}$ is 3.5 hr.

(b) If identical average plasma levels are to be maintained with a 500-mg capsule, how often should it be administered?

Answer: (a) 783 mg
         (b) 3.83 hr

D. Repetitive Dosing for Minimum Effective Concentrations

1. Prediction of P^∞_{min} from Single-Dose Plots

Figure 8 illustrates how the choice of τ can influence the relative contribution of each exponential to the steady-state time course. If τ is sufficiently large, the value for P^∞_{min} can be calculated directly from the line representing the slower exponential (or rate-determining step). The minimum τ (τ_{min}) that will satisfy this condition may be estimated by inspection. If $\tau \geq t'$ where t' is the time at which the first data point (P_t) falls on the terminal long-linear plot, then the rapid exponential will be insignificant in the calculation of P^∞_{min} and $\tau_{min} \approx t'$. This is more easily visualized with graphical examples. In Fig. 5, τ_{min} is approximately 14 hr since this is the time at which the first data point falls on the β line. Therefore if $\tau \geq 14$ hr, then P^∞_{min} can be estimated from this reference line. We can test this method using Fig. 6. When $\tau = 24$ hr, $P^\infty_{min} = 2$ $\mu g/ml$ [Fig. 6(a)]. Using the β line in Fig. 5 provides X = $[1/(1 - 0.23)]$ = 1.3, which predicts $P^\infty_{min} = (P^1_{24\,hr})$ (X) = $(1.6)(1.3) = 2$ $\mu g/ml$. When $\tau < \tau_{min}$ both exponentials will contribute to P^∞_{min}. For example, at $\tau = 6$ hr [Fig. 6(b)], $P^\infty_{min} = 16.1$ $\mu g/ml$, which is the sum of the contributions from the β line (15.46 $\mu g/ml$) and the α line (0.66 $\mu g/ml$). (The α-line contribution is small even at $\tau = 6$ hr in this particular example since at t = 6 hr in Fig. 5 the α line represents only 10% of the total. This is but one example and should not be misconstrued as the general case.)

Thus, if $\tau \geq \tau_{min}$, P^∞_{min} may be predicted from the β line of a two-compartment I.V. semilog plot. This may be stated using equations as follows. If the time course for drug concentration in blood can be described by

$$P = Ae^{-\alpha t} + B^{-\beta t} \qquad (21)$$

the steady-state equation may be written by applying Eq. (11) with n = ∞ to give

$$P^\infty = \frac{Ae^{-\alpha t}}{(1 - e^{-\alpha \tau})} + \frac{Be^{-\beta t}}{(1 - e^{-\beta \tau})} \qquad (22)$$

Since P^∞_{min} occurs at t = τ,

$$P^\infty_{min} = \frac{Af'}{(1 - f')} + \frac{Bf}{(1 - f)} \qquad (23)$$

where $f' = e^{-\alpha \tau}$ and $f = e^{-\beta \tau}$. When $Ae^{-\alpha t}$ is insignificant the data points in Eq. (21) may be described by $P_t \approx Be^{-\beta t}$ at which time the data appear to lie on the β line. The P^∞_{min} value in Eq. (23) then becomes $Bf/(1 - f)$. In the process described above we calculated f from $(P^1_{t=\tau})/(B)$. Therefore $Bf = P^1_{t=\tau}$, which is the data point on the single-dose curve at time τ. Substituting in Eq. (23), when $\tau > \tau_{min}$ so that $Af'/(1 - f')$ becomes insignificant gives

$$P^{\infty}_{min} \approx \frac{fB}{(1 - f)} = \frac{P^1_{t=\tau}}{(1 - f)} \tag{24}$$

which is the equation describing the process used above to convert the single-dose data point in Fig. 5 to the P^{∞}_{min} value in Fig. 6(a) when $\tau = 24$ hr.

A similar approach can be used for the biexponential oral curve shown in Fig. 7 where $\tau_{min} \approx 8$ hr. Figure 8 shows examples wherein $\tau_{min} > \tau = 3$ hr and $\tau_{min} < \tau = 12$ hr. The P^{∞}_{min} value of 17.51 at $\tau = 3$ hr is the difference between the slower (S_1) exponential contribution (18.65 mg%) less the faster (S_2) exponential (1.14 mg%). However, at $\tau = 24$ hr, P^{∞}_{min} is calculated directly from the S_2 line: $P^{\infty}_{min} = (2)(1.33) = 2.66$ mg%. Equation (15) may be converted to the steady-state minimum using Eq. (11), as done above for Eq. (21), to give

$$P^{\infty}_{min} = \frac{fB_{app}}{(1 - f)} - \frac{f'B_{app}}{(1 - f')} \tag{25}$$

where $f = e^{-S_1\tau}$ and $f' = e^{-S_2\tau}$. When $\tau > \tau_{min}$ and $f'B_{app}/(1 - f')$ becomes insignificant, then

$$P^{\infty}_{min} \approx \frac{fB_{app}}{(1 - f)} = \frac{P^1_{t=\tau}}{(1 - f)} \tag{26}$$

Thus, the line associated with the rate-determining exponential (S_1 in Fig. 7) can be used to calculate the steady-state minimum in the same way as the β line, since in both cases $P^{\infty}_{min} \approx P^1_{t=\tau}/(1 - f)$ when $\tau \geqslant \tau_{min}$.

2. Calculating Dosage Regimens to Maintain Minimum Plasma Levels

In the previous section it was shown that P^{∞}_{min} can be estimated from the terminal log-linear plot provided that τ is equal to or greater than the time required for the single-dose semilog plot to become linear. When this condition is satisfied the τ values will be based on the terminal or rate-determining slope. For a one-compartment I.V. dose this will be the observed first-order rate constant, which is the negative slope of the entire plot. For a two-compartment I.V. dose, it will be β. For an extravascular route described by two exponentials, it will be S_1 (Fig. 7). Thus, we may define the dosing interval as $\tau = -\ln f/k_{rds}$ where f and k_{rds} are the fraction remaining and the negative slope associated with the terminal log-linear plot. It is reasonable to assume that τ is normally sufficiently large to make P^{∞}_{min} primarily a function of the k_{rds} line. That is, contrary to $\tau = 3$ hr in Fig. 8, the examples representing $\tau = 12$ hr (Fig. 8) and $\tau = 24$ hr (Practice Problem 3) wherein the rapid exponential is no longer significant are considered more realistic. The validity of this assumption may be illustrated by the case where $\tau = 3$ hr. Examination of Figs. 7 and 8 will show that the 3-hr dosage interval is not rational. It is unlikely that one would choose to administer a dose at 3 hr when Fig. 7 clearly shows that blood levels following one dose persist at least 12 hr. Since blood levels are prolonged by the rate-determining exponential, it is reasonable to assume that the value normally chosen for τ will correspond to a time on the terminal log-linear plot.

We have seen from the previous discussion that it is relatively simple and practical to select a τ which will result in a P^{∞}_{min} value that may be safely predicted using only the terminal log-linear data line. A single equation, $P^{\infty}_{min} \approx P^{1}_{t=\tau}/(1 - f)$, may then be employed to calculate a dosage regimen to maintain a given value for the steady-state minimum. This may also be written as

$$P^{\infty}_{min} = \frac{fB_i}{(1 - f)} \tag{27}$$

where B_i is the intercept of the terminal log-linear plot previously defined as $B_i = B$ (one- and two-compartment rapid I.V.), $B_i = B_{app}$ (biexponential oral). There are two variables which may be adjusted in developing a regimen with Eq. (27). These are B_i [which is proportional to dose] and f [which is related to τ by Eq. (6)]. Thus, the size of the dose and the dosage interval can be altered to design a convenient regimen to provide any desired minimum steady-state plasma concentration.

Although the values for D_0 and τ may be altered, there will be an ideal combination if plasma levels are to be maintained within a narrow range. This is illustrated in Fig. 9, where the dose size is constant for all three cases but the values for τ are altered. However, once the size of the dose is fixed the ideal value for τ is also fixed and vice versa. This can be illustrated with two examples taken from Schumacher [10]. In Practice Problem 9 the dose size is fixed and the interval must be calculated. In Practice Problem 10 the interval is fixed and the dose must therefore be adjusted.

Practice Problem 9: Calculation of the Dosage Interval to Maintain M.I.C. with 500-mg Capsules of Tetracycline.
A single oral dose of tetracycline (500-mg capsule) is found to give a linear terminal semilog plot for total drug in blood vs. time. The equation for this line is $\ln(P_t) = \ln(3.9 \ \mu g/ml) - (0.0729 \ hr^{-1}) \ (t)$. Calculate the dosage interval that will provide an M.I.C. of 0.8 $\mu g/ml$ of free tetracycline if 50% of the drug in the blood is bound to serum protein.
Answer: 16.9 hr

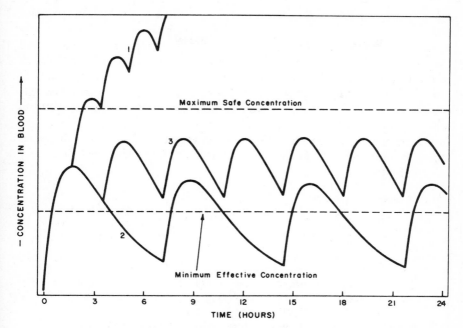

Fig. 9   The objective of the multiple-dosage regimen is to maintain the patient's blood level within the maximum and minimum concentrations shown in the figure. The dosage interval, τ, is too short in curve 1, too long in curve 2, and ideal in curve 3. The initial dose used for this simulation is 33% more than the maintenance dose, and k_1 is three times larger than k_2.

Practice Problem 10:   Calculation of the Oral Dose of Tetracycline to Maintain M.I.C. with a 12-hr Dosage Interval.
In the previous problem 500-mg capsules were used to calculate a dosage interval. The regimen which resulted was one capsule every 16 or 17 hr. This is not a convenient interval. A regimen of morning and night (every 12 hr) would be more reasonable. Using the information in Practice Problem 9, calculate the dose to be administered every 12 hr.
Answer: 287 mg (Hint: Assuming that blood levels are proportional to dose, calculate the value for B_{app} when $\tau = 12$ hr and therefore $f = 0.417$. The value for B_{app} is 2.24, which is 57.4% of 3.90. Therefore the new dose is 57.4% of 500 mg.)

During the steady state a drug is administered on a fixed dose and dosage interval. The patient thereby maintains a relatively constant amount of drug in the body. The previous problem demonstrates the manner in which the dose or time interval may be altered and still maintain the steady state. When the 12-hr interval was employed, a maintenance dose of 287 mg was sufficient. However, 500 mg was needed when the 17-hr interval was used. In the steady state, a single dose of drug is eliminated during each τ interval and then replaced by the next dose. Therefore the difference between the minimum and maximum in the steady state is a single maintenance dose. This was illustrated in Table 1. The shorter the interval chosen for τ, the smaller the maintenance dose. This was just observed in the previous two problems, where 287 mg replaced 500 mg. Thus, the shorter the τ interval, the smoother the blood-time profile during steady state and the less the difference between P_{min}^{∞} and P_{max}^{∞}. This is an important consideration in developing a regimen for a drug with a narrow margin of safety.

Practice Problem 11:
A 3-g I.V. dose of ticarcillin provided the following serum levels as a function of time:

hr:	0.25	0.50	1.0	2.0	3.0	4.0	6.0
(μ/ml):	190	140	107	52.2	31.3	13.8	4.2

The *minimum inhibitory concentration* (M.I.C.) for treating the detected strain of pseudomonas is 60 μg/ml. What τ value is required to maintain this M.I.C. value using the 3-g I.V. dose?
Answer: A first-order plot is linear with $\beta = 0.655$ hr^{-1} and B = 206 μg/ml. Using Eq. (27) where P_{min}^{∞} = M.I.C. = 60 μg/ml and B = 206, gives f = 0.226. Then $\tau = -\ln f/\beta = 2.3$ hr.

In the above problem the τ value of 2.3 hr would not be convenient to use. If increased slightly to $\tau = 3$ hr the regimen would be greatly simplified. But the dose size must be increased. This may be done by finding the new value for B as follows: $-\ln f = \beta\tau = (0.655)(3) = 1.965$; f = 0.140. Then B = (P_{min}^{∞}) $(1 - f)/f = 368$ μg/ml. Since the intercept is proportional to the dose, D_0 = $(3\ g)(368/206) = 5.36$ g. The new regimen is therefore 5.36 g every 3 hr.

3. Calculating the Minimum Dosage Interval (τ_{min}) to Use the Monoexponential Approximation

It was demonstrated previously that $P_{min}^{\infty} = fB_i/(1 - f)$ if τ is sufficiently large $(\tau \geqslant \tau_{min})$ to be equal to or greater than the time required to reach the mono-exponential phase of a semilog plot. This can be estimated on inspection by simply observing when the data points fall on the terminal log-linear plot. However, it was noted that at $\tau = 6$ hr, the P_{min}^{∞} value in Fig. 6(b) could be approximated using only the β line even though estimated τ_{min} was 14 hr by inspection. Estimates obtained for τ_{min} by the method of inspection will ensure reliable predictions when using Eq. (27). They may, however, be larger than the actual minimum required for approximating monoexponential loss. The following equation may be employed to calculate the *minimum* time required, τ_{min}, to ensure that the contribution of the rapid exponential will not exceed some chosen percentage of the rate-determining exponential. [Eq. (28) was adapted from Ref. 5.]

$$\tau_{min} = \frac{\ln (R/Pct)}{\Delta} \tag{28}$$

The value for Pct is (% chosen)/100, R is the rapid/slow intercept ratio, and Δ is the positive difference between the slopes. In the case of an oral dose, R = 1 (Fig. 7). For a two-compartment I.V. case, R will generally not be unity. In the example shown in Fig. 5, R = 0.29. Equation (28) will predict the time after which the slow exponential alone will describe the single-dose time course with the maximum contribution of the rapid phase occurring at $t = \tau_{min}$. Take, for example, a 5% contribution by the rapid exponential in the case of Figs. 5 and 7. For Fig. 5, τ_{min} = 10 hr and for Fig. 7, τ_{min} = 5 hr. (The estimates by inspection were 14 and 8 hr.) Since the estimates using Eq. (28) are based on a single dose, the percent contribution would be even less during steady state since the $[1/(1 - f)]$ factor will always be greater for the slower exponential. This is due to the fact that f must be larger for the slower exponential making its factor $[1/(1 - f)]$ greater, thus further reducing the percent contribution by the rapid exponential.

E. Calculation of Loading Dose

In Fig. 1, a fixed dose was administered every 4 hr and roughly 16 hr were required to achieve the steady state. Contrast that to the time course of curve 3 in Fig. 9, where the steady state is practically attained with the first dose. The difference is the fact that a loading dose equal to 33% more than the maintenance dose was used in curve 3 of Fig. 9. Kruger-Thiemer [11] has pointed out that a nearly optimum regimen with little or no lag time results when the loading dose is twice that of the maintenance dose and $\tau = t_{0.5}$ (provided that $k_1 \gg \beta$). Thus, for a dosage regimen which accumulates drug, a loading dose can provide the shortest onset.

If a drug has a short half-life, a dosage regimen may not be designed to result in accumulation. The various penicillins, for example, have $t_{0.5}$ values of 0.5-1.0 hr. Oral penicillin tablets are generally administered every 4-6 hr. Assuming that absorption is relatively rapid and elimination is first-order, one would estimate that 94% of a dose is eliminated in four half-lives or 2-4 hr. Thus administration of tablets every 4-6 hr will not result in significant accumulation, since each dose is administered to an empty patient. The time course of drug in blood after each dose would therefore appear like a single-dose treatment.

For those drugs which *do* accumulate during a multiple-dose regimen, an onset period may be defined as the time required to reach the steady-state blood levels. As seen for the case of constant I.V. infusion, this onset is related to the $t_{0.5}$ of the drug. In other words, a drug with a long $t_{0.5}$ will have a longer onset than one with a shorter $t_{0.5}$ (all other parameters being equal). In Table 1, where $\tau = t_{0.5}$, one can observe that 94% of the steady-state minimum occurs just prior to $n = 5$ or 4 times τ which is equal to four half-lives. Just prior to $n = 6$ (or five half-lives), 97% of the steady-state minimum is achieved. Thus, a one-compartment I.V. repetitive dose regimen will approach the steady-state minimum in four to five half-lives [12].

A two-compartment drug may require even longer [13]. If one accepts that roughly four half-lives are required for accumulation, it follows that a drug with a 12-hr half-life will not reach steady state for 2.0 days. In such a case a loading dose may significantly improve therapy. Applying this estimate to a more extreme example, a 4-day regimen of a drug with a 24-hr half life would not achieve the steady-state level during the course of therapy. The use of a sufficiently large initial dose will result in steady-state levels throughout the 4 days.

How does one calculate the initial dose or the loading dose, D^*? If $\tau \geqslant \tau_{min}$ or if the single-dose curve is monoexponential, the D^* may be calculated from the maintenance dose, D_0, according to

$$D^* = \frac{D_0}{1 - f} \tag{29}$$

where the fraction remaining is related to the rate-determining step by $t_f = -\ln f/k_{rds}$. Thus, the initial dose, D^*, is calculated from the maintenance dose, D_0, and the fraction, f. Equation (29) may be used for either the oral or I.V. route of administration provided that the maintenance dose, D_0, has been determined for the same route. That is why Eq. (29) is identical to Eq. (8) for calculating D_{max}^∞ by the I.V. route, where the bioavailability factor, F, is equal to 1. Thus, for the I.V. case, the loading dose is equal to D_{max}^∞. For an extravascular route, D^* will generally be larger than D_{max}^∞, since the bioavailability factor will be less than 1.

Practice Problem 12: Calculating Loading Dose.

Calculate a loading dose to be used for each of the maintenance regimens (doses and intervals) that you estimated in Practice Problems 8–10.

Answer: (Problem 8a) 1.13g; (Problem 8b) 940 mg; (Problem 9) 705 mg; (Problem 10) 492 mg.

It is important to distinguish between those factors controlling onset and those controlling the resultant steady-state plasma levels. *Onset*, as defined above, refers to the time required to achieve steady state and is therefore a function of half-life [or apparent half-life, Eq. (17)] only. The *degree of accumulation* was previously defined as the quantitative relationship between the plasma level following a single dose (n = 1) and that following dose n. If $\tau > \tau_{min}$ and the terminal log-linear phase is considered, then the accumulation factor is $X = (1 - f^n)/(1 - f)$. The degree of accumulation in the steady state (n = ∞) was shown to depend on both τ and $t_{0.5}^*$ since $-\ln f = (0.693)(\tau)/t_{0.5}^*$ (see the summary of X values in Table 4). Thus, *onset* depends only on $t_{0.5}^*$ while *degree of accumulation* depends on both $t_{0.5}^*$ and τ.

The amount of drug in the body at the steady state is dependent upon the bioavailable dose, the dosage interval, and the $t_{0.5}$. The average steady-state plasma level, $\bar{P}_{ss}$, has been defined by Eq. (18). This equation shows that $\bar{P}_{ss}$ will increase with increasing bioavailable dose (FD_0) and $t_{0.5}$ but will decrease with increasing τ. However, for any given $t_{0.5}$, only FD_0 and τ will influence $\bar{P}_{ss}$. *Onset* will still require four times $t_{0.5}$. (The onset time is mathematically t = ∞ but four times $t_{0.5}$ will be considered a clinically acceptable approximation.)

Equation (18) may be rearranged to calculate the ratio of drug in the body to bioavailable dose as defined by the equation

$$\frac{\bar{D}_{ss}}{FD_0} = \frac{(1.44)(t_{0.5})}{\tau} \tag{30}$$

Thus, a drug that is completely absorbed (F = 1) will accumulate 1.44 times the dose if administered every half-life. If it is administered at intervals that are one-half of the value for the half-life, $\tau = (0.5)(t_{0.5})$, then 2.88 times the dose will accumulate. Thus, we see that the average steady-state number of bioavailable doses which accumulate is directly proportional to the $t_{0.5}$ and inversely proportional to the dosage interval. This equation does *not* indicate degree of accumulation. For example when $\tau = t_{0.5}$, at n = ∞ Eq. (30) predicts $\bar{D}_{ss}/FD_0 = 1.44$ while the accumulation relative to a single dose is $X = 1/(1 - f) = 2$. The ratio $\bar{D}_{ss}/FD_0$ is not a measure of degree of accumulation since it does not compare steady-state results to those of a single dose. Therefore it will *not* be employed in this text when discussing accumulation. Equation (30) is included here to emphasize the fact that $\bar{D}_{ss}$ is proportional to $(t_{0.5}/\tau)$ while onset time remains a function of $t_{0.5}$.

One final complication, which will be noted but not solved, is the problem of calculating a dosage regimen when drugs are not administered at uniform time intervals "around the clock." If the indicated dosage regimen for a drug is four times a day, it is unlikely that it will be taken once every 6 hr. The most common definition found in hospital formularies for q.i.d. is either

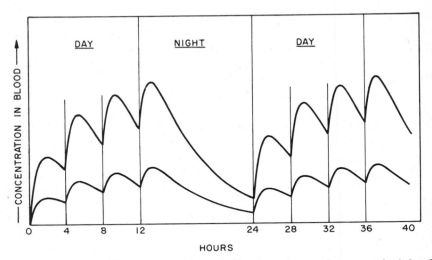

Fig. 10   A Typical regimen of one tablet four times a day on a schedule of 10-2-6-10 or 9-1-5-9. Two different doses are illustrated over the first and second day of the regimen.

10-2-6-10 or 9-1-5-9 [14]. Thus a 12-hr period follows the last dose each night. Figure 10 illustrates drug plasma-time profiles for this type of dosage regimen at two different doses. Methods have been devised for computerized calculations of plasma level-time courses for such cases [14].

III.   ADJUSTMENT OF DOSAGE REGIMEN IN RENAL FAILURE

A.   Minimum and Maximum Desired Blood Levels

There are many specific examples of recommendations for adjustment of the dosage regimen for a drug that is administered to a patient during renal failure. This precaution is of paramount importance in cases where the drug has a narrow margin of safety. Administration of such a drug on the normal or average basis can result in higher levels of drug accumulation during the steady state, thus providing the basis for potential side effects to the patients.

Two factors dictate the potential danger of drug accumulation due to renal failure. One is the effect of renal failure on elimination of the drug. The second is the acceptable range of drug concentration in blood. Winek [15] has prepared a comprehensive list of values for the therapeutic range, the toxic level, and the lethal concentration of various compounds in blood. Some of those data are listed in Table 5 together with their ratios for P_{max}/P_{min}, $P_{toxic}/\bar{P}$, and $P_{lethal}/\bar{P}$

where $\bar{P}$ is the average of P_{max} and P_{min}. It is clear that useful drugs may have a very narrow range between the desired blood levels and those which can cause serious side effects.

The second factor is whether or not renal failure will cause an increase in the blood level of the drug. A narrow range of safety together with increased accumulation due to renal failure mandate a correction in the dosage regimen.

Table 5

Concentration of Drug in Blood (mg% unless specified) Following Therapeutic Dosage (therapeutic range), Associated with Serious Toxic Symptoms (toxic) and Reported or Judged Sufficient to Cause Death (lethal)[a]

Drug	Thera-peutic Range	Toxic	Lethal	Ratios[b] R_1	R_2	R_3
Acetaminophen	1–2	40	150	2	27	100
Acetohexamide	2.1–5.6	–	–	2.7	–	–
Amitriptyline	5–20 µg%	40 µg%	1.0–2.0 mg%	4	3	80
Barbiturates						
Phenobarbital	ca. 1.0	4–6	8–15	–	4	8
Barbital	ca. 1.0	6–8	10 & >	–	6	10
Chloral hydrate	1.0	10	25	–	10	25
Chlordiazepozide	0.1–0.2	0.55	2	3	3	10
Chlorpromazine	0.05	0.1–0.2	0.3–1.2	–	2	6
Dextropropoxyphene	5–20 µg%	0.5–1 mg%	5.7 mg%	4	40	450
Diazepam	0.05–0.25	0.5–2.0	2.0	5	3	13
Ethchlorvynol	ca. 0.5	2	15	–	4	30
Glutethimide	0.02	1–8	3–10	–	50	150
Lithium	0.42–0.83 (0.6–1.2 meq./liter)	1.39 (2.0 meq./liter)	1.39–3.47 (2.0–5.0 meq./liter)	2	2	2
Meperidine	60–65 µg%	500 µg%	ca. 3 mg%	1.1	8	48
Meprobamate	1	10	20	–	10	20
Methaqualone	0.5	1–3	3	–	2	6
Methyprylon	1.0	3–6	10	–	3	10
Paraldehyde	ca. 5.0	20–40	50	–	4	10
Phenytoin	0.6–1.7	2–5	10 & >	3	2	8
Salicylate (acetyl-salicylic acid)	2–10	15–30	50	5	2	8

[a]Adapted from Winek [15].

[b]$R_1 = (P_{max}/P_{min})_{therapeutic}$; $R_2 = P_{toxic}/\bar{P}_{normal}$; $R_3 = P_{lethal}/\bar{P}_{normal}$; where $\bar{P} = (P_{max} + P_{min})/2$.

B. Kinetic Basis for Renal Effects

The adjustment of a dosage regimen in the presence of renal failure is based on the kinetic principles discussed previously under parallel drug loss. In that section, the total elimination rate constant, β, is defined as

$$\beta = \beta_m + \beta_e \tag{31}$$

where β_m is the apparent first-order rate constant for metabolism and β_e represents excretion. This may be written in a more general form as

$$\beta = \beta_{NR} + \beta_R \tag{32}$$

where β_{NR} represents the sum of all first-order rate constants for loss of drug by *nonrenal* routes and β_R represents *renal* excretion. The assumptions in applying this equation to correct for renal failure are that β remains first-order and that β_{NR} remains constant. This means that the decrease in renal function does not result in saturation of the remaining elimination processes such as metabolism and that there is no compensatory increase in β_{NR}. If Eq. (32) does not remain linear, it is necessary to describe the effect of renal clearance on the elimination constant (or the $t_{0.5}$) and use those data for dosage correction. Since clearance = (rate constant) (volume), multiplying through Eq. (32) by Vd results in

$$C_T = C_{NR} + C_R \tag{33}$$

where $C_T = \beta Vd$, $C_{NR} = \beta_{NR} Vd$, and $C_R = \beta_R Vd$. The relationship between β and renal clearance for the drug can be written as

$$\beta = \beta_{NR} + \frac{1}{Vd} \, C_R \tag{34}$$

by substituting for β_R in Eq. (32). If the renal clearance value for the drug (C_R) can be related to glomerular filtration rate (GFR), it is possible to write Eq. (34) in terms of a kidney function test for GFR. Creatine renal clearance (C_{Cr}) is a commonly employed test to measure GFR. Thus if $C_R \propto C_{Cr} = GFR$, then Eq. (34) may be written in terms of creatinine renal clearance:

$$\beta = \beta_{NR} + QC_{Cr} \tag{35}$$

where β_{NR} is assumed to be constant and Q is the slope of the linear plot for β versus C_{Cr} with intercept β_{NR}.

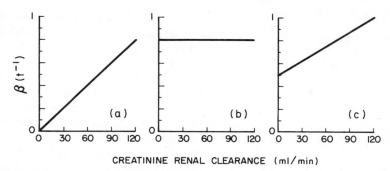

CREATININE RENAL CLEARANCE (ml/min)

Fig. 11   Three hypothetical plots based on Eq. (35), which assumes a linear relationship between the overall drug elimination constant (β) and the glomerular filtration rate (GFR) as estimated from creatinine renal clearance (C_{Cr}). These three examples illustrate (a) negligible non-renal elimination ($\beta_{NR} \approx 0$) resulting in $\beta \approx 0$ when GFR ≈ 0, (b) negligible renal excretion ($\beta_R \approx 0$) so that β is represented by β_{NR} which is independent of GFR, and (c) $\beta_R = \beta_{NR}$ since $\beta = \beta_{NR} + \beta_R = 1$ at a normal GFR value ($C_{Cr} = 120$ ml/min) and $\beta = \beta_{NR} = 0.5$ when GFR $= 0$.

This suggests three general classes of drugs as illustrated by Fig. 11 where the normal C_{Cr} value has been set at 120 ml/min. Figure 11(a) illustrates the effect of GFR on the β values for a drug that is eliminated only by renal excretion. Figure 11(b) shows the case where the drug is eliminated only by nonrenal routes. Figure 11(c) shows the dependence of β on C_{Cr} for a drug that is eliminated by both renal and nonrenal routes. In this example, Fig. 11(c) has been constructed to represent a drug that is normally excreted 50% intact in the urine and 50% by other routes such as metabolism. This is reflected by the fact that the value for β at normal clearance (120 ml/min) is twice that at $C_{Cr} = 0$. Since β_{NR} is the intercept at $C_{Cr} = 0$, the normal β value is the sum of two equal values for β_{NR} and β_R. If the specific plot or equation [such as Fig. 11 or Eq. (35)] is known for a drug, then the β value may be calculated for any given C_{Cr} value and the dosage regimen can be adjusted if necessary.

While the assumptions in arriving at Eq. (35) are commonly made, they do not represent the only approach which may be used. Several studies have demonstrated an empirical relationship between the observed half-life for the drug (or the total elimination constant as defined by β) and the renal clearance value of creatinine or inulin. The resulting "calibration" plot can then be used for the patient in renal failure whose clearance value for the test substance is known. In fact, experimental data such as these should be sought and preferentially employed when available.

C. Individualization of Dosage Regimens

The adjustment of dosage for patients in renal failure may be deemed necessary for drugs such as those in Fig. 11(a) and (c) when the resulting increase in drug accumulation is considered undesirable. One summary tabulates the effect of renal insufficiency on the behavior of 117 drugs in addition to reviewing the concepts and presenting specific recommendations for the dosage adjustment of 16 drugs [16]. Another, containing more than 60 drugs, lists the probable side effects in patients with renal failure and the recommended maintenance dosage intervals to avoid toxicities [17]. It contains a brief discussion of the use of creatinine clearance values in dosage adjustment and an excellent bibliography containing 78 references complete with titles. A number of investigators have recommended dosage adjustment based upon creatinine or inulin clearance values as an indicator of GFR. Notable among these examples are cephalosporins, digoxin, digitoxin, gentamicin, kanamycin, and procainamide.

The most frequently employed equation is derived from Eqs. (18) and (19).

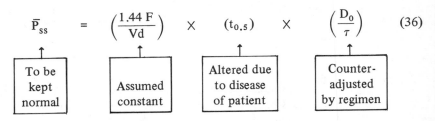

$$\bar{P}_{ss} = \left(\frac{1.44\ F}{Vd} \right) \times (t_{0.5}) \times \left(\frac{D_0}{\tau} \right) \qquad (36)$$

| To be kept normal | Assumed constant | Altered due to disease of patient | Counter-adjusted by regimen |

The goal is to provide the renal failure patient with average steady-state plasma levels, $\bar{P}_{ss}$, that are equal to those obtained in the patient with normal kidney function. It is assumed that the fraction absorbed and volume of distribution remain constant, i.e., the first term (1.44F/Vd). Information to the contrary should be used if available. The biological half-life for the drug in the renal failure patient must be calculated from a known relationship such as illustrated in Fig. 11(a) and (c). This requires a clinical study to establish the effect of renal insufficiency on the observed $t_{0.5}$ of the drug. Creatinine and inulin clearance tests are most frequently employed as a measure of renal function. It is necessary to study a wide range of renal insufficiency in order to clearly define the relationship between the observed β and C_{Cr}. In working Practice Problem 13, an illustration of such a plot will be constructed from the data in the table. The value for $t_{0.5}$ in Eq. (36) will increase in renal failure for drugs behaving like those shown in Fig. 11(a) and (c). If the patient cannot excrete the drug, the half-life will be longer and more drug will accumulate in the patient. The method for adjustment obviously resides in the final term of the equation (D_0/τ). One can decrease the dose, increase τ, or both. The product $(t_{0.5})(D_0/\tau)$ must be kept constant.

Consider a drug with Vd = 140 liters, $t_{0.5}$ = 3.5 hr, F = 0.85, and desired $\bar{P}_{ss}$ of 0.2 mg% that is normally administered every 6 hr. The dose may be calculated from Eq. (36) as $D_0 \approx$ 400 mg. If the $t_{0.5}$ value is extended to 7 hr due to renal insufficiency the regimen may be adjusted by decreasing (D_0/τ) in half. The original value for (D_0/τ) was (400/6) = 66.7. Any combination providing a (D_0/τ) ratio of 33.3 will maintain $\bar{P}_{ss}$ constant. Thus, $\bar{P}_{ss}$ will be kept at 0.2 mg% by any of the following: (1) 200 mg every 6 hr, (2) 400 mg every 12 hr, (3) 266 mg every 8 hr, (4) 133 mg every 4 hr, etc. Note, however, that the normal steady-state time *profile* cannot be duplicated in the renal patient. This is because of the change in $t_{0.5}$. The shape of a blood level curve will change when $t_{0.5}$ is changed. The use of Eq. (36) will maintain the normal $\bar{P}_{ss}$ value but not the normal time course. In the previous example, for dosage regimen (1), the P_{max}^{∞} value will be lower and the P_{min}^{∞} value higher than normal.

Practice Problem 13

An adult male patient normally taking a drug as a 50-mg dose every 8 hr is found to have a creatinine clearance value of 65 ml/min as a result of a renal complication. It is considered necessary to adjust the dosage of this drug for this patient. Tablets are available as 10-, 25-, and 50-mg sizes. Using the data in Table 6, recommend an adjusted regimen.

Table 6
Relationship of Creatinine Clearance Values to Observed
Elimination Rate Constants ($\beta = 0.693/t_{0.5}$) for Drug

C_{Cr} (ml/min)	β (hr)	C_{Cr} (ml/min)	β (hr)
10	0.033	50	0.049
22	0.037	69	0.058
33	0.044	86	0.069
40	0.048	132	0.089
50	0.053	128	0.084

Answer: A plot of β versus C_{Cr} is linear with a slope of 0.000448 and an intercept of 0.0286. Therefore β_{65} = 0.058 and the half-life is 12 hr. If C_{Cr} = 128–132 ml/min is considered normal, then the normal $t_{0.5}$ is 8 hr and the $t_{0.5}$ has increased 1.5-fold. This can also be calculated directly from the values for β since (β_{130}/β_{65}) = (0.087/0.058) = 1.5. The adjusted dosage regimen may be (1) 25 mg every 6 hr or (2) 50 mg every 12 hr.

After therapy is initiated using an adjusted dosage regimen, the concentration of drug in the blood during steady state should be determined if possible and compared to the desired value. Further adjustment may then be made on an empirical basis.

D. A Method of Approximation by Dettli

Data for $t_{0.5}$ (or β) versus C_{Cr}, such as those given in Table 6, are not always available in the literature. Dettli [18, 19] has pointed out that the $t_{0.5}$ values in normal and anuric patients are often reported and he has suggested an approximate method using these data when the calibration plots are not known. Assuming that Eq. (35) is applicable, the data for normal renal function, β, and for the absence of renal function, β_{NR}, can be used to estimate the slopes and intercepts of plots such as those in Fig. 11(a) and (c). Dettli has published several tables listing literature values for the elimination rate constants in normal and anuric patients. Some typical examples taken from Dettli [18, 19] are listed in Table 7. The data are used in the manner described above. It is assumed that β is a linear function of renal clearance as described by Eq. (35). Thus the value for the anuric patient represents the intercept value, β_{NR}, in Fig. 11. The value for β in the presence of normal renal function is taken as that corresponding to 100 ml/min. By using 100 ml/min instead of 120 ml/min, no correction is used for minor changes in GFR.

Consider gentamicin, for example. Substitution into Eq. (35) yields β_{calc} (hr^{-1}) = 0.006 (hr^{-1}) + slope   (min/ml·hr) C_{Cr} (ml/min where slope = 0.003. What dosage adjustment must be made for a patient with a creatinine clearance value of 30 ml/min? The value for β_{30} may be calculated as 0.006 + 0.003(30) $\approx$ 0.1 hr^{-1}. Since the normal value for β was 0.3 hr^{-1}, the $(t_{0.5})_{30}$ = 3 $(t_{0.5})_{normal}$. Therefore the adjusted dosage regimen (D_0/τ) must be decreased to one-third of the normal. The recommended dosage in the prescribing information for gentamicin at a creatinine clearance value of 30 ml/min is 35% of the normal dosage at the normal τ value of 8 hr [20], which agrees with the above approximation. This oversimplification is recommended as a first approximation when data are not available. In the case of gentamicin the problem of individualization of dosage is quite complex as can be appreciated from Secs. II.A.4. of Chap. 6 and III.B.2. of Chap. 7.

Practice Problem 14

Answer the following questions using the data from Dettli as found in Table 7.
(a)   How would you classify chlortetracycline, lincomycin, and procainamide relative to Fig. 11?
(b)   An adult patient normally receives 0.25 mg/day as a single dose of digoxin. What regimen do you recommend if the patient has renal failure and the creatinine clearance value decreases to 40 ml/min?

Answer: (a) Chlortetracycline, Fig. 11(b); lincomycin, Fig. 11(c); and procainamide, Fig. 11(a).

(b) $\beta_{40} = 0.15 + [(0.45 - 0.15)/100]40 = 0.27$ day^{-1}. The $(t_{0.5})_{40} = 1.67$ $t_{0.5}$. Since $\tau = 1$ day is both convenient and infrequent, it should be kept constant and the dosage size changed to $(0.25$ mg$/1.66) = 0.15$ mg. The recommended adjusted regimen is 0.15 mg every 24 hr.

The method of approximation of the dosage regimen was based on known data for β and β_{NR} in the above examples. This principle can be extended to cases where the only data available are the normal $t_{0.5}$ value and the fraction of drug excreted intact in the urine. Equation (35) may be employed as a *first approximation.* Again it is necessary to monitor blood levels and correct the dosage empirically. The assumption is made that β_{NR} is constant and may be calculated from $\beta[1 - $ (fraction excreted intact)]. The average normal renal clearance value for the patient's age and weight may be used or the actual value for the patient before renal failure may be used. The following illustration is adapted from a literature response for drug information [21]. The drug, ethambutol, is normally administered once daily. Since the $t_{0.5}$ is given as 6.5 hr, the expected accumulation would be insignificant. The steady-state degree of accumulation using this value would be 108% that of a single dose. (The apparent $t_{0.5}$ values during the 12 hr following oral administration to normal subjects has been estimated at 4.1 hr from tablets and 4.8 hr from solutions with estimates increasing up to 10 hr when 24-hr and 72-hr data were included [22].) If renal failure prolongs the $t_{0.5}$ sufficiently, then increased accumulation could occur. Since the usual dosage interval is so long (24 hr), it is more practical to correct the size of the maintenance dose rather than τ as shown in the following problem.

Practice Problem 15

A 60-kg patient with a normal creatinine clearance value of 120 ml/min was taking 1.5 g of ethambutol in a single oral daily dose and has undergone a kidney transplant. The creatinine clearance value has decreased to 40 ml/min. Should the daily dosage of ethambutol be altered in order to maintain a body content which is similar to that before the operation? Assume the half-life for this drug in this patient was 6.5 hr before the transplant and that 80% of the drug was excreted intact by the kidneys (normally).

Answer: The value for β (normal) is 0.107 hr^{-1} and $\beta_{NR} = (0.20)$ $(0.107) = 0.0214$ hr^{-1}. Using Eq. (35), $\beta_{40} = 0.0214 + [(0.107 - 0.0214)/120](40) = 0.0498$ hr^{-1}. Thus $(t_{0.5})_{40} = 2.14$ $t_{0.5}$ and the dose should be reduced to 1.5 g$/2.14 = 0.7$ g every 24 hr.

Table 7

Average Elimination Rate Constants in Patients with Normal Renal Function (β in hr^{-1} unless marked * = in day^{-1}) and in Anuric Patients (β_{NR} in hr^{-1} unless marked * = in day^{-1}) as Reported by Dettli[a]

Drug	β_{NR}	β	Drug	β_{NR}	β
Ampicillin	0.06	0.6	Methicillin	0.17	1.4
Carbenicillin	0.06	0.6	α-Methyldopa	0.03 (?)	0.17
Cephacetril	0.03	0.7	Minocycline	0.05	0.06
Cephalexin	0.03	0.7	Nafcillin	0.5	1.2
Cephaloridine	0.03	0.4	Oxacillin	0.35	1.4
Cephalothin	0.06 (?)	1.4	Penicillin G	0.14	1.4
Cephazolin	0.02	0.35	Peruvoside[b]	0.24*	0.3*
Chloramphenicol	0.24	0.3	Polymyxin B	0.02	0.15
Chloretetracycline[b]	0.08	0.1	Practolol	0.01	0.07
Ciclacillin	0.1	1.0	Procainamide	0.007	0.21
Clindamycin	0.16	0.2	Rifampicin	0.25	0.25
Colistimethate	0.06	0.2	Rolitetracycline	0.02	0.06
Digitoxin	0.07*	0.1*	Sisomycin	0.0005	0.25
Digoxin	0.14*	0.45*	Streptomycin	0.01	0.25
α-Acetyldigoxin	0.21*	0.7*	Strophanthin G (Ouabaine)[b]	0.3*	1.2*
β-Methyldigoxin	0.13*	0.25*	Strophanthin K[b]	0.25*	1.0*
Doxycycline	0.025	0.03	Sulfadiazine	0.03	0.07
Erythromycin	0.35	0.5	Sulfamethoxazole	0.06	0.07
5-Fluorocytosine	0.007	0.25	Sulfisomidine	0.01	0.12
Gentamicin	0.006	0.3	Tetracycline	0.01	0.08
Isoniazid (fast inactivators)	0.4	0.5	Thiamphenicol	0.02 (?)	0.25
Isoniazid (slow inactivators)	0.13	0.25	Ticarcillin	0.06	0.6
Kanamycin	0.01	0.35	Tobramycin	0.007	0.35
Lidocaine	0.36	0.4	Trimethoprim	0.03	0.06
Lincomycin	0.06	0.15	Vancomycin	0.004	0.12

[a] From Refs. 18 and 19.
[b] The clinical consequences of the formation of active metabolites in patients with renal disease are still to be determined.

REFERENCES

1. E. Kruger-Thiemer, Formal Theory of Drug Dosage Regimens. I., *J. Theor. Biol. 13*, 212(1966).
2. E. Kruger-Thiemer, Formal Theory of Drug Dosage Regimens. II., The Exact Plateau Effect, *J. Theor. Biol. 23*, 169(1969).
3. E. Kruger-Thiemer, P. Bunger, L. Dettli, P. Spring, and E. Wempe, Dosage Regimen Calculation of Chemotherapeutic Agents. Part III., Sulfasymazine. *Chemotherapia 10*, 325(1965/66); see also *Chemotherapia 10*, 61 and 129 (1965) for Parts 1 and 2.
4. M. Gibaldi and D. Perrier, *Pharmacokinetics*, Marcel Dekker, Inc., N.Y., 1975, p. 101.
5. P. R. Byron and R. E. Notari, Critical Analysis of "Flip-Flop" Phenomenon in Two-Compartment Pharmacokinetic Model, *J. Pharm. Sci. 65*, 1140 (1976).
6. R. E. Notari, M-Y. Huang, and P. R. Byron, Calculations of Optimum Pharmacokinetic Drug Supply Rates for Maximum Duration During Multiple Dose Therapy by Prodrug Administration, *Int. J. Pharm. 1*, 233 (1978).
7. J. G. Wagner, J. I. Northram, C. D. Alway, and O. S. Carpenter, Blood Levels of Drug at the Equilibrium State After Multiple Dosing, *Nature 207*, 1301(1965).
8. M. Gibaldi and H. Weintraub, Some Considerations as to the Determination and Significance of Biological Half-life, *J. Pharm. Sci. 60*, 624(1971).
9. D. Perrier and M. Gibaldi, Relationship Between Plasma or Serum Drug Concentration and Amount of Drug in the Body at Steady State Upon Multiple Dosing, *J. Pharmacokin. Biopharm. 1*, 17(1973).
10. G. E. Schumacher, Practical Pharmacokinetic Techniques for Drug Consultation and Evaluation. I. Use of Dosage Regimen Calculations, *Amer. J. Hosp. Pharm. 29*, 474(1972).
11. E. Kruger-Thiemer, Dosage Schedule and Pharmacokinetics in Chemotherapy, *J. Pharm. Sci. 49*, 311(1960).
12. J. M. Van Rossum, Pharmacokinetics of Accumulation, *J. Pharm. Sci. 57*, 2162(1968).
13. J. G. Wagner, *Pharmacokinetics*, J. M. Richard Laboratory, Grosse Pointe Park, Mich., 1969, p. 139.
14. P. J. Niebergall, E. T. Sugita, and R. L. Schnaare, Calculation of Plasma Versus Time Profiles for Variable Dosing Regimens, *J. Pharm. Sci. 63*, 100(1974).
15. C. L. Winek, A Role For the Hospital Pharmacist in Toxicology and Drug Blood Level Information, *Amer. J. Hosp. Pharm. 28*, 351(1971).
16. J. Fabre and L. Balant, Renal Failure, Drug Pharmacokinetics and Drug Action, *Clin. Pharmacokin. 1*, 99(1976).
17. W. M. Bennett, I. Singer, and C. H. Coggins, A Practical Guide to Drug Usage in Adult Patients with Impaired Renal Function, *JAMA 214*, 1468 (1970); see also *Guide to Drug Usage in Adult Patients with Impaired Renal Function. A Supplement, JAMA 223*, 991(1973).

18. L. Dettli, Elimination Kinetics and Dosage Adjustment of Drugs in Patients With Kidney Disease, *Progr. Pharmacol. 1,* No. 4 (1977).
19. L. Dettli, Drug Dosage in Renal Disease, *Clin. Pharmacokin. 1,* 126(1976).
20. Litton Industries, Inc., *Physician's Desk Reference,* 33rd ed., Oradell, N.J., 1979, p. 1538.
21. Dias Rounds, Request Number 4, *Drug Intell. Clin. Pharm. 5,* 251(1971).
22. C. S. Lee, J. G. Gambertoglio, D. C. Brater, and L. Z. Benet, Kinetics of Oral Ethambutol in the Normal Patient, *Clin. Pharmacol. Ther. 22,* 615 (1977).

Chapter 6

PHARMACOKINETIC ASPECTS OF STRUCTURAL
MODIFICATIONS IN DRUG DESIGN AND THERAPY*

I. INTRODUCTION   215
   A. Status   215
   B. Structure Pharmacokinetic Activity Relationships (SPAR)   215
   C. Modification of Absorption, Distribution, or Elimination   217
   D. Potency of Analogs   218
      Sample Problem 1   220
      Practice Problem 1   222

II. ANTIMICROBIAL AGENTS   223
   A. Systemic Antibiotics   223
      1. Goals for Derivative Formation   223
      2. Penicillins   223
         a. Structural Requirements and Ideal Properties   223
         b. Effect of Molecular Modification on Gastric Stability
            and Dissolution Rate   226
         c. Pharmacokinetic Analysis of Structural Changes   226
            Sample Problem 2   228
            Sample Problem 3   229
      3. Tetracyclines   233
         a. Structural Requirements and Ideal Properties   233
         b. Absorption and Distribution   234
         c. Binding to Dairy Products and Various Divalent or
            Trivalent Cations   235
            Sample Problem 4   235
         d. Effect of Binding on Distribution and Elimination   237
         e. Tetracycline Half-Lives   239
      4. Aminoglycoside Antibiotics   240
         a. Introduction and Ideal Properties   240

*Adapted with permission of the copyright owner from the following two reviews by the author: Pharmacokinetics and Molecular Modification: Implication in Drug Design and Evaluation, *J. Pharm. Sci. 62*, 865(1973); Alteration of Pharmacokinetics Through Structural Modification, in *Design of Biopharmaceutical Properties through Prodrugs and Analogs*, E. B. Roche, ed., A. Ph.A., Washington, D.C., 1977, pp. 68-97.

213

        b.   Tissue Accumulation and Serum Pharmacokinetics   241
              Sample Problem 5   243
        c.   Explanation for Apparent Inconsistencies in Literature   244
    5. Cephalosporins   245
        a.   Structural Requirements and Ideal Properties   245
        b.   Pharmacokinetics   250
        c.   Clinical Use   252
    6. Sulfonamides   254
        a.   Half-Lives, Indications, and Dosage Intervals   254
        b.   Renal Tubular Resorption   254
  B. Urinary Tract Antimicrobial Agents   255
    1. Intrinsic Activity and Urinary pH   256
    2. Urinary Concentration, Half-Life, and Protein Binding   257
    3. Volume of Distribution   258
    4. Potential Toxicity Due to Renal Insufficiency   258

III. ORAL BIOAVAILABILITY   258
  A. Presystemic Metabolism; First-Pass Metabolism   258
  B. Optimizing Oral Absorption   260
    1. Partition Coefficients   261
    2. Partition Coefficient Adjustment Through
        Molecular Modification   262
    3. Model Systems for Absorption Studies   262
    4. Partition Coefficient Effects in Absorption Data   263

IV. PHARMACOKINETICS OF PRODRUGS   264
  A. Kinetic Profiles   264
  B. Goals   265
    1. Increased Absorption   265
    2. Assay Specificity and Nonspecificity   267
        a.   Rapid Prodrug Conversion   267
        b.   Prodrug Conversion Rates Which Result
           in Circulating Prodrug   271
        c.   Conversion of Prodrug in the Intestines   272
    3. Increase in Duration   274
        a.   The Rate-Determining Step   274
        b.   The Optimum Rate-Determining Input Constant   276
           Sample Problem 6   278

REFERENCES   278

I. INTRODUCTION

A. Status

The clinical implications of bioavailability differences among various dosage forms have received widespread attention. It is well recognized that dosage form design plays a major role in determining the rate and extent of drug release following administration of the product to the patient. Consideration has been given to the effects of prolonged action products, dissolution rate, particle size, inert ingredients, pH, and other factors on the absorption of drugs following oral administration. Much of what has been reported applies to gastrointestinal absorption of oral products and may be described as attempts to

1. Maximize absorption rate by increasing the dissolution rate (as in micronization, salts of acids or bases, buffers, amorphous or metastable polymorphs, etc.)
2. Extend duration by decreasing release rate from the dosage form (sustained release, repository injections of slowly soluble salts, microcrystals, free acid or base instead of salt, etc.)
3. Decrease degradation in the stomach (acid insoluble salts or esters, enteric coating, etc.)

Thus, pharmacokinetic studies are significant in the design, evaluation, and rational use of drug *products*.

These modifications of the dosage form (or drug delivery system) can improve the kinetics of drug input. Structural modification of the drug itself may alter any of the kinetic processes for that drug. A minor chemical modification may result in a significant change in pharmacokinetics and in the clinical results. Although generalities are few, numerous examples of the successful chemical manipulation of pharmacokinetic properties can be observed. The ultimate goal is to design a drug molecule having a desired pharmacological effect resulting from the proper balance of absorption, distribution, intrinsic activity, metabolism, and excretion without resorting to the costly and time-consuming process of screening large numbers of analogs.

B. Structure Pharmacokinetic Activity Relationships (SPAR)

An acceptable therapeutic agent which has a single pharmacokinetic limitation would represent an ideal candiate for chemical modification. The derivative may be either a *prodrug* (see Sec. IV) or an *analog*. In either case, the primary goal is to alter that single pharmacokinetic process without affecting any others. Absolute selectivity is unlikely since each process is influenced by the physical chemical characteristics of the drug. In the end a compromise representing optimization of the overall pharmacokinetic pattern must be accepted.

Consider the model in Fig. 1 representing substituent group effects in a series of molecules upon the "drug–receptor" interaction. Typically assumptions are made regarding the interaction between the parent compound and the "receptor." The basic assumptions are tested by molecular modifications. Unexpected results are explained by modifying the theory and occasionally by modifying the concept of the drug structure by arguing for a particular preferred conformation for that molecule *only* when it is in the vicinity of that receptor. Conclusions are often based upon dose–response curves. In doing so the dose is assumed to be responsible for the magnitude of the response. It is widely recognized (albeit seldom evaluated) that the time course for a drug at the receptor must be considered. The onset, duration, and intensity of effect may be considered as a function of at least two factors:

1. Transport processes affecting the time course at the receptor site; delivery to and removal from the site
2. Interaction between drug and receptor after arrival at the site

Figure 2 illustrates how modification of a parent structure can influence the drug time course at the receptor site. The following processes may be altered by changing a substituent group on a drug (D):

1. Supply and loss
    a. Release from dosage form (rate and/or amount)
    b. Stability in depot
    c. Binding in depot (DB)
    d. Transfer from depot to central compartment (rate and/or amount)
    e. Elimination rate from central compartment
2. Distribution
    a. Binding in central compartment (DB)
    b. Binding in peripheral compartment (DB)
    c. Rate and volume of distribution
    d. Transfer to receptor site
3. Drug–receptor interaction

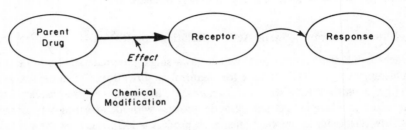

Fig. 1 Simplified model for considering the effect of various substituent groups on the drug–receptor interaction.

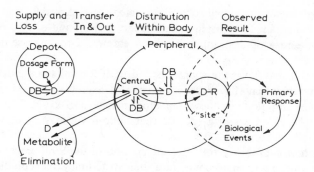

Fig. 2 Diagram of various rate processes which may be altered by chemical modification of a drug, thereby affecting the time course for drug at its site of action. The symbols and interactions are explained in the text.

Consider the case where two "equipotent" drugs are administered but one results in a decreased biological response due to failure to reach the site. How many potential explanations for this can you identify in Fig. 2? (There are more than 10.)

One obvious challenge in "optimizing" the above factors is locating the receptor site and defining an ideal time course for the drug–receptor interaction. An ideal drug should

1. Reach the site of action
2. Arrive rapidly in sufficient quantity
3. Remain for a sufficient duration
4. Be excluded from other sites
5. Be removed from the site when appropriate

The most significant question ultimately is, "Does this alteration in pharmacokinetic behavior improve the course of therapy with this drug?" It is difficult to envision a model system that will lend itself to simple assessments of such questions.

C. Modification of Absorption, Distribution, or Elimination

Figure 2 may be divided into three areas where chemical modification can alter pharmacokinetics: (1) the *input function,* (2) *elimination* (excretion and/or metabolism), and (3) *distribution* to active and inactive binding sites.

The *input function* is the most frequently altered pharmacokinetic property. The two most common goals are (1) to increase bioavilability or (2) to program the drug time course. Oral bioavailability has been increased by optimizing the partition coefficient, increasing solubility, increasing gastric stability, decreasing binding to foods, and decreasing intestinal metabolism and/or first-pass effect. Control of the rate of drug input has been employed to increase duration of action or to decrease toxicity.

Elimination may limit the success of a drug if it results in a short duration. Molecular modification may reduce the rate of excretion and/or metabolism thus increasing duration. Reduced metabolism may also avoid formation of a toxic metabolite. Conversely a specific metabolic route may be desirable if an active metabolite is formed.

Distribution is probably the least understood of the three areas. Few generalities can be made with confidence regarding structural effects on distribution. The goals, if less predictable, are perhaps more significant. Specificity is undoubtedly the single most important desirable trait. Increased distribution to a specific site is a primary goal for increasing specificity and decreasing toxicity. Increasing tissue distribution can also increase duration through the deposition of drugs in sites that are less available to metabolism or excretion.

D. Potency of Analogs

Any comparison of the potency of drug analogs must begin by introducing each drug into what is called the site of administration. Several pharmacokinetic rate processes separate the site of *action* from the site of *administration*. The pharmacological response is influenced by the time course which results from these processes. The drug time course at the site of action may determine the response time profile which in turn is used to define potency. In such a system the term potency may be inadequate. For example the observed difference in potency between two drugs could be a difference in their rate of loss to inactive metabolite. The rank order of the pharmacological responses of analogs may also change as a function of time. These problems cannot be overcome by using rapid I.V. injections. It thus appears misleading to rank the relative potency of the analogs by a single set of numbers. Yet these values are readily available.

It might be more useful to determine potency–time profiles for a series of analogs. Three questions may be considered in using this approach.

1. How much of each drug is needed at the target organ?
2. How much drug arrives at the target organ?
3. How does the time course of each drug in the target organ differ?

Studies on three apomorphine analogs (Fig. 3) will be used to illustrate this concept [1].

The brain is considered to be the target organ for the measured response. The time course following rapid I.V. injections of each analog was investigated using the pharmacokinetic model represented by Scheme I.

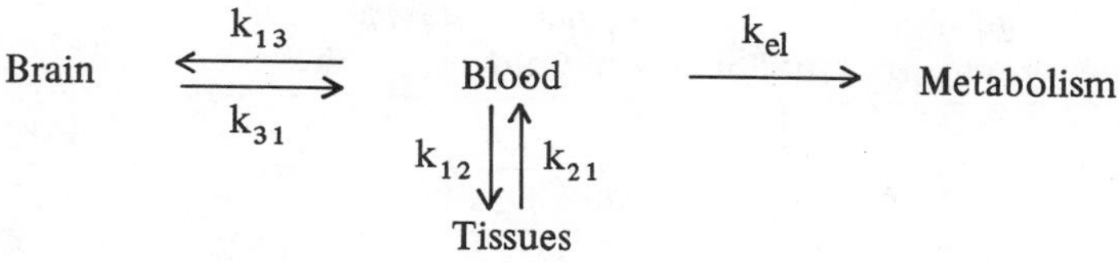

$$\text{Brain} \quad \underset{k_{31}}{\overset{k_{13}}{\rightleftarrows}} \quad \text{Blood} \quad \overset{k_{el}}{\longrightarrow} \quad \text{Metabolism}$$

with k_{12} and k_{21} exchanging between Blood and Tissues.

Scheme I

Let us now consider the three questions posed above.

How much of each drug is required at the target organ? Using the response and the time course in brain it was possible to define EC50 as that concentration in the brain which would be expected to produce a response in 50% of a population. These values are given in Table 1, where it can be seen that apomorphine (R = CH$_3$) is the most potent since the required concentration is least. The potency relative to apomorphine (taken as 100%) is thus 39% for the N-n-propyl derivative while the nor compound is only 6% as potent. For each analog to provide a 50% response, the N-n-propyl compound must be present in 2.5 times more than the concentration of apomorphine while 17.5 times more of the nor compound is required.

Results based on observations following intraperitoneal (I.P.) dosing are also given in Table 1. These data are not based on drug content in the brain but are based on the dose placed in the peritoneal cavity. Results are potentially influenced by bioavailability as well as the other processes in Fig. 2. Here the

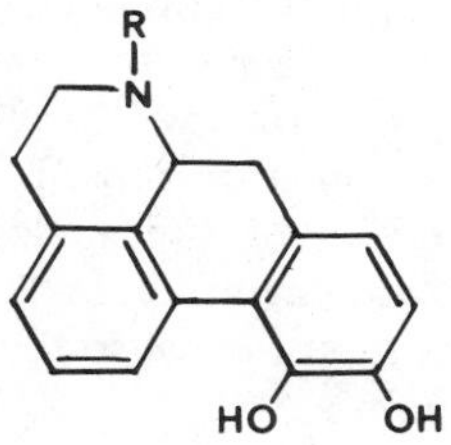

DRUG	-R
NORAPOMORPHINE	-H
APOMORPHINE	-CH$_3$
N-n-PROPYLNORAPO-	-C$_3$H$_7$

Fig. 3 Structures for the apomorphines used to relate the pharmacokinetic data to pharmacological response in mice.

Table 1
Comparison of Potency of Compounds Shown in Fig. 3

R	I.V. dose		I.P. dose	
	EC50 in brain	Relative potency, %	ED50	Relative effect, %
$-C_3H_7$	3.05	39	7.5	114
$-CH_3$	1.20	100	8.4	100
$-H$	21.05	6	213	4

n-propyl compound appears to be 14% more effective as seen from the values for relative effect. Since 2.5 times more N-n-propyl is required in the brain to provide the same activity as apomorphine, it follows that the brain time course of the N-n-propyl compound appears more favorable than that of apomorphine when each is administered I.P.

The remaining questions may be considered together. How much of each drug arrives in the brain and how do the three time courses in brain differ? Figure 4 shows the time course for each compound in the brain following I.V. administration. The N-n-propyl derivative shows the highest initial level while the norapomorphine has the longest duration. Thus, the rank order for the percent dose of the three analogs in brain changes as a function of time.

Sample Problem 1

(a) Consider the pharmacological response for the three analogs in Fig. 4 given by I.V. administration. The relative potency values are given in Table 1. If response is examined at *one* specific time, after injection, what time would provide values for relative potency that are most similar to those in Table 1?

Solution: The time when all of the analogs are present at equal concentration would provide the values in Table 1. The closest point is 14 min although they are not equal so the values cannot be duplicated at any single time point.

(b) Figure 4 shows the time course for each analog in brain and Table 1 shows the relative potency. Construct a plot which compares the three analogs as a function of time with respect to the amount in the brain and the amount required in the brain following equal I.V. doses.

Solution: If apomorphine is used as the standard, then curve B in Fig. 4 can remain constant. Curve A represents the compound that is only 39% as effective. It can be compared by multiplying each data point by 0.39. Similarly, curve C must be multiplied by 0.06. Results are shown in Fig. 5.

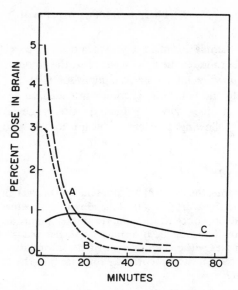

Fig. 4 The percent of the I.V. dose in the brain as a function of time for N-n-propylnorapomorphine (A), apomorphine (B), and norapomorphine (C). Structures are shown in Fig. 3.

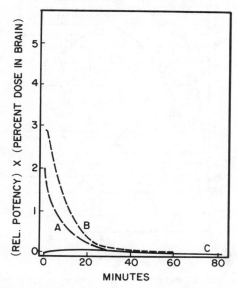

Fig. 5 The profiles in Fig. 4 have been normalized to reflect both the *bioavailability* to the brain and the amount required for equivalent response by multiplying each data point by (relative potency)/(100%) where relative potency is based on EC50 in the brain (Table 1).

The solution to Sample Problem 1 provides one response to all three previous questions. It incorporates the amount *needed,* the amount that *arrives,* and the *time-dependent profiles* into a single comparison (Fig. 5). This example is used only to illustrate the concepts. It is not intended to be ideal or to have clinical significance. It does serve to illustrate the vague nature of relative potency values. The following problem is meant to test your perception of these principles.

Practice Problem 1

Figure 6 represents the percent of dose in the "target organ" as a function of time for a drug A and its analog B. The values obtained for EC50 based on concentration in the target organ are 0.45 for drug A and 0.09 for drug B. If a pharmacologist was testing these drugs at equal doses without knowledge of the information in Fig. 6, at what time would his test incorrectly indicate that the compounds were equipotent?
Answer: 1 hr

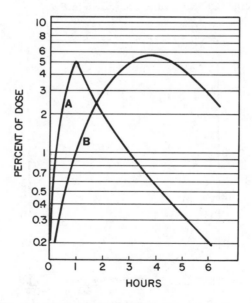

Fig. 6 Hypothetical example illustrating a semilog plot of the time course for the percent of dose of drug A and its analog, B, in the target organ where the EC50 values are 0.45 for A and 0.09 for B (see Practice Problem 1).

II. ANTIMICROBIAL AGENTS

A. Systemic Antibiotics

1. Goals for Derivative Formation

Some of the goals in improving the clinical effectiveness of known systemic antibiotic agents are

1. Increase the amount and/or rate of oral absorption
2. Increase the distribution of the drug
3. Increase the biological half-life
4. Decrease the binding to food and/or plasma proteins
5. Decrease the minimum inhibitory concentration (M.I.C.)

Increased rates of oral absorption have been obtained by using salt forms of the parent drug such as potassium salts of penicillins or sodium salts of sulfonamides. Penicillin absorption has been improved by increasing gastric stability through molecular modification. Altering the oil–water partition coefficient through ester prodrug formation has resulted in improved oral absorption of erythromycin, lincomycin, and ampicillin. Molecular modification of tetracyclines has resulted in increased tissue distribution.

The significance of tissue distribution of antimicrobial agents has been emphasized by several authors. Spitzy and Hitzenberger [2] stated that "bacteria germinate more frequently in the tissues than in blood," while Pratt [3] stated that "bacteria are more common in other tissues than blood." Several authors stress the importance of tissue concentrations [4-7]. Fabre et al. [7] stated that antibiotic effectiveness depends upon penetration into tissues and particularly inflamed tissues. Thus, if binding values were equal, an antibiotic with greater tissue distribution would appear to be reaching the site of action with better efficiency.

The development of β-lactamase-resistant penicillins has resulted in increased biological half-life and higher postdistribution body levels. Both penicillins and tetracyclines serve as examples where attempts to increase half-life and to reduce binding to food and/or plasma proteins have been attempted.

2. Penicillins

a. Structural Requirements and Ideal Properties. The penicillin molecule has two parts; the 6-aminopenicillanic acid nucleus and various side chains (R) attached through an amide linkage (Table 2). Rupture of the β-lactam ring at any point results in loss of activity [8,9]. The presence of the free carboxyl group and sulfur atom are also necessary [8-10]. The side chain can vary widely and appears to control the relative potency and the pharmacokinetics of various derivatives. An ideal penicillin would be stable toward acids and β-lactamases,

Table 2

Structures of Some Common Penicillins

NAME	R
Amoxicillin	
Ampicillin	
Carbenicillin	
Cloxacillin	
Dicloxacillin	
Epicillin	

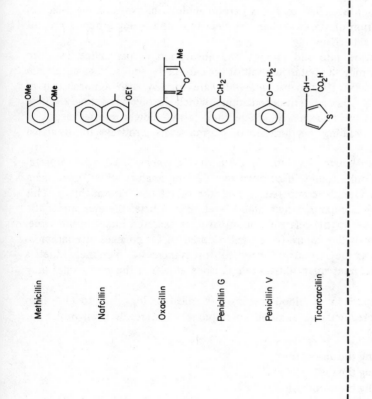

Methicillin

Nafcillin

Oxacillin

Penicillin G

Penicillin V

Ticarcillin

Mecillinam

well absorbed and distributed, less bound to plasma proteins, have a broad spectrum and high antibacterial activity. In terms of pharmacokinetic parameters, it should possess a large F value, a long $t_{0.5}$, and a large Vd.

   b.   *Effect of Molecular Modification on Gastric Stability and Dissolution Rate.* Schwartz and Buckwalter [11] have discussed gastric stability of penicillins as a primary factor in determining bioavailability. Penicillin G and methicillin are very unstable in acid, having half-lives of 3.5 and 2.3 min, respectively, at pH 1.3, 35°C. On the other hand, ampicillin has a half-life of 660 min under the same conditions. The dramatic change in $t_{0.5}$ appears to be due to electronic effects of the protonated amine in acidic solution. In general, an electron-withdrawing group attached to the α carbon inhibits cleavage of the β-lactam ring. The inhibition diminishes when the electron-withdrawing group is present elsewhere in the side chain.

   The dissolution rate and rate of oral absorption of penicillins has been increased by forming the potassium salt of the carboxylic acid such as potassium penicillin G and V. Highly insoluble salts are formed with amines such as procaine and N,N'-dibenzylethylenediamine, which dissolve very slowly. These salts are injected intramuscularly, where they form a slowly released depot of the drug thus extending the duration of plasma levels. Prodrugs are discussed in a later section.

   c.   *Pharmacokinetic Analysis of Structural Changes.* Two misinterpretations are commonly found in comparisons of drug analogs. First, pharmacokinetic data are directly compared as evidence of relative bioavailability. This error is made by comparing their blood level time course, the area under the curve (AUC) values or the relative amount of drug excreted intact in the urine. The second error is the failure to recognize potential for changes in pharmacokinetic patterns as the amount of absorbed drug is increased. Nonlinear kinetics can result in incorrect quantitative comparisons although the rank order may remain the same.

   Direct comparison of blood levels of chemical analogs fails to take into account that three pharmacokinetic consequences can result from molecular modification:

   1.   Changing the absorption
   2.   Changing the distribution
   3.   Changing the elimination

In order to assess minor differences in structurally related drugs it is necessary to consider all three of these aspects. The assessment of effect of molecular modification of the penicillin side chain can be illustrated by considering the isoxazolyl penicillins, which are closely related derivatives with varied pharmacokinetic behavior. They differ in structure only in the number of chlorine atoms present on the benzene ring in the side chain (see Table 2). The time course for each of these analogs in blood has been studied by Modr and Dvoracek [12].

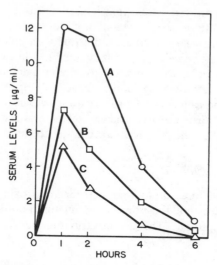

Fig. 7 Average serum levels following 500-mg oral doses of dicloxacillin (A), cloxacillin (B), and oxacillin (C). (Drawn from data in Ref. 12.)

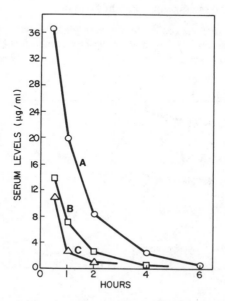

Fig. 8 Average serum levels following 500-mg I.V. doses of dicloxacillin (A), cloxacillin (B), and oxacillin (C). (Drawn from data in Ref. 12.)

Figure 7 shows the comparison following oral administration of 500 mg. The direct comparison of these curves would lead to the erroneous conclusion that absorption was increased by the addition of each chlorine atom. But if one examines these same three drugs given by rapid I.V. injection, it is apparent that the same relative order exists with dicloxacillin dramatically higher than cloxacillin, which is somewhat higher than oxacillin (Fig. 8). Therefore, it is obvious that absorption cannot be the sole cause for observed differences in the plasma time profiles. When the AUC values for the oral route were compared with the AUC values for the I.V. route, according to the following equation:

$$F = \text{fraction absorbed} = \frac{(\text{AUC})_{\text{oral}}}{(\text{AUC})_{\text{I.V.}}} \tag{1}$$

results showed that all three drugs were absorbed approximately 74% (±6%). Thus, oral absorption is not the primary reason for the drastic difference in the blood level time profiles. Therefore distribution and/or elimination must be considered.

Sample Problem 2

Rosenblatt et al. [13] compared dicloxacillin, cloxacillin, and oxacillin by constant I.V. infusion (250 mg/hr). The results are shown in Fig. 9. They reported $t_{0.5}$ values of 0.71 hr for dicloxacillin, 0.42 hr for cloxacillin, and 0.38 hr for oxacillin.

(a) Explain the differences in steady-state plasma levels.
Solution: The values for β and Vd calculated from $\beta = (0.693/t_{0.5})$ and $Vd = (k_0/\beta P_{ss})$ are given in Table 3.

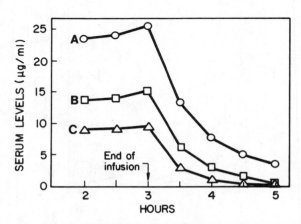

Fig. 9   Average serum levels following I.V. infusions at 250 mg/ hr for dicloxacillin (A), cloxacillin (B), and oxacillin (C). (Drawn from data in Ref. 13.)

Table 3
Steady-State Plasma Levels Obtained During I.V. Infusion
at 250 mg/hr

Penicillin	P_{ss} (mg/liter)	β (hr^{-1})	Vd (liters)
Oxacillin	9.7	1.82	14
Cloxacillin	15.0	1.65	10
Dicloxacillin	25.0	0.98	10

It can be seen that cloxacillin and oxacillin have similar values for their elimination rate constants but differ in volume of distribution. The primary reason for higher blood levels of cloxacillin during steady state, as compared to oxacillin, is therefore the value for Vd. Conversely, dicloxacillin and cloxacillin have similar distribution volumes. The primary difference in this case is that dicloxacillin has a smaller elimination rate constant than cloxacillin and therefore achieves higher blood levels. By comparing both the elimination rate constants and the volumes of distribution during steady state we can observe in more detail the effect of the chlorine atoms on these penicillins.

(b) Rosenblatt et al. [13] also showed that the urinary excretion of intact penicillin (as percentage of I.V. dose) was 56%, 62%, and 73% for oxacillin, cloxacillin, and dicloxacillin. Predict the steady-state P_{ss} values that would result from the 250 mg/hr infusion in the absence of renal function.
Solution: Assuming that $\beta = \beta_R + \beta_{NR}$, then β_{NR} (in hr^{-1}) = (0.44)(1.80) = 0.80 (oxacillin); β_{NR} = (0.38)(1.65) = 0.63 (cloxacillin) and β_{NR} = (0.27)(0.98) = 0.26 (dicloxacillin). The resulting P_{ss} values (mg/liter) would be 22 for oxacillin, 39 for cloxacillin, and 93 for dicloxacillin.

Sample Problem 3

The observed steady-state plasma levels for various penicillins following I.V. infusions of 500 mg/hr and half-life values are given in Table 4.

(a) What rank order would be predicted solely on the basis of elimination?
Solution: Based solely on elimination, the penicillin with the longest half-life would be predicted to have the highest plasma concentration. Therefore, the rank order would be carbenicillin > ampicillin > dicloxacillin > penicillin G > nafcillin > cloxacillin > oxacillin.

(b) Another parameter must be considered in order to predict the observed steady-state plasma levels correctly. Calculate the value of this parameter for each penicillin.

Table 4
Observed Steady-State Plasma Concentrations for
Various Penicillins Following I.V. Infusion of 500 mg/hr

Penicillin	P_{ss} (mg/liter)	$t_{1/2}$ (hr)
Carbenicillin	73	1.00
Dicloxacillin	51	0.71
Cloxacillin	30	0.42
Ampicillin	29	0.98
Oxacillin	19	0.39
Nafcillin	18	0.55
Penicillin G	16	0.61

Solution: The value of Vd must also be considered when predicting the observed steady-state plasma concentrations. The value of Vd for each penicillin can be calculated using the equation

$$Vd = \frac{k_0}{\beta P_{ss}} \tag{2}$$

The value for β may be calculated from the half-life values given in the table.

The values of some selected pharmacokinetic parameters are given in Table 5. These parameters are the ones used most often to make comparisons between analogs. These parameters also can be used to calculate other parameters of interest, as discussed. Nauta and Mattie [18] examined dicloxacillin and cloxacillin at higher dosage levels, and showed that increasing the dose of dicloxacillin gave higher AUC values and lower urinary recovery. For example, the AUC following a 1-g I.V. dose was 114 (mg/liter) hr while it was 310 (mg/liter) hr after a 2-g I.V. dose. The fraction recovered in the urine was 0.726 for the 1-g dose and 0.592 for the 2-g. The fraction absorbed orally, F, was calculated from the AUC values, Eq. (1), and from the ratio of drug excreted in the urine after oral administration relative to I.V. The answers obviously do not agree. The value for F is 0.63 (urine) and 0.73 (AUC) for 1 g; 0.74 (urine) and 0.53 (AUC) for 2 g. In view of the dose effects it is likely that the F values are incorrect. If the I.V. dose is doubled (from 1 to 2 g) the AUC increases by a factor of 2.7 (from 114 to 310). Since the observed oral AUC for 2 g is (0.53)(310) = 164 (mg/liter) hr, it can be seen to be larger than that expected from I.V. administration of 1 g, 114 (mg/liter) hr. Therefore the conclusion that F = 0.53 is doubtful.

This problem must be taken into account in comparisons of analogs. If one is to use the quations for linear kinetics, such as Eq. (1), it is necessary to demonstrate the validity of the assumptions. The values for AUC (or for the fraction excreted in the urine) must be a linear function of the I.V. doses and the oral values for AUC (or for fraction excreted) must fall within the calibration range if simple comparisons are to be made. Many examples of failure to demonstrate linearity may be found in the literature. In some instances the fraction excreted in the urine is seen to decrease with increased dosage within the same paper where comparisons of plasma AUC values are used directly for bioavailability. Apparent structural effects may be due to misuse of pharmacokinetic equations.

Several investigators had reported direct comparisons of amoxicillin plasma level data to that of ampicillin after oral administration. The AUC values for amoxicillin were in excess of 50% more than ampicillin. This would indicate an increase in bioavailability of roughly $F_{amox} > 1.5\ F_{amp}$. However, it is fortuitous that this estimate is so close to the value found using Eq. (1).

The reason for this agreement lies in the fact that the clearance values for the drugs are very similar. The effect of this coincidence can be appreciated by examining the equations for AUC (see Appendix C),

$$(AUC)_{I.V.} = \int_0^\infty Pdt = \frac{A}{\alpha} + \frac{B}{\beta} \qquad\qquad (3)$$

Table 5
Values for Selected Pharmacokinetic Parameters[a]
for Several Penicillins

Penicillin	$t_{1/2}$ (hr)	Vd (liters)	C_R (ml/min)[b]
Carbenicillin	1.0	10	86
Dicloxacillin	0.88, 0.71, 0.7	13, 10, 9.4, 16	88, 162, 130
Cloxacillin	0.42, 0.6	10, 11, 23	162, 287
Ampicillin	1.0, 0.8	22, 20, 25, 30	283, 210,[c] 312
Oxacillin	0.7, 0.38, 0.40	27, 14, 13, 15, 26	190,[c] 402
Nafcillin	0.55	21	160[c]
Methicillin	0.43	22	350
Penicillin V	0.53, 0.43, 0.52	51, 54	393
Penicillin G	0.70, 0.5, 0.84– 0.93,[d] 0.6–0.99,[e] 0.54, 0.65, 0.78	26, 22, 37–47,[d] 35	433, 386,[c] 340–480,[d] 393

[a]The values were taken from Ref. 12–17 or calculated from data contained in them.
[b]Renal clearance values.
[c]Units are ml/min/1.72 m^2.
[d]Variation due to ambulatory vs bed rest.
[e]Variation attributed to size of dose.

where P is the plasma concentration and A, α, B, β are the usual pharmacokinetic parameters associated with the equation:

$$P = Ae^{-\alpha t} + Be^{-\beta t} \tag{4}$$

It can be shown from the relationships $\alpha\beta = k_{21} k_{el}$ and $(A\beta + B\alpha) = k_{21} D/V_1$ that

$$\left(\frac{A}{\alpha} + \frac{B}{\beta}\right) = \frac{D_0}{k_2 V_1} = (AUC)_{I.V.} \tag{5}$$

Equation (5) shows that the $(AUC)_{I.V.}$ is equal to the dose, D_0, divided by the plasma clearance, C_T, defined as

$$C_T = k_2 V_1 \tag{6}$$

where V_1 is the volume of the central compartment. A similar equation can be derived for the oral administration of drug wherein

$$(AUC)_{oral} = F\left(\frac{A}{\alpha} + \frac{B}{\beta}\right) = \frac{FD_0}{k_2 V_1} = \frac{FD_0}{C_T} \tag{7}$$

Although the shape of a plasma profile is influenced by all of the rate constants, k_1, k_{12}, k_{21}, k_2, Eq. (7) shows that the area is proportional to FD_0 and inversely related to clearance.

This explains why the comparison of amoxicillin and ampicillin (AUC) values were nearly correct. Examination of the literature values for the pharmacokinetic parameters describing these derivatives shows that their clearance values are nearly equal. Thus, although the values for the individual constants are different, the clearance values, C_T, are similar as shown in Table 6.

Table 6

Comparison of Pharmacokinetic Parameters for Ampicillin and Amoxicillin

	k_{12} (hr^{-1})	k_{21} (hr^{-1})	k_2 (hr^{-1})	V_1 (liter)	C_T (ml/min)
Ampicillin[a]	0.384	0.733	1.73	12.0	335
Amoxicillin[b]	1.29	1.94	1.43	13.9[c]	332[d]

[a]Ref. 19.
[b]Ref. 20.
[c]Calculated from mean weight of 74.5 kg and reported value of V_1 = 0.187 liter/kg.
[d]Calculated from Eq. (6).

Rearranging Eq. (7) yields

$$FD_0 = [(AUC)_{oral}] C_T \tag{8}$$

If two drugs with equal values for C_T are given in equal doses, the ratio of observed values of $(AUC)_{oral}$ will provide the ratio of their F values. This is a coincidence. One could not predict a priori that analogs do or do not have similar clearance values. Clearance is best determined by I.V. administration and the calculation of $[dose/(AUC)_{I.V.}] = C_T$. The determination of $(AUC)_{I.V.}$ allows the use of Eq. (1), which obviates the necessity of determining clearance.

Ampicillin, epicillin, and amoxicillin have similar antibacterial spectra and M.I.C. values. The nearly complete oral absorption of amoxicillin is generally regarded as advantageous relative to ampicillin. A triple crossover study of 500-mg oral doses of amoxicillin, ampicillin, and epicillin demonstrated a significant sequence effect on ampicillin peak levels which were 6.4 μg/ml if epicillin was taken the previous week and 2.7 μg/ml when ampicillin was first [21]. Total 24-hr urinary recoveries and apparent $t_{0.5}$ estimates were amoxicillin, 57%, 1 hr; ampicillin, 50%, 1.3 hr; and epicillin, 23%, 1.4 hr. Mean renal clearance values (C_R) were similar, being 278, 268, and 208 ml/min for amoxicillin, ampicillin, and epicillin. Reported comparisons of serum levels may not be appropriate in the epicillin case since its lower urinary recovery and roughly equal C_R implies that its total body clearance (C_T) may not be similar [Eqs. (6) and (7)].

Ticarcillin, like carbenicillin, is not orally absorbed as one would expect with the additional carboxylic acid substituent. (For a discussion of the oral prodrug, carbenicillin indanyl sodium, see Sec. IV.) Ticarcillin has been shown to be two to four times as active against *Pseudomonas* strains and has been compared kinetically to carbenicillin. Following I.V. administration to healthy adults the C_T values were identical in the steady-state determinations (134 ml/min) while the 5-min infusion resulted in 154 ml/min for ticarcillin and 132 ml/min for carbenicillin. Half-lives and C_R values were similar. Urinary recovery (24 hr) and % binding in serum were ticarillin (86%, 65%) and carbenicillin (99%, 50%). The similarity in average serum time profiles following 5 min, 30 min, and 2.75 hr (with loading dose) is remarkable [22].

Mecillinam is also limited to parenteral use showing a maximum urinary excretion of 5% following oral administration [23]. Its prodrug, pivmecillinam, is discussed in Sec. IV.

3. Tetracyclines

a. Structural Requirements and Ideal Properties. Since the isolation in 1947 of the first known member of the tetracycline family, many semisynthetic derivatives have been prepared and their properties extensively studied. Typical structures are shown in Table 7.

Table 7
Structures of Various Tetracyclines

Name	R_1	R_2	R_3	R_4
Tetracycline	H	OH	CH_3	H
Chlortetracycline	H	OH	CH_3	Cl
Demethylchlortetracycline	H	OH	H	Cl
Oxytetracycline	OH	OH	CH_3	H
Methacycline	OH	$=CH_2$	–	H
Minocycline	H	H	H	$-N(CH_3)_2$
Doxycycline	OH	H	CH_3	H

In general, molecular modifications of the basic tetracycline structure have reflected attempts to improve absorption, decrease binding to plasma proteins, improve distribution to the tissues, and decrease minimum inhibitory concentrations. These attempts are examples of research directed toward preparation of an ideal tetracycline. The ideal tetracycline is one which would be rapidly and completely absorbed, only slightly bound to plasma protein, distributed throughout the proper tissues, of long duration, and possess high intrinsic antimicrobial activity. In terms of pharmacokinetic parameters, an ideal tetracycline might therefore have a large Vd and long $t_{0.5}$.

   b. Absorption and Distribution. The basic tetracycline molecule has three pK_a values of 3.3, 7.7, and 9.5 [24] associated with the tricarbonylmethane, phenyl diketone, and dimethylamino groups, and thus will be ionized over the entire pH range which a molecule would encounter after oral administration. This fact, coupled with the tendency of tetracyclines to form complexes with substances in the stomach, implies that their oral absorption might be slow and incomplete. Oral administration of tetracycline HCl with 200 ml of water containing 2.0 g of $NaHCO_3$ resulted in a 50% decrease in absorption relative to absence of $NaHCO_3$ [25]. When the tetracycline was dissolved prior to administration, no differences were observed. (See further discussion in Chap. 7, Sec. II.A.3.)

There is some indication that lipid solubility plays a major role in the distribution of tetracyclines and that serum protein binding may be less of a factor. Tetracyclines permeate both extra and intracellular fluid, and calculated values of Vd in man exceed the volume of total body water. In a comparison of four tetracyclines in dogs, no linear relationships could be found between PC or log PC and any of the nine concentration gradients determined between tissues or body fluids and blood [26]. An inverse relationship was observed between lipid solubility and both urinary excretion and absolute renal extraction.

   c. Binding to Dairy Products and Various Divalent or Trivalent Cations. It became apparent soon after the introduction of chlortetracycline in 1948 that concomitant administration of aluminum hydroxide gel resulted in decreased biological activity for the antibiotic. Decreased gastrointenstinal absorption due to complexation with divalent and trivalent cations, such as calcium, magnesium, aluminum, and so on, indicates that the co-administration of milk or antacids to diminish the potential side effects of anorexia, nausea, and vomiting (often observed with tetracycline therapy) must be avoided. In Chap. 4 the data of Scheiner and Altemeir [27] were used to demonstrate the dramatic sensitivity of demethylchlortetracycline to complexation with heavy metals. Relative to equal doses in the fasting state, only 13% oral absorption takes place when the antibiotic is administered with 8 oz of milk and 22% with 20 ml of aluminum hydroxide gel. Thus, development of tetracyclines with a lesser tendency toward complexation became a clinically significant research goal. However, since the sites considered most likely to be the site of complexation [28-30] are also necessary for antimicrobial activity, any direct molecular modification of these sites in order to reduce complexation is precluded. Modifications can be made only in positions such as 5-9, where the substituents may exert either electronic or steric effects upon binding.

   Some measure of success has been obtained with newer tetracyclines. Doxycycline oral absorption is markedly less sensitive to food and homogenized milk. This is illustrated in the following problem.

Sample Problem 4

   Rosenblatt et al. [31] studied the effect of diet on oral bioavailability of doxycycline and demethylchlortetracycline. Some of the results are illustrated in Fig.10. The reported maximum plasma value (or peak height) and the time at which it occurred (t_{max}) for each of these eight curves is given in Table 8.

   (a) Summarize the effect of (1) food, (2) skim milk, and (3) whole milk and food on the bioavailability of these two antibiotics and include a rough estimate on the percent reduction of oral absorption in each case.

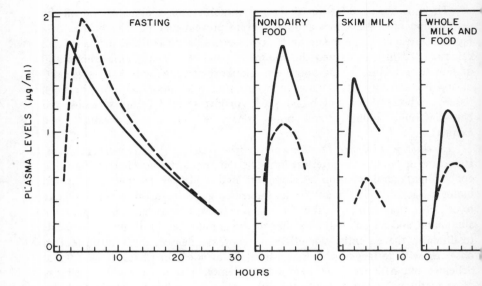

Fig. 10   The data of Rosenblatt et al. [31] have been used to construct these curves representing the time course in blood following single oral doses of 100 mg of doxycycline (solid line) or 300 mg of demethylchlortetracycline (dashed line).

Solution: The peak height may be used for a rough estimate provided that k_1 is relatively constant as indicated by the constancy of the t_{max} values (see Chap. 3). The t_{max} values for demethylchlortetracycline are constant at 4 hr. The estimates are therefore (1) food: (108/1.98) = 54% (or 46% reduction); (2) skim milk: (59/1.98) = 30% (70% reduction); (3) food and whole milk: (71/1.98) = 36% (64% reduction).

The t_{max} values for doxycycline are given as 2 hr and 4 hr. Therefore: (1) food appears to have delayed absorption but provided the same peak value, (2) skim milk: (145/1.79) = 81% (19% reduction), (3) food and whole milk: again absorption appears to be delayed. Since food and food with whole milk both have a t_{max} value of 4 hr, the effect of the whole milk can be estimated from (118/1.75) = 67% (33% reduction).

(b) How do these results compare with those calculated from the data of Scheiner and Altemeir?

Solution: See Practice Problem 7 in Chap. 4.

(c) Figure 10 shows fairly similar time profiles for the two tetracyclines in the fasting state for doses of 300 and 100 mg. What

Table 8

Literature Values (Ref. 31) for Peak Plasma Levels (P_{max}, μg/ml) and
Their Time of Occurrence (t_{max}, hr) Following Single Oral Doses of
300 mg of Demethylchlortetracycline or 100 mg of Doxycycline to
Healthy Volunteers in a Crossover Study

Drug	Fasting		Nondairy food		Skim milk		Whole milk and food	
	P_{max}	t_{max}	P_{max}	t_{max}	P_{max}	t_{max}	P_{max}	t_{max}
Doxycycline	1.79	2	1.75	4	1.45	2	1.18	4
Demethylchlor-tetracycline	1.98	4	1.08	4	0.59	4	0.71	4

conclusions can be made regarding the oral absorption of demethylchlortetracycline relative to doxycycline?

Solution: None; additional information is required because these are two different chemical entities.

(d) Product information supplied with doxycyline hyclate for injection indicates that 40% of the dose is excreted by the kidney within 72 hr after administration to individuals with normal renal function. Rosenblatt et al. [31] recovered 45.4 mg during 72 hr following oral ingestion of 100 mg by normal volunteers (creatinine clearance roughly 130 ml/min). What percent of the orally administered dose was absorbed in the Rosenblatt study?

Solution: It was apparently 100% absorbed, since urinary recovery or 45.4 mg exceeds the value calculated based on the 40% figure (or 40% of 100 mg = 40 mg).

Thus doxycycline absorption has been shown to be less sensitive to skim milk, food, and homogenized milk when compared to demethylchlortetracycline. However, ingestion of antacids containing divalent or trivalent cations resulted in negligible absorption for both drugs. In another study food was shown to reduce tetracycline plasma levels 50% and doxycyline levels 20% when compared to the fasting state [32]. The formulations provided blood levels similar to that of solutions for both drugs when compared in the fasting state.

d. Effect of Binding on Distribution and Elimination. A number of excellent reviews which discuss binding of antibiotics [33] and other agents [34, 35] have been published. In spite of widespread attention the clinical significance of tissue and protein binding in relation to therapeutic efficacy remains unclear for many antibiotics. Readily reversible binding by serum or tissues may serve as a pool of active drug to prolong therapeutic levels [5]. Antibacterial activity of three long-acting sulfonamides may be independent of their protein binding, but this binding may determine their duration [36]. Research indicates that penicillins bound to protein lose their activity. It has been stated [5] that absorption, distribution, and inactivation may be more important than binding in determining penicillin therapy, presumably because of reversibility. Other data [37] emphasize the decrease in availability of penicillins due to inactivation by protein binding. The M.I.C. of eight penicillins in human serum is the same as that in broth when corrected for the bound fraction. Methicillin was least active in broth where there was no binding. In serum where it was bound to a lesser extent than the others, it required the lowest total concentration drug to kill 99% of the inoculum and acted more rapidly than the other penicillins.

Some of the confusion regarding the significance of percent protein binding is the lack of appreciation for the meaning of these values. Literature values for percent protein bound generally refer to in vitro values determined in blood. They do not refer to the percent bound of the total drug in the body. It is therefore possible to have a drug with a high value for percent bound which results in a large free fraction of total body content. This is discussed in greater detail in Chap. 7. Without this consideration it would seem that tissue distribution would always decrease with increasing serum binding as a result of the inability of the protein-bound form to diffuse. Data exist [15, 37] which do not support this hypothesis in the case of penicillins. Similar values of Vd were obtained for four penicillins whose percent binding in plasma varied from 22% to 94% [15]. The fraction of the dose in the peripheral compartment was considered by the authors to be similar for all five penicillins studied [15].

Reversibility is another key factor. It has been noted and documented by authors of seemingly opposing views that reversible binding can serve to prolong drug action [5,37], whereas irreversible binding removes the drug from the biophase. Clinical significance of drug binding is probably dependent upon the strength of binding, and it has been calculated that protein binding will affect drug distribution only if the binding constant exceeds 10^4 [38].

The renal clearance of tetracyclines decreases with increasing protein binding [7]. Urinary clearance is greater for oxytetracycline (73% free) and least for doxycycline (18% free). Chlortetracycline and minocycline are exceptions since they are excreted mainly in bile. The $t_{0.5}$ appears to be related to protein binding only for those drugs that are primarily cleared by glomerular filtration. A drug that is excreted by tubular secretion does not appear to be influenced by protein binding. Penicillins which have high clearance values (reflecting tubular secretion) have half-lives which are relatively insensitive to protein binding. Data suggest that tetracyclines are primarily excreted by glomerular filtration rather than by tubular secretion, although the lack of precise serum protein binding measurements makes it difficult to calculate the individual contributions. Tetracyclines tend to accumulate during renal insufficiency, with chlortetracycline, minocycline, and doxycycline being exceptions. Fabre et al. [7] reported that doxycycline clearance decreased during renal insufficiency without a concurrent increase in hepatic excretion despite a relatively constant $t_{0.5}$ in normal and anuric patients. Studies [39] into the extent of metabolic degradation of doxycycline in man and dog indicate that more than 90% of the intact drug was recovered from the urine and feces in both species. Thus excretion of intact doxycycline in feces appeared to compensate for decreased renal clearance in uremic patients. The urinary recovery of minocycline was only 6–9% following I.V. injections [40]. The lack of sensitivity to renal failure was apparent when the biological $t_{0.5}$ of minocycline did not vary statistically in patients with C_{Cr} of 3.9, 26.2, and 93.9 ml/min [41].

  e. *Tetracycline Half-Lives.* The extension of biological half-life to increase duration and decrease the frequency of administration has been a major research goal. Chlortetracycline first appeared in 1948 with a reported $t_{0.5}$ of 5.6 hr and a recommended dosage interval of 6 hr. Oxytetracycline and tetracycline were introduced soon after with reported half-lives of 8.2 and 9.2 hr, respectively. In 1958, demethylchlortetracycline ($t_{0.5}$ of 11.8 hr) and methacycline were introduced as useful on a 12 hr regimen. Doxycycline ($t_{0.5}$ of 18–22 hr) marked a new stage in this evolution with the advent of once-a-day therapy and minocycline is roughly equal in $t_{0.5}$ (Table 9).

  It has been suggested that the increased $t_{0.5}$ values following multiple dosing might be due to a failure to obtain an accurate assessment of the terminal (or β) slope following a single oral dose [43]. Inclusion of part of the absorption or distribution phase could tend to make the $t_{0.5}$ appear smaller with a single dose, whereas this problem is decreased during the steady state where plasma

Table 9
Apparent Biological $t_{0.5}$ Values for Tetracyclines[a]

Antibiotic	Single dose	Multiple doses	Steady state
Tetracycline	6.3, 5.6–9.3, 8.2, 8.0, 7.2, 7.3	10,[b] 9.5, 11	10.8
Demethylchlor-tetracycline	9.0, 6.3–13.3, 12.6, 10, 11, 12.7	14.7,[b] 14.7, 15	13.6
Methacycline	7.0, 14.3, 8.5, 9.6, 7.7	11.0,[b] 10.5, 11.5	14.3
Minocycline	16	19	—
Doxycycline	8.3, 11.7, 15, 15.1	14.5,[b] 22	16.6

[a]From Ref. 42 except minocycline [41].
[b]Values determined on days 4 and 5 of a multiple-dose regimen.

concentrations and intercept values defined by $B_{app}^{\infty} = B_{app}/(1 - e^{-\beta\tau})$ are higher.

4. Aminolglycoside Antibiotics

a. Introduction and Ideal Properties. The first aminoglycoside antibiotic to be used clinically was streptomycin which was isolated in 1944. This group has since gained in clinical significance. More recent additions show a broad spectrum of activity against both gram-positive and gram-negative pathogens with some being very active against *Pseudomonas aeruginosa.* Hospital acquired ("nosocomial") infections of resistant strains of *Enterobacteriaceae* often respond to aminoglycoside therapy. Potent bactericidal action against gram-negative bacilli has resulted in their widespread use in the treatment of coliform bacteria. In the treatment of infections which are resistant to antibiotics in general, the aminoglycosides may often be regarded as life saving [44].

Aminoglycoside antibiotics are not absorbed sufficiently well to be used orally for systemic infections. They are administered parenterally which, together with their ototoxicity and nephrotoxicity, somewhat limits their use. In spite of these disadvantages they have gained a prominent role in combating serious infections caused by organisms that are resistant to other antibiotics.

Gentamicin represents the reference standard against which improvement in aminoglycoside chemotherapy is measured. As clinical usage has become more prevalent, bacterial resistance has developed. The major research goals in this area have been to overcome the development of resistance and to decrease toxicity. While accumulation in tissues and tissue fluids has been implicated in ototoxicity and nephrotoxicity, it has become clear that intrinsic toxicity also differs among aminoglycosides. Netilmicin appears to be less oto- and nephrotoxic than gentamicin and tobramycin in spite of its high tissue accumulation [45].

Aminoglycosides are excreted intact in the urine. They are neither metabolized nor eliminated in the bile. Renal excretion is generally attributed to glomerular filtration while tubular reabsorption has been demonstrated for gentamicin in dogs [46] and man [47], netilmicin in dogs [48] and implicated in man for gentamicin [49], tobramycin [50], netilmicin [51,52], and others. The elimination of aminoglycosides is significantly altered by renal failure making the adjustment of dosage necessary in order to decrease the known potential for toxicity. There are numerous reviews of dosage nomograms based on glomerular filtration rate as estimated by creatinine renal clearance values. The success of these methods has somewhat obscured the complexity of aminoglycoside pharmacokinetics which are analyzed in the following sections where it is demonstrated that most of the drug is eliminated prior to the terminal log-linear phase.

b. Tissue Accumulation and Serum Pharmacokinetics. The biological half-lives of aminoglycoside antibiotics are commonly reported as 2-3 hr in patients with normal renal function [44]. These values are based on data normally collected over an 8-24 hr period. Although the aminoglycosides are neither metabolized nor excreted in the bile, urinary recovery in 24-hr collections is incomplete even with normal renal function. Serum and urine levels were reportedly detectable for weeks after termination of drug administration [53-56]. The extended terminal phase $t_{0.5}$ values reported for several aminoglycosides are 37 hr, netilmicin [57]; 17 hr, sisomicin [57]; 1-28 days, gentamicin [52,53,56]; 1.5-18 days, tobramycin [50,58].

Studies were undertaken specifically to examine the "washout" period following gentamicin and tobramycin multiple-dose therapy [49,50,55]. In order to characterize their elimination, it was necessary to determine the serum levels and urinary excretion for as long as 20 days. A radioimmunoassay (RIA), reportedly sensitive to 0.03 μg/ml [55], was used to supplement the usual microbiological assay. The biphasic plasma profiles were described by a two-compartment model with a rapid slope of α and a terminal slope of β. As we shall see shortly the α phase corresponds to that reported by others for $t_{0.5}$. The terminal phase appeared to begin more than 24 hr after the final dose when serum levels were typically below 0.5 μg/ml. The apparent β half-lives were varied with a maximum value of 29 days for 47 patients on gentamicin [55] and 18 days for tobramycin [50]. Previous studies reporting 2- to 3-hr half-lives generally used a duration that was too brief and/or an assay that was not sensitive enough to observe this effect.

Both tobramycin [50] and gentamicin [49,55] doses were completely recovered in the urine when patients were available for long-term studies. In postmortem tissue analyses for gentamicin (six patients [55], one patient [49]) or tobramycin (four patients [50]) these antibiotics were recovered from several tissues and fluids. Edwards et al. [59] had previously measured high kidney concentrations of gentamicin or amikacin in 9 out of 10 patients who died during aminoglycoside therapy. It thus appears that the β phase observed during washout periods is due to release from tissues. This is further supported by the observation that the observed β values for both gentamicin and tobramycin were not related to renal function whereas the *initial slopes* of the semilog plots do correlate with creatinine clearance values. (Although the actual α values were not tested for dependence on renal function [50], they would be nearly identical to the *initial slope* of an unfeathered semilog plot as is demonstrated below in Sample Problem 5.)

The terminal phases showed extreme intersubject variability as might be expected for release of aminoglycoside bound to tissue. The reported averages (and ranges) are gentamicin, 112 hr (27-693 hr) in 47 patients [55]; tobra-

Table 10

Two-Compartment Pharmacokinetic Parameters Based on Washout Periods
up to 20 Days Following Multiple-Dose I.V. Administration[a]

Drug	C_{Cr} (ml/min)	Rate constants (hr^{-1})					
		k_{12}	k_2	$(k_{12} + k_2)$	α	k_{21}	β
Gentamicin[b]	42	0.016	0.154	0.170	0.172	0.009	0.008
Gentamicin[b]	~55	0.012	0.173	0.185	0.186	0.004	0.004
Gentamicin[c]	50–75	0.047	0.160	0.207	0.211[d]	0.016	0.012[d]
Tobramycin[c]	0–50	0.01	0.07	0.08	0.083	0.006	0.005
Tobramycin[c]	51–75	0.02	0.16	0.18	0.18[d]	0.008	0.007
Tobramycin[c]	76–150	0.03	0.22	0.25	0.25	0.008	0.007

[a]Taken from Refs. 49 and 50.
[b]One patient.
[c]Mean of groups of 9–16 patients.
[d]Calculated from reported values for k_{12}, k_{21} and k_2 using

$$\alpha, \beta = 0.5 (k_{12} + k_{21} + k_2 \pm \sqrt{(k_{12} + k_{21} + k_2)^2 - 4k_{21}k_2}).$$

mycin, 146 hr (33–428 hr) in 35 patients [50]. This slow release would not be
expected to be dependent on renal function since diffusion from the tissues
rather than glomerular filtration has become rate determining. This can be
appreciated by examining Table 10. In each case the value for α agrees well
with the sum of the values for $(k_{12} + k_2)$ while k_2 predominates with (k_2/k_{12})
ratios ranging from 3.4 to 14.4. Thus, the rapid initial decline of serum concentration is primarily loss to urinary excretion and secondarily to tissue binding
sites. This may be envisioned as

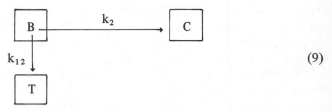

(9)

where return from the tissues is negligible during this period since k_{21} varies
from 1/10th to 1/43rd of k_2. It was noted that 24 or more hr (depending on
renal function) was required before the slower phase was observed. By this
time 80-90% of the dose has been recovered in the urine and the serum levels
are extremely low [49,50,60,61] representing only a small fraction of the
maximum value. Since most of the drug has been excreted and the α slope is
roughly the same as what would be obtained from a simple first-order plot

where $k_{obs} = k_{12} + k_2$, the initial slope values are consistent with one-compartment analyses and highly dependent on glomerular filtration rate.

When the slower phase becomes evident the model effectively behaves as two consecutive first-order processes $(A \rightarrow B \rightarrow C)$ where the first step $(A \rightarrow B)$ is rate-determining. Under these conditions, as shown in Fig. 14 of Chap. 3, the observed rate constant for $B \rightarrow C$ will appraoch that of $A \rightarrow B$. Thus, the above model will behave as

$$ \boxed{T} \xrightarrow[\text{rds}]{k_{21}} \boxed{B} \xrightarrow{k_2} \boxed{C} \qquad (10) $$

where the observed constant for loss from B (β) approaches the value for k_{21} as shown in Table 10. This rate-determining release from tissues is not affected by renal function since at all C_{Cr} values, release from tissues is a much slower process than elimination as can be seen by comparing k_{21} to k_2 in Table 10.

This β phase contributes very little to the serum levels during the normal course of therapy which is 7–10 days. This is because B and β are relatively small. The accumulation due to this phase is probably within the normal assay and/or biological variability. The resulting tissue accumulation is probably clinically significant and should be cause for some concern especially in long-term therapy. The following problem is designed to illustrate how incorrectly assuming the data are one-compartment will lead to inconsequential errors in predicting the plasma levels following the final dose $(n = 21)$ in a 7-day treatment.

Sample Problem 5

The data in Table 11 represent serum gentamicin levels for a patient receiving a single 80-mg I.V. dose.

(a) If the patient receives 80 mg every 8 hr for 7 days, how will the final plasma profile compare to that observed in Table 11? *Solution:* A semilog plot of the data appears linear with negative slope of 0.170 hr^{-1} and intercept of 5 $\mu g/ml$. At $\tau = 8$ hr the value for the fraction remaining (f) is 0.256 and $X = [(1 - f^n)/(1 - f)] = 1.344$ where $n = 21$. Thus, $P_{max}^{21} = (1.344)(5) = 6.72$ $\mu g/ml$ and $P_{min}^{21} = (1.344)(1.28) = 1.72$ $\mu g/ml$ where $P_{max}^1 = 5$ $\mu g/ml$ and $P_{min}^1 = 1.28$ $\mu g/ml$.

(b) The above patient was treated for 7 days and a sensitive radioimmunoassay was employed to determine serum levels for an additional 9 days. The curve was found to be biphasic with the β phase appearing roughly 24 hr after the last dose. This was not observed in solving part (a) since the final data point was 8 hr. The data given in Table 11 may be described by $P = Ae^{-\alpha t}$

Table 11
Concentration of Gentamicin in Serum Following I.V. Injection
of 80 mg[a]

Time (hr)	μg/ml	Time (hr)	μg/ml
1	4.21	4	2.53
2	3.55	6	1.80
3	3.00	8	1.28

[a]Data are based on the pharmacokinetic constants for patient 1 in Ref. 49.

$+ Be^{-\beta t}$, where P is the plasma concentration (μg/ml) and the reported values for this patient are A = 4.97 μg/ml, α = 0.172 hr^{-1}, B = 0.03 μg/ml, and β = 0.008 hr^{-1} [49]. Calculate the P_{max}^{21} and P_{min}^{21} values and compare them to those predicted in part (a) where a one-compartment model was assumed.
Solution: At τ = 8 hr the fraction of the α curve remaining is $e^{-\alpha\tau}$ = $e^{-1.376}$ = 0.253 = f_A. (This may also be done from $-\ln f_A = \alpha\tau$, f_A = antiln$[-\alpha\tau]$.) For the β curve, $f_B = e^{-\beta\tau} = e^{-0.064}$ = 0.938. Thus, X_A = $[(1 - f_A^n)/(1 - f_A)]$ = 1.338 and X_B = $[(1 - f_B^n)/(1 - f_B)]$ = (0.739)/(0.0620) = 11.92. The maximum will be P_{max}^{21} = $A(X_A) + B(X_B)$ = 4.97(1.338) + 0.03(11.92) = 7.00 μg/ml. The 6.72 μg/ml value estimated in part (a) is 4% less. The minimum value will be P_{min}^{21} = $Af_A(X_A) + Bf_B(X_B)$ = 4.97(0.253)(1.338) + 0.03 (0.938)(11.92) = 2.02 μg/ml making the estimate in part (a) 15% less. It is easily appreciated how these small errors are readily obscured by patient and assay variability in clinical practice.

c. Explanation for Apparent Inconsistencies in Literature. Plasma level data following single I.V. injections in six healthy adults were described by a three-compartment open model with half-lives (in hours) of 0.41, 1.93, and 17.3 for sisomicin and 0.47, 1.99, and 36.9 for netilmicin [57]. Since each phase is 94% complete after four times its $t_{0.5}$ value, we can estimate that the initial rapid phase requires 2 hr, the intermediate phase 8 hr, and the terminal phase 3–6 days. The large difference between the three slopes has resulted in workers reporting one-, two-, and three-compartment model analyses depending on when samples were taken. There is ample evidence in the literature to suggest that a three-compartment open model may be generally applicable to these aminoglycosides. The use of one-, two-, and three-compartment models has caused considerable confusion since, for example, the α slope of one report can be the β slope of another. If one compares the dominant slope for aminoglycoside blood level decay, during roughly 1–10 hr in normal renal function, there appears to be good consistency in the literature. To avoid confusion we will define the aminoglycoside plasma time course following I.V. injection as

$$P = Ae^{-S_1 t} + Be^{-S_2 t} + Ce^{-S_3 t} \tag{11}$$

where S_1 is the initial rapid slope, S_2 is the intermediate slope (during roughly 1-10 hr), and S_3 is the prolonged terminal phase. This will allow a comparison of literature values based on consideration of the sampling time.

Several workers have initiated sampling at 1 hr ending at roughly 8 or 10 hr and have reported monoexponential first-order plots (one-compartment model). These slopes represent S_2 with minor errors due to the contributions of the other exponentials. On the other hand, some reports include sampling every 5 min over the first hour but terminate sampling at 8-10 hr. These have reported two-compartment model behavior wherein the β phase begins at t $\sim$ 1 hr. The latter values for β probably correspond to S_2, which also represents the one-compartment model slope and the reported α slopes in the washout studies. In those washout studies designed to accurately determine drug persistence after termination of multiple-dose therapy of gentamicin [49] or tobramycin [50], the two-compartment model rate constants α and β correspond to S_2 and S_3. In Table 12, the comparison of literature values which correspond to the predominant log-linear slope (S_2) shows good agreement regardless of the model. This is probably due to the large differences in rates of the three exponentials allowing reasonable estimates for each slope in spite of disregard for the contributions of others.

5. Cephalosporins

a. *Structural Requirements and Ideal Properties.* Cephalosporin research began as early as 1945 but not until 1964 did these antibiotics gain clinical recognition. Three distinct chemical structures were originally isolated from the *Cephalosporium* fungus. One of the first was cephalosporin C which, although active, was never clinically useful. The hydrolysis of cephalosporin C provided the initial source for 7-aminocephalosporanic acid (7-ACA; shown in Table 13), which served as the nucleus for production of semisynthetics such as cephalothin, cephaloridine, and cephaloglycine. Thousands of semisynthetic analogs have since been reported involving alteration of the C7-amide substituent or displacement of the acetoxy function at the C3 methylene position. Some common examples are shown in Table 13. The nomenclatue has been simplified by assigning the name cephem to the bicyclic nucleus including the β-lactam ring oxygen. When the double bond occurs between C2 and C3, it is called 2-cephen or Δ^2-cephem and these compounds are inactive.

Much of the cephalosporin chemistry and structural requirements for antimicrobial activity resembles that of the penicillins and has been thoroughly reviewed [6,73]. An intact β-lactam ring is essential for activity [8] and

Table 12

Comparison of the Predominant Log-Linear Slope (S₂) for Decay of Aminoglycoside Serum Levels During the Period 1–10 hr Following I.V. Administration

Ref.	Drug	No. comp.	Ref. symbol	C_{Cr} (ml/min)	% Recovered in urine/time (hr)	[S_2] Rate const. (hr^{-1})	[$0.693/S_2$] Half-life (hr)
[62]	Amikacin	1	$t_{0.5}$	–	–	–	~3
[63]	Amikacin	1	$t_{0.5}$	120	94%/24 hr	0.31	2.3
[49]	Gentamicin	2	α	50–75	complete[a]	0.21	3.3
[52]	Gentamicin	1	$t_{0.5}$	normal	85%/24 hr	0.35[e]	2.0[e]
[61]	Gentamicin	2	β	normal	69%/24 hr	0.43[c]	1.6[c]
[64]	Gentamicin	1	$t_{0.5}$	normal	–	0.27	2.6
[63]	Kanamycin	1	$t_{0.5}$	119	94%/24 hr	0.34	2.1
[65]	Kanamycin	1	$t_{0.5}$	>90	–	0.31	2.3
[66]	Kanamycin	1	k_D	normal	81%/24 hr	0.3[e]	2.4[e]

[52]	Netilmicin	1	$t_{0.5}$	normal	87%/24 hr	~0.37	~1.9
[67]	Netilmicin	1	$t_{0.5}$	normal	45%/6 hr	~0.3	~2.2
[68]	Netilmicin	2	β	normal	90%/24 hr	0.31	2.3
[69]	Netilmicin	1	$t_{0.5}$	>90	complete/8 h_1	0.22	3.2
[70]	Netilmicin	2	β	normal	45%/24 hr	0.21	3.3
[51]	Netilmicin	2	β	>92	76%/24 hr	0.29	2.4
[57]	Netilmicin	3	β	normal	~75%/24 hr	0.35	2.0
[57]	Sisomicin	3	β	normal	~75%/24 hr	0.36	1.9
[72]	Sisomicin	2	β	normal	40%/24 hr	0.27	2.6
[71]	Sisomicin	2	β	normal	55%/8 hr	0.43[b]	1.6[b]
[61]	Sisomicin	2	β	normal	77%/24 hr	0.34[c]	2.0[c]
[50]	Tobramycin	2	α	76–150	complete[a]	0.25	2.8
[61]	Tobramycin	2	β	normal	74%/24 hr	0.35[c]	2.0[c]

[a] Studies carried out sufficiently long to recover all of the dose.

[b] Calculated from reported k_{12}, k_{21}, and k_2 values; reported β value is 0.87 hr^{-1}.

[c] Taken from terminal slopes of figures in Ref. 61; $t_{0.5}$ values calculated from reported microconstants: gentamicin, 2.3 hr; sisomicin, 6.1 hr; and tobramycin, 4.8 hr.

[e] Based on terminal slope following I.M. administration.

Table 13

Structures of Some Common Cephalosporins

7-ACA: $R_1 = H$, $R_2 = -OOCCH_3$

NAME	R_1	R_2
Cefadroxil		-H
Cefamandole		
Cefatrizine		
Cefazolin		
Cefoxitin		-OCONH_2

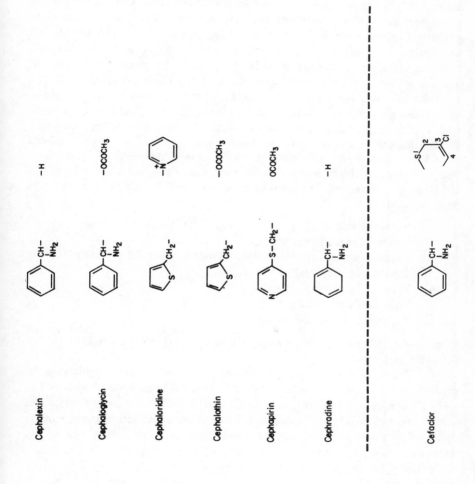

Cephalexin

Cephaloglycin

Cephaloridine

Cephalothin

Cephapirin

Cephradine

Cefaclor

derivative formation of the free carboxyl group results in complete loss or significant decrease in activity [8]. Although cephalosporins are more acid-stable than penicillins and are resistant to penicillin β-lactmase, they have shared a similar history with regard to developmental problems. Oral absorption of early analogs was not sufficient for systemic use, thus limiting several to parenteral administration incuding cefazolin, cephaloridine, cephalothin, and cephapirin. A brief summary of the outstanding features of the available cephalosporins was published in 1976 [74]. Like the penicillins, storage of aqueous solutions is a problem due to chemical degradation. Cephaloridine and cefazolin are considered the least painful on I.M. injection. Although cephalosporins are penicillinase resistant, their widespread use has resulted in cephalosporin-resistant bacterial which do produce β-lactam hydrolyzing enzymes. Partial cross-allergenicity with penicillins appears to occur. Cephalosporins should be administered cautiously to penicillin-sensitive patients. There have been instances in which patients react to both drug classes including anaphylaxis following parenteral use. The goals of molecular modification of cephalosporins have included

1. Increased acid stability
2. Improved oral absorption
3. Increased activity against resistant strains (particularly those producing destructuve enzymes)
4. Decreased pain on injection
5. Decreased allergenicity
6. Prolonged biological half-life

Considerable success has been realized and selected examples are reviewed in the following section.

   b. Pharmacokinetics. An extensive and excellent review of cephalosporin pharmacokinetics together with some reworking of literature data appeared in 1975 [75]. Kinetic studies for all of the analogs in Table 13 except cefamandole, cefatrizine, and cefaclor were included. Some of the significant pharmacokinetic information from several sources is summarized in Table 14. A few of the derivatives have achieved some increase in the biological half-life values: cephanone (2.8 hr; withdrawn from clinical trial), cefazolin (1.7 hr), and cephacetrile (1.3 hr). The rest fall roughly in the range of 30 min to 1 hr as seen for the penicillins (Table 5). Like the penicillins, this short half-life precludes significant accumulation during the usual dosage regimen with normal kidney function. Several cephalosporins are eliminated by renal tubular secretion as evidenced by high renal clearance values (Table 14: cephradine, 367 ml/min; cephalothin, 274 ml/min; cephalexin, 252 ml/min; cephacetrile, 235 ml/min) whereas cephanone (47 ml/min) and cefazolin (64 ml/min) appear to undergo tubular reabsorption. In general, the cephalosporins are excreted intact in the urine with little, if any, evidence for metabolism. Two notable exceptions are

Table 14
Average Reported Values for Biological Half-Lives, % Excreted Unchanged in Urine, Renal Clearance Values and Oral Absorption for Cephalosporins in Adults with Normal Renal Function

Cephalosporin	Terminal $t_{0.5}$ (hr)	% dose recovered in urine	C_R (ml/min)	Oral abs	Ref.
Cefaclor[a]	0.67–1.0; 0.58	50–70 in 8 hr; 70	–	good[b]	[78, 82]
Cefadroxil[a]	1.3	88, 93	–	~complete[b]	[80, 89]
Cefamandole	0.86; 0.87; 1.7; 0.57; 0.5	47–61, 80, ~100	234, 257	poor	[83–85; 90, 91]
Cefatrizine	1.1	45(I.M.)	–	~78%(?)[c]	[79]
Cefazolin	1.9; 1.8; 1.4	89; 100; 76	64	poor	[75, 86, 88]
Cefoxitin	0.67	90–100	–	poor	[75]
Cephacetrile	1.3; 1.3	88; 60–100	235	poor	[75]
Cephalexin	0.80[a]; 0.76; 0.61; 0.94	96[a]; 96; 87; 80–100	252	~complete	[75, 78, 87, 88]
Cephaloglycin	–	18–25	–	~27%[c]	[75]
Cephaloridine	0.6–1.5; 1.4; 1.1	85	125	poor	[75, 87, 88]
Cephalothin	0.56; 0.63; 0.47, 0.65; 0.34	52, 64, 38	274	poor	[75, 83, 86–88]
Cephapirin	0.71, 0.72, 0.36	41, 48	–	poor	[75, 76, 83]
Cephradine	0.76; 0.61[a]	79–100	367	~complete	[75, 80]

[a] Following oral administration.
[b] Assuming % excreted in urine following oral administration represents a minimum value for absorption.
[c] Estimated by comparison of urinary excretion following oral administration to that following I.M.

cephapirin (43% [76]) and cephalothin (33% [75]), both of which are rapidly deacetylated. Since urinary excretion is the primary route for cephalosporin elimination, it may become necessary to adjust the dosage regimen during renal failure. Among those in current use, the prescribing information for cefazolin, cephalothin, and cephaloridine includes dosage adjustments based on creatinine clearance values whereas that for cephradine provides guidelines when $C_{Cr} <$ 20 ml/min. Cephaloglycin, cephalexin, and cephapirin dosage instructions suggest caution in the presence of severe renal impairment. The use of nomograms for adjustment of cefaclor dosage in renal failure was shown to make little difference since the dosage interval (τ = 6 hr) is roughly three times the maximum half-life values of 2-3 hr observed in anephric patients ($C_{Cr} \approx 0$ ml/ min) [77]. For most cephalosporins the short half-life in normal renal function (~1 hr) relative to the long dosage interval ($\tau \approx$ 6-12 hr) obviates the need for adjustment in moderate renal failure.

Cephalexin and cephradine appear to be completely bioavailable by the oral route and they are employed clinically as oral dosage forms. Cefaclor, cephaloglycin, cefadroxil, and cefatrizine are also administered orally. When examined against cephalexin, 70% of the oral cefaclor dose was recovered in the urine as compared to 96% for cephalexin [78]. Twelve-hour urinary recovery of cefatrizine was 35% orally and 45% I.M. as compared with 68% and 74% for cephalexin [79]. The total cumulative urinary excretion of cefadroxil and cephalexin were statistically equivalent with a mean of 88% whereas cephradine recovery was complete following oral doses of 250-500 mg in fasting subjects [80]. These studies as well as many others compare the blood level time profiles of the test cephalosporins to a reference standard such as cephalexin. As discussed previously (and illustrated in Figs. 7 and 8 and Sample Problems 2 and 3), the direct comparison of blood levels for different chemical entities can lead to erroneous conclusions. Measurement of cephaloglycin blood levels have been complicated by the formation of the active deacetylated metabolite. A comparison of peak heights after oral and I.M. administration concluded only 25% oral absorption [75]. As with many newer antibiotics the necessary I.V. studies to establish a linear relationship between AUC and dose for the assessment of absolute bioavaibility, Eq. (1), are often lacking.

    c. Clinical Use. An in vitro study compared four oral cephalosporins (cefaclor, cefatrizine, cephalexin, and cephradine) to penicillin V, ampicillin, carbenicillin, oxacillin, clindamycin, and tetracycline on more than 30 organisms in 342 respiratory, skin, soft-tissue, and urinary isolates [81]. Against *Staphylococcus aureus* and streptococci (other than enterococci) cefatrizine was the most active cephalosporin but was less active than penicillin V, ampicillin, oxacillin, and clindamycin. It was also the most active cephalosporin against anerobes (other than *Bacteroides fragilis*), where it was similar to oxacillin but less active than penicillin V, ampicillin, and clindamycin which was the most active and the only antibiotic active against *B. fragilis*. Tetracycline was more active than cefaclor, which was similar to ampicillin and greater than other cephalosporins, penicillin V, and clindamycin against *Hemophilus influenzae*. The rank order for percentages of strains susceptible to cephalosporins among *Eschericia coli, Klebsiella* (where cephalosporins were more active than penicillin V, ampicillin, carbenicillin, and tetracycline), and *Proteus mirabilis* was cefaclor > cefatrizine > cephalexin > cephradine. These in vitro studies provide information for potential effectiveness without the many complications which accompany clinical use. They do not predict optimum therapy which must provide adequate drug concentrations at the site of the pathogen without producing serious side effects.

The 1975 review [75] provided several critical recommendations regarding cephalosporin use. Noting that cephalosporin popularity stems mainly from a broad spectrum, high safety, and small frequency of cross-sensitivity with penicillins, it was stated that other antibiotics are generally preferable once the bacteria are identified. This conclusion was based on either greater activity or reduced likelihood of suprainfection. Cephalosporins were thought to have the advantage against *Klebsiella* based on activity in the case of penicillins and toxicity in the case of aminoglycosides. That review recommends penicillin G for group A streptococcus, nonpenicillinase-producing staphylococci, "pneumococcus," and anaerobic streptococci; ampicillin for *Hemophilus*; oxacillin for penicillinase-producing *S. aureus.* Of the cephalosporins reviewed, cefazolin was recommended for parenteral use and cephaloridine was criticized due to significant nephrotoxicity. Cephalexin and cephradine were considered similar in oral use and superior to cephaloglycin which is not absorbed as well. Less expensive oral antibiotics were considered better choices except for either the follow-up of initial cephalosporin therapy or for urinary tract infections where patients are penicillin-hypersensitive or organisms are resistant to other antibiotics. Cefaclor, cefamandole, and cefadroxil were not included in the review.

The clinical use of cephalosporins has increased since that review. Many strains of *H. influenzae* have become resistant to ampicillin. Some clinicians consider cefaclor as the drug of choice for *H. influenzae* otitis media because of its safety and efficacy.* Other strains that are resistant to cefazolin are susceptible to cefamandole and cefoxitin.

Three new parenteral cephalosporins were introduced at the October 1979 joint meeting of the 11th International Congress of Chemotherapy and the 19th Interscience Conference on Antimicrobial Agents and Chemotherapy in Boston. Although they share the 7-ACA nucleus, one (LY 127935) is a 1-oxy cephem wherein the 1-sulfur is replaced by oxygen making it a new chemical

---

*For example, see J. Nelson, *Pocketbook of Pediatric Antimicrobial Therapy,* 3rd ed., University of Texas, Dallas, 1980, pp. 14, 24, 39.

class of cephalosporins. It is also a dicarboxylic acid somewhat resembling ticarcillin. Because of its long biological half-life (2.3 hr) it may prove useful on regimens of two or three times daily, given I.M. or I.V. In cefotaxime, the amide-linked side chain is replaced by aminothiazolyl and methoxyimino groups. In the third new cephalosporin, cefopyrazone, the amide-linked side chain contains dioxo-1-piperazine while the acetate group in R_2 (Table 13) is replaced by thiomethyl and methyltetrazole groups. All three appeared to be more active than established cephalosporins against aerobic gram-negative enteric bacilli. Cefopyrazone was notably active agains *P. aeruginosa* while cefotaxime and LY 127935 were effective for *Serratia* and *Klebsiella*. Their clinical usefulness remains to be established.

6. Sulfonamides

a. Half-Lives, Indications, and Dosage Intervals. Although sulfanilamide was known in 1908, it was not until 1935 that the antibacterial activity of sulfonamides was discovered with the drug Prontosil. Since that time thousands of sulfonamide derivatives have been synthesized. The therapeutically useful agents are all derivatives of sulfanilamide, and some of these are shown in Table 15.

For a single chemical class of compounds the sulfonamides exhibit a rather wide range of half-lives as shown in Table 15. The clinical utility of the various sulfonamides depends in part upon their half-lives. For example, sulfisoxazole, with a relatively short half-life of 6 hr, is excreted as the free drug into the urine where it rapidly reaches bacteriostatic levels. Sufladimethoxine, on the other hand, has a $t_{0.5}$ of 41 hr, accumulates slowly in the urinary tract, and is used primarily for upper respiratory tract infections or other systemic soft-tissue infections. Thus, $t_{1/2}$ serves as a qualitative guide as to whether a sulfonamide would have more potential in urinary tract or systemic infections.

Sulfonamides with long half-lives have been implicated in the development of Stevens-Johnson syndrome in children. The use of sulfas such as sulfadimethoxine, sulfamethoxypyridine, and sulfameter is associated with the possible occurrence of this sometimes fatal side effect. Sulfonamides with short or intermediate half-lives do not appear to present this danger. They should be preferentially employed when sulfonamide therapy is indicated.

b. Renal Tubular Resorption. The pK_a affects both the protein binding and the urinary excretion of sulfonamides. Once the sulfonamide has passed through the glomerulus into the tubule, it may be passively reabsorbed via the un-ionized form. Thus, the biological half-life is increased by factors which favor this passive resorption process. The amount resorbed will depend upon the pK_a of the sulfonamide and the urinary pH, which in turn determines how much of the un-ionized species will be present. The $t_{0.5}$ of sulfaethidole, which has a pK_a of 5.1, was markedly increased from 4.2 to 11.4 hr when the urinary pH

Table 15
Structure, Half-Life, and Dosing Interval of Some Common Sulfonamides[a]

$$H_2N\!-\!\!\overset{4}{\underset{}{\bigcirc}}\!\!-SO_2-NH-R$$

Name	R	$t_{1/2}$ (hr)	τ (hr)
Sulfanilamide	H	9	8
Sulfathiazole	(thiazole ring, S–N)	4	4
Sulfisoxazole	(isoxazole ring, O–N, 3,4-di-CH_3)	6	6
Sulfamethoxazole	(isoxazole ring, 5-CH_3, N–O)	11	12
Sulfadiazine	(pyrimidine ring, N, N)	17	12
Sulfadimethoxine	(pyrimidine ring, 2,6-di-OCH_3, N, N)	41	24
Sulfamethoxypyridazine	(pyridazine ring, OCH_3, N=N)	35	24

[a] From Ref. 92.

was changed from 8 to 5 [92]. It would also be expected that the more lipophilic the un-ionized species, the greater would be the resorption.

B. Urinary Tract Antimicrobial Agents

The goals of molecular modification of agents used in the treatment of urinary tract infections are often contrary to some of those stated previously for systemic antimicrobial drugs. Although the following list of characteristics for an idealized urinary tract antimicrobial agent may seem somewhat arbitrary, examples from the current literature indicate that the goals of research in this area generally reflect these characteristics. The ideal urinary tract antimicrobial agent should possess the following properties:

1. High intrinsic antimicrobial activity
2. High urinary concentrations of intact drug and/or active metabolite
3. Short plasma half-life with high affinity for the target site
4. Low volume of distribution
5. Poor or rapidly reversible serum protein binding

1. Intrinsic Activity and Urinary pH

High intrinsic antimicrobial activity is a common goal to both systemic and urinary tract antibacterials. The organisms more frequently responsible for urinary tract infections are gram-negative bacilli such as *E. coli, Enterobacter (Aerobacter) aerogenes, Pseudomonas aeruginosa, Proteus vulgaris,* and various salmonellae and gram-positive streptococci and staphlococci [93]. In patients developing symptoms of urinary tract infections for the first time (and who have not been previously catheterized or examined with the use of instruments), it would be reasonable to assume that the infection is due to either *E. coli* or one of the *Proteus* species and to initiate drug therapy on that basis. The choice of the drug to be used may be altered if necessary after the results of sensitivity tests performed on a urinary specimen have been obtained and assessment of the clinical response has been made. The importance of sensitivity tests in those cases where a high level of activity is desired against a particular organism cannot be overemphasized.

Urinary pH may also play an important role in limiting the activity of anti-infective agents. The minimum inhibitory concentrations of several sulfonamides have been correlated with their pK_a values [94], and the ionized species appear to possess greater activity than the un-ionized species [95]. Gentamicin activity against *Klebsiella, P. aeruginosa,* and *P. mirabilis* has been shown to increase with increasing pH (Fig. 11).

Streptomycin and kanamycin also have greater activity in alkaline urine [97]. Conversely, drugs such as penicillin G, tetracycline, nitrofurantoin, and methenamine are more active in acidic urine [97]. The necessity of an acidic urine for the activity of methamine will be discussed later in the section. Kunin [98] has discussed the management of pH during the treatment of urinary tract infections. He points out that daily use of pH-sensitive paper (Nitrazine ribbons) is necessary because of the varying response to agents used to alter urinary pH. Agents used orally to acidify the urine (and their total daily doses) are ammonium chloride (8-12 g), methionine (8-12 g), ascorbic acid (2 g), NaH_2SO_4 (2 g); and those to alkalize are Na_2HPO_4 (2 g), $NaHCO_3$ (12-24 g), acetazolamide (0.5-1.5 g), according to Kunin [98].

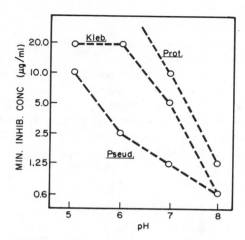

Fig. 11 The effect of pH on gentamicin activity against *Klebsiella, Pseudomonas aerugenosa,* and *Proteus mirabilis.* As the pH incrases the M.I.C. decreases, illustrating an apparent increase in gentamicin activity. (Drawn from data in Ref. 96.)

2. Urinary Concentration, Half-Life, and Protein Binding

The ability to produce high concentrations of the drug and/or its active metabolite at the site of action is a desirable trait shared by both systemic and urinary tract antimicrobial agents. It is preferred that systemic agents possess a long half-life in order to maintain tissue levels at minimum inhibitory concentrations for a sufficient duration. For urinary tract antibacterials the half-life should be relatively short so that the drug will reach the site of action rapidly and in sufficient quantity. Implicit in this statement is that urinary clearance is primarily responsible for the short half-life and not metabolism to inactive forms or other clearance processes.

Urinary clearance is a function of the mechanism of clearance, protein binding, and urinary pH. Since only the unbound form of a drug will undergo glomerular filtration, the extent and strength of protein binding will affect this type of urinary clearance. Protein binding has been indicated as a possible cause of extended duration of several sulfonamides [36]. Drugs which are actively secreted appear to be eliminated in a manner which is independent of protein binding [99]. Passive resorption of the drug can occur from the tubules, which results in lowering of the observed clearance. Maintenance of the urinary pH at a value where the drug exists primarily in the ionized form will inhibit this process. Thus, for weak acids such as the solfonamides, an alkaline urine would result in minimal resorption.

3. Volume of Distribution

In general, urinary tract antimicrobial agents should have a low volume of distribution, which increases their selectivity for the urinary tract. The degree of tissue penetration desired will depend upon the site of infection. Infections of the lower urinary tract (bladder and urethra) such as cystitis are best treated with those agents which have low volumes of distribution and short half-lives. In cases where infection involves the upper urinary tract (kidney and ureters), tissue penetration becomes important and agents with a low Vd, such as nitrofurantoin, are ineffective. For this reason, pyelonephritis—which requires high, steady bacteriostatic levels in the parenchymal cells [7]—is often treated using one of the tetracycline derivatives.

4. Potential Toxicity Due to Renal Insufficiency

Although cephaloridine, chloramphenicol, the colistins, neomycin, polymyxin, kanamycin, streptomycin, and gentamicin are effective against many of the organisms responsible for urinary tract infections, their use should be reserved for those cases which are resistant to other commonly used agents because of their potential for causing severe side effects. Ototoxicity has occurred with the use of gentamicin, kanamycin, and neomycin. Gentamicin and cephaloridine may result in nephrotoxicity, while blood dyscrasias are well-known side effects of chloramphenicol. The probability of the occurrence of these side effects is increased in those cases involving renal insufficiency due to higher and prolonged levels of these drugs and the increased difficulty in controlling their plasma levels.

III. ORAL BIOAVAILABILITY

A. Presystemic Metabolism; First-Pass Metabolism

Several types of drugs have demonstrated a reduction in bioavailability by the oral route due to presystemic metabolism in the liver, in the intestine, or during passage through the intestinal wall. This increase in metabolism by liver following oral administration is often called "first-pass" metabolism since drug passes directly to the liver before reaching the systemic circulation. Prodrugs may sometimes present a potential solution to this problem and are discussed in Sec. IV.

It has often been observed that the degree of first-pass metabolism may be reduced by increasing the rate of drug input to the liver. Thus, larger oral doses may result in increased values for F in Eq. (1). This is sometimes referred to as approaching saturation of the enzyme system, a notion that is conceptually (though probably not quantitatively) sound in most cases. The chemist should be aware that because of this effect, decreasing the absorption rate can

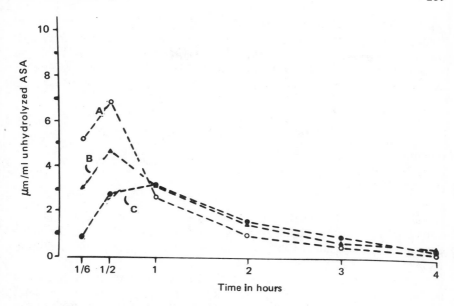

Fig. 12   The data of Hollister [100] have been used to construct these curves showing the plasma levels of unmetabolized aspirin following oral administration of equal doses of buffered tablets (A), regular tablets (B), and sustained release tablets (C).

be counterproductive. In the limit, if the drug is supplied slowly enough it could be completely metabolized in the first pass. Hollister [100] has provided an excellent demonstration of this phenomenon using acetylsalicylic acid in three dosage forms. As shown in Fig. 12, the bioavailability of unmetabolized aspirin is greatest from the most rapid release rate tablets (buffered) and least from the slow release tablets (sustained action) while regular tablets are intermediate. The primary difference in these three products is in rate of absorption rather than amount absorbed. The slow release form increases the hydrolysis of aspirin with a net reduction in its bioavailability. A chemical alteration which reduces the rate of absorption can result in an increased first-pass effect in spite of the fact that the modification increased enzymatic stability.

Tocainide represents an interesting example of a successful chemical modification to avoid first-pass metabolism. The I.V. administration of lidocaine has been reported to exert an antiarrhythmic effect which is useful in treating acute myocardial infarction. Approximately 90% of the administered dose is metabolized in the liver and 10% excreted unchanged via the kidneys. The metabolism of lidocaine involves N-de-ethylation to form monoethylglycinexylidide and glycinexylidide, both of which are active and contribute to the toxicity observed following lidocaine administration [101-103]. Side effects, noted with some of the oral doses, were absent in the I.V. studies which provided higher lidocaine levels [103]. Oral administration of lidocaine results in poor and variable absorption (21-46% with a mean of 35%) [103]. This was attributed in part to a large first-pass metabolism. Liver tissue can rapidly hydrolyze the

amide in monoethylglycinexylidide while its activity toward lidocaine and de-ethyl lidocaine (glycinexylidide) is low [104]. Thus, de-ethylation to the mono-ethyl metabolite would be expected to result in increased amide hydrolysis during first-pass metabolism.

Tocainide is a primary amine which therefore inhibits amide hydrolysis and circumvents the problem of N-de-ethylation. Oral absorption of tocainide appears to be both rapid and complete [105]. Renal clearance with acidified or uncontrolled urine was roughly 40% of the total body clearance which averaged 166 ml/min [105]. The pharmacokinetic parameters for tocainide are markedly different from those for lidocaine. The value for F is reported to be nearly 1.0 for tocainide as compared to only 0.35 for licodaine. The lido-caine elimination constant (β) as well as its total clearance value (C_T) is six times that of tocainide. Thus, reduced tocainide metabolism appears to greatly enhance both absorption and duration as indicated by the relative values for bioavailability, biological half-life, and total body clearance.

B. Optimizing Oral Absorption

Several factors are of primary importance for oral absorption of drugs, These are the drug's partition coefficient, its aqueous solubility, and its resis-tance to loss from the absorption site due to enzymatic or chemical degra-dation. Attempts to quantify the effects of molecular modification on these factors have been made and models proposed to explain the observed effects based on passive diffusion of drugs to, into, and through simulated membranes. Often a set of rules or constants derived from this type of research enable pre-dictions to be made concerning the absorption and physicochemical properties of a new compound. Thus, a priori design of molecules having the desired absorption behavior and physicochemical properties may become possible. While this is not yet a reality, considerable progress has been made in the form of linear relationships that are predictive within a given series. An excellent review on the use of physical models to the design of drugs with improved intestinal absorption has been published [106]. That same book contains excellent chapters on structural effects on partitioning, distribution, membrane transport, and other significant areas.

1. Partition Coefficients

The pH partition hypothesis for gastrointestinal drug absorption is discussed in Chap. 4. A few reviews summarize the pertinent data [106-109]. The theory states that only the un-ionized form of the drug passes through a biological membrane. The membrane is regarded as lipoidal in nature, and the ease with which the drug passes through it increases with increasing lipophilicity of the drug. While there are undoubtedly many compounds whose absorption behavior follows this theory, a growing list of exceptions has necessitated refinement of the theory. For example, the absorption rate constants for both ionized and un-ionized species of sulfaethidole and barbital have been determined in situ using rat stomach and intestine [110]. The ratios of the first-order constants for the neutral species to that of the ionized form was roughly 5 for sulfaethidole and 3 for barbital. At pH 6.1, approximately 42% of the sulfonamide is absorbed in the ionized form.

Other studies have been made concerning the absorption of compounds which are ionized over the entire pH range of the gastrointestinal tract either due to fixed ionic charges in compounds such as the quaternary ammonium drugs [111, 112] or due to the pK_a of the compound such as in the case of methylene blue [113] and the tetracyclines [114]. Tetracyclines exist in the cationic form at acidic pH values, as anions at alkaline pH, and in zwitterionic form at relatively neutral pH values. They are too polar to partition into a nonpolar solvent, but will partition into n-octanol from pH 5.2 and 7.4 buffered aqueous solutions [115]. Thus, tetracyclines may have sufficient lipid solubility to be passively absorbed in vivo even though ionized. The partitioning of tetracycline into n-octanol as a function of the pH of the aqueous solution and its ionic form has been examined [114]. It was found that partitioning was greatest at those pH values where the concentration of the zwitterion species was highest. This is also the pH range where tetracyclines exhibit their greatest antibiotic effect [116]. In general, minocycline, doxycycline, and methacycline have the same pH partition profile as tetracycline, but all are much more lipid-soluble, having zwitterions whose partition coefficients are 20-30 times that of tetracycline. These large differences in partition coefficients may also explain the large differences in tissue penetration and distribution discussed in earlier sections.

In some cases, what appears to be evidence contradicting the pH partition hypothesis is really data showing dominance of other factors. For example, phenobarbital and pentobarbital are weak acids having pK_a values of 7.2 and 8.1, respectively. Therefore, it would be predicted that these drugs would be more rapidly absorbed from the acidic environment of the stomach than from the intestine. Instead, two to three times as much is absorbed from the intestine during a 10-min period as is absorbed from the stomach in 1 hr [117]. This large difference is not due to preferential absorption of the ionized species but is due primarily to the much larger surface area of the intestine, which more than compensates for the decreased absorption of drug per unit area. Thus, the results of absorption experiments must be interpreted carefully and variables such as surface area controlled.

2. Partition Coefficient Adjustment Through Molecular Modification

In 1964, Fujita, Iwasa, and Hansch derived a substituent constant, π, which can be used to predict partition coefficients by summing the π values of the component parts of the molecule [118]. The π constant was defined by the Hammett-like relationship,

$$\pi x = \log \frac{Px}{Ph} = \log Px - \log Ph \tag{12}$$

where Px is the partition coefficient of the molecule bearing the substituent x and Ph is the partition coefficient of the unsubstituted compound. The n-octanol-water system was chosen as the standard for determination of these constants, since it was felt that n-octanol possesses several properties which allow it to serve as a model for the hydrophobic and H-bonding effects that might be encountered in biological membranes [119]. This method for predicting partition coefficients has been demonstrated for many compounds with widely varying structures, such as diphenhydramine, diethylstilbesterol, and 6, α-fluroprednisolone [120-122]. A library of partition coefficients for the basic structures of various classes of chemotherapeutic agents, such as penicillins [123], phenothiazines [124], barbiturates [125], and so on, have been compiled and serve as a data base for a priori calculation of the partition coefficients of various derivatives. However, caution should be used when calculating π values, since various interactions may cause deviations from the π-value additivity rules [118, 122, 126-129].

3. Model Systems for Absorption Studies

The buccal absorption of drugs has been suggested as an in vivo method for studying the passage of drugs across biological membranes [130] and lends itself well toward studying the effects of the lipid solubility and pK_a of various compounds. This method has been used to examine the absorption of amines, alkyl-substituted acids, substituted phenylacetic acids, and various other carboxylic acids [130-136]. Several important relationships were derived from these studies. Absorption across the buccal membrane was shown to occur by passive diffusion. For a series of unbranched aliphatic acids ranging in chain length from butyric to dodecanoic, absorption was shown to increase with decreasing pH and increasing chain length. Rate constants, expressed as clearance values, for the absorption of 10 carboxylic acids at pH 4 increased linearly with increasing partition coefficients (n-heptane: 1 N HCl). A linear relationship was also found between the absorption of a series of amines and acids and log partition coefficient when the drugs were either 1% or 10% ionized. This linear relationship also held for amphetamines and 10 fluramines. It had been previously calculated that the log transfer rate through a lipoidal barrier would be expected to increase linearly with log partition coefficient until a maximum constant value was approached [137].

Other investigators have developed an in vitro diffusion model for absorption studies [106,138]. This physical model consisted of a bulk aqueous diffusion layer and a lipid phase and has been used to interpret quantitatively and mechanistically the above in vitro buccal absorption data. For the alkanoic acids, a factor of 2.3 per methylene group for the buccal membrane-aqueous phase incremental partition coefficient was determined. This same model was satisfactorily tested on data for buccal absorption of various acids, and a value of 2.2 was obtained for the p-alkylphenylacetic acid series [139]. This provided further evidence for the applicability of the diffusional model and the significance of the diffusion layer in buccal transport. The theory was extended to a multicompartment diffusion model, and data for the gastric, intestinal, and rectal absorption of sulfonamides and barbiturates was shown to fit the model [140, 141].

Studies on the intestinal absorption rate of more than 50 compounds were conducted in rats [142,143]. From extrathermodynamic considerations, an additivity rule was proposed to predict the effect of substituents on the absorption rate constant.

The effect of alkyl chain length of a series of p-aminobenzoate esters on their physiochemical properties and ability to penetrate biological barriers has also been examined [144]. This diffusional model predicts a parabolic dependence of the maximum steady-state flux on chain length as the homologous series is ascended. Other studies also point to a parabolic relationship between biological activity and lipophilic character [145-148]. The parabolic nature of these relationships suggest that an optimum partition coefficient should exist for a given system. For example, optimum log partition coefficients for the absorption of various acids and bases from rat stomach and intestine have been estimated to be 1.97 and 1.39, respectively [149].

4. Partition Coefficient Effects in Absorption Data

Both in vivo and in vitro absorption studies indicate that the absorption of compounds with very small partition coefficients may be improved by increasing their lipophilicity. For example, clindamycin has a larger partition coefficient value and is much better absorbed than is lincomycin.

Esterification is a common method of increasing the partition coefficients of molecules. Applying the π-additivity principle, calculations indicate that the acetate ester of an alcohol will have a log partition coefficient value which is 0.89 unit larger than that of the alcohol. Increasing the chain length of the ester will increase the log partition coefficient by 0.5 for each additional methylene group in the chain. Thus, the butyrate ester would have a value which is 1.89 units more than the parent alcohol. The C-2 propionate ester of lincomycin is more extensively absorbed than the parent compound [150], and the C-2 and C-7 butyrates are better absorbed from rat intestinal loops [151]. The oral absorption of a series of erythromycin esters has been examined and, based on areas under the plasma curves, the acetate and propionate esters appear to be better absorbed than the parent drug while the butyrate was absorbed markedly less [152]. However, these curves may not be indicative of absorption differences alone, since intact ester was present in significant amounts. If the blood level curves represent total erythromycin due to hydrolysis of the ester prior to assay, the differences cannot be attributed solely to absorption without further data.

IV. PHARMACOKINETICS OF PRODRUGS

A. Kinetic Profiles

The optimum kinetic profile for any given prodrug is dictated by (1) the purpose for which the prodrug is designed and (2) the characteristics of the original drug itself. Some of the problems inherent in bringing these two considerations into play can be appreciated by examining Scheme II, which illustrates the processes involved in the administration of a drug by use of a prodrug. The symbols PD and D represent prodrug and drug at the site of administration prior to the absorption phase. Prodrug or drug in the first compartment or central compartment is shown by PD_1 and D_1. These compartments would have the same concentration as blood. Prodrug or drug distributed throughout the remainder of the body is represented by the symbol PD_2 or D_2. Distribution throughout rest of the body may be described by a two-compartment model, a three-compartment model, etc. Equations for the time course of a two-compartment drug and prodrug have been published [153]. The conversion of prodrug to drug may occur at the site of administration, within the blood compartment, or at some other site in the body. The site for conversion of prodrug to drug is the key to achieving the desired goal. Values for the rate constants associated with the drug itself are a property of that drug. The constants associated with prodrug must be controlled through the chemistry of the prodrug in order to achieve the optimum kinetic pattern for the drug. Thus, the behavior of the prodrug must vary to meet the particular goal for which it was designed.

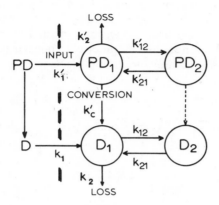

Scheme II

B. Goals

There are many possible reasons for employing prodrugs. Typical goals are

1. To increase absorption by
   (a) increasing gastric stability
   (b) obtaining optimum partition coefficient
   (c) increasing dissolution rate
   (d) decreasing first-pass or intestinal metabolism
2. To increase duration
3. To increase solubility for formulations
4. To increase site specificity

The optimum pharmacokinetic patterns for each of these goals may vary widely. This variation in pharmacokinetic behavior can cause problems in the evaluation of prodrugs. Failure to recognize the difference between optimum pharmacokinetic profiles for prodrugs designed with different goals in mind can lead to erroneous experimental design and/or erroneous interpretation of data. Let us consider some of the typical problems as they relate to these goals.

1. Increased Absorption

Scheme III illustrates the optimum pharmacokinetic pattern for a prodrug whose sole function is to increase the bioavailability or absorption of the drug. This may be achieved by having either a larger fraction of prodrug absorbed (F') than of the original drug (F) or a faster rate constant for absorption (k_1')

of prodrug or both. It is desirable to have the conversion of prodrug to drug occur in the central compartment at a rate that is more rapid than any competing rates in the system. Since the goal is to increase absorption, circulating prodrug, which should be biologically inactive, is not desirable. Ideally, both the rate and amount of absorption of prodrug should be increased followed by rapid conversion to active drug immediately upon arrival in the blood. This would decrease the potential loss of prodrug to nonactive species and the distribution of the inactive prodrug throughout the body.

Scheme III

In addition, the circulating prodrug can cause a problem by interfering with analytical methodology. Figure 13 shows a theoretical profile for a nearly ideal prodrug designed to increase bioavailability of the drug. In this example the rate constant for absorption of the prodrug has been kept equal to that of

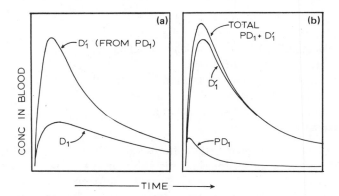

Fig. 13 (a) Molar concentration time course for drug in the blood following extravascular administration of either the drug itself (curve D_1) or an equimolar dose of its prodrug (curve D_1'), which is described by Scheme III wherein $F' = 2F$, $k_1' = k_1$, and the prodrug conversion constant, k_c', is 12 times faster than its absorption constant, k_1'. (b) As shown in Scheme III the blood contains both prodrug (PD_1) and drug (D_1') following the administration of prodrug as in Fig. 13(a). Because $k_c' = 12k_1$ the curve for the total of ($PD_1 + D_1'$) is only slightly higher than the D_1' curve. An assay that is specific for drug would provide results nearly the same as a non-specific assay for prodrug plus drug.

the rate constant for absorption of the original drug. However, the bioavailable fraction F' was increased to $2F$. Figure 13 shows a large increase in the AUC of drug (D_1') from administration of prodrug (PD) as compared to that obtained after administration of an equimolar dose of drug itself (D_1). The value of the conversion constant, k_c', is $12 \times k_1'$. Note that there is very little difference between the time course for total of prodrug plus drug from the prodrug $(PD_1 + D_1')$ and the time course for free drug from the prodrug (D_1'). The unconverted or intact circulating prodrug (PD_1) is very small. The ratio $(k_c'/k_1') = 12$ has been chosen so that the time profile for prodrug could be illustrated in the figure. If a sufficiently large ratio was chosen the intact prodrug concentration could be made so insignificant that its presence would not be detected. When conversion of prodrug to drug is sufficiently fast, comparisons of I.V. doses of the two forms will yield apparently identical data. This is nearly the case for the prodrug hetacillin wherein conversion is sufficiently rapid to produce ampicillin blood levels that are nearly identical with those obtained by an equimolar injection of ampicillin itself [19,154]. If the prodrug time course is significant relative to the drug itself then the assessment of bioavailability requires assay specificity.

2. Assay Specificity and Nonspecificity

Ampicillin has been widely used presumably due to its broad spectrum of activity. However, its oral absorption has been less than ideal. The *absolute* bioavailability of ampicillin varies from 30 to 50% [12,19,155,156] where percent = 100F in Eq. (1). This combination of widespread utilization and incomplete bioavailability has caused a high degree of interest in the synthesis of ampicillin derivatives (Table 16). *Absolute* bioavailability of the analog amoxicillin ($\sim$ 89%) is roughly twice that of ampicillin [20]. The comparison of these two analogs has been discussed in Sec. II.A.2.c.

  a. Rapid Prodrug Conversion. In contrast to analogs, the plasma levels of drug from prodrug may be compared directly provided that either the assay is specific for drug or the reversal is sufficiently fast. If the assay is nonspecific, serious misinterpretation of the data can result. The degree of error is inversely related to the rate of conversion of prodrug. If conversion of prodrug to drug is sufficiently rapid relative to prodrug absorption the circulating prodrug concentration will be minimal and its contribution to the assay will be insignificant.

  Of the ampicillin prodrugs in Table 16 only hetacillin has been found to circulate intact (Fig. 14). However, its conversion is so rapid ($t_{0.5}$ for conversion is 11 min [19]) that the observed difference between a nonspecific assay and a specific assay [157] is not dramatic. This small difference was sufficient to cause early investigators to erroneously conclude that parenteral doses of hetacillin provided greater AUC values than ampicillin itself. Quantitative assessments of hetacillin pharmacokinetics in man using a specific assay for ampicillin

Table 16

Structures for Ampicillin, Its Analog, Amoxicillin,
and Some of Its Prodrugs

	R	R'
AMPICILLIN	-H	-H
AMOXICILLIN	-OH	-H
BACAMPICILLIN	-H	-CH-OCOC$_2$H$_5$ / CH$_3$ O
PIVAMPICILLIN	-H	-CH$_2$-OC-C(CH$_3$)$_3$ / O
TALAMPICILLIN	-H	-CH / O / C / O (phthalidyl)

HETACILLIN

showed that this was not the case [19, 154, 157] as one would expect from pharmacokinetic theory. Hetacillin oral absorption appears to be equal to that of ampicillin although there is conflicting evidence regarding this. Its primary advantage would appear to be its increased storage time in concentrated solutions. This is attributed to blocking the primary amine which inhibits dimerization and polymerization [158,159].

Prodrug esters of penicillins are inactive since the free carboxyl group is a prerequisite for antibacterial activity (see also Sec. II.A.2.a). It is therefore necessary for the ampicillin esters in Table 16 to readily hydrolyze releasing

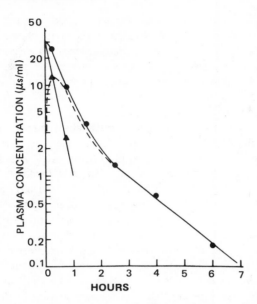

Fig. 14   Data of Jusko and Lewis [19] have been used to construct these semilog plots showing the time course for hetacillin (▲), ampicillin (———), and the sum of both (●) following the I.V. administration of the prodrug hetacillin.

free ampicillin to blood and tissues after facilitating absorption. Simple alkyl and aryl esters of penicillins are somewhat resistant to hydrolysis by human blood or tissues. Conversely, rapid conversion with little or no evidence for circulating intact prodrug has been reported for pivampicillin [155,160], bacampicillin [156, 161, 162], and talampicillin [163-165] (Table 16). Each of these has achieved increased oral absorption followed by rapid bioreversal.

Loo et al. [155] have shown that the percent of ampicillin absorbed from oral administration of pivampicillin is roughly 82% as opposed to 49% and 53% for the trihydrate and anhydrous forms of ampicillin. While the conversion rate was not reported in that study, pivampicillin has been shown to have a half-life of 5 min in whole blood [166]. The suggestion that formaldehyde release during pivampicillin reversal may cause side effects prompted the synthesis of lactonyl esters such as talampicillin [164,167]. Mean ampicillin plasma levels during 6 hr following talampicillin oral administration in man were approximately 6 times higher at 20 min and equivalent at 4 hr when compared with ampicillin itself [164]. Another study reported that the AUC values in man roughly doubled following talampicillin as compared to ampicillin and the P_{max} value (at $t_{max} \approx 1$ hr for both) was 2.6 times higher [165]. Hydrolysis in human blood was complete in less than 2 min in both studies [164,165]. This rapid conversion in vitro is qualitative proof that circulating prodrug is unlikely. However, the half-life obtained in whole blood cannot be extrapolated to the half-life for conversion in clinical use. There are many factors which prevent the use of in vitro data to quantitatively predict in vivo conversion rates. Two opposing influences are a first-pass effect which would be expected to increase the rate of conversion and distribution of prodrug into nonmetabolizing tissues which would decrease the rate of conversion.

Bacampicillin was reported to be 40% better absorbed than ampicillin based on the comparision of both the AUC values and urinary excretion data following oral administration [161]. In another study *relative* AUC values following oral administration of equimolar doses was found to be ampicillin = 1, bacampicillin = 1.5, and pivampicillin = 1.5 [168]. The *absolute* oral bioavailability of bacampicillin relative to ampicillin I.V. [Eq. (1)] has been reported as 0.87 with no detectable prodrug in serum [169]. The aqueous solubility of bacampicillin is similar to that of ampicillin but its lipid solubility is increased [169].

When a prodrug is rapidly converted to drug the pharmacokinetic parameters estimated from plasma data should agree with those for drug itself. If agreement is lacking this may be evidence for circulating prodrug and lack of assay specificity. This had led to some confusion in the comparison of prodrugs. Bacampicillin has show increased ampicillin levels in several organs and in tissue cage transudates [161]. This has been attributed to higher levels of ampicillin in plasma since no bacampicillin has been found in the circulation. This interpretation is most likely correct in spite of the fact that organ (or transudate) to plasma ratios were not the same following administration of drug and drug from administered prodrug. It is important to realize that rapidly converting prodrugs can only alter the input function of the drug and not the pharmacokinetic parameters associated with equivalent plasma levels of the drug itself.

Mecillinam (Table 2) is poorly absorbed when administered orally. The prodrug pivmecillinam (pivaloylmethyl ester) appears to show satisfactory oral absorption in human volunteers [23] and in both young volunteers and elderly patients [170]. The mecillinam AUC values following oral administration of 400 mg of pivmecillinam HCl in solutions, capsules, or tablets were roughly 45% of the AUC values following either I.V. or I.M. administration of 400 mg of mecillinam. The AUC values following oral doses of 200, 400, and 800 mg of prodrug were proportional to dose but the percent of the dose excreted in the urine as mecillinam decreased with increasing dose (51%, 46%, and 32%). A 400-mg oral dose of pivmecillinam HCl tablets provided mecillinam AUC values equal to that of a 200-mg I.M. injection of mecillinam, but urinary recovery was only 39% of the dose for the tablets as compared to 58% for the injection [23]. Correcting for the increased molecular weight of the prodrug as compared to the drug would increase all of the above reported values that were expressed as percent dose of pivmecillinam. There is some evidence that the serum half-life of mecillinam, following 400-mg oral doses of pivmecillinam, was increased in patients over 65 years of age with normal renal function ($t_{0.5}$ = 4 hr) compared with that of young (< 30 years) volunteers ($t_{0.5}$ = 0.9 hr) [170].

Carbenicillin is a penicillin that is limited to parenteral use due to poor bioavailability (see also Sec. II.A.2.c). This is presumably due to its low lipid solubility (it is a dicarboxylic acid) or its acid instability or both. At pH 2.0 it has a half-life of less than 30 min [171]. Once again esterification has been used to prepare a prodrug which would be more lipophilic and acid-stable, thereby decreasing loss at the site of absorption due to degradation. The indanol ester of carbenicillin was stable when incubated in simulated gastric juice at pH 2.0 and 37°C for 1 hr, while under these same conditions carbenicillin was almost totally destroyed [171]. The prodrug is rapidly hydrolyzed after absorption. The 5-indanol moiety is excreted in various conjugated forms, and differential assays have shown that only trace amounts of intact ester are present in the serum and urine [171]. In experimental urinary tract infections in one study, the effectiveness of the oral prodrug was generally as good or better than that of parenteral carbenicillin. The oral prodrug is useful only in urinary tract infections, since it has been shown that serum levels of carbenicillin from the oral prodrug are suboptimal [172].

b. Prodrug Conversion Rates Which Result in Circulating Prodrug. In the case where conversion is not sufficiently rapid to prevent circulation of intact prodrug, misinterpretation can result when assays are not sufficiently specific. Figure 15 is an illustration of a prodrug whose absorption rate constant is 2.7 times that of the original drug but whose bioavailability is only 0.8 that of the original drug. Contrary to Fig. 13, the conversion of prodrug to drug in the plasma is slower than its absorption. In this case, the conversion constant has been set at 75% of the value of the absorption constant. Figure 15(a) illustrates a comparison of plasma levels wherein the assay method is not specific. Here the analytical method detects not only free drug but some fraction of the prodrug. This case can occur with antibiotic prodrugs using microbiological assays. For example, an ester prodrug might hydrolyze in the culture media and liberate free drug during the assay. Figure 15(a) might be misinterpreted as an example of a dramatic increase of bioavailability of drug by use of the prodrug. The same data are examined using a specific assay in Fig. 15(b). It can now be seen that the actual effect of the prodrug is to decrease the bioavailability of the drug. Thus, the prodrug has interfered with delivery of drug rather than improved it. This example has intentionally been designed to illustrate how a nonspecific assay could lead to a conclusion which is contrary to the actual effect of prodrug administration.

One example illustrating this problem of assay nonspecificity in the presence of circulating prodrug is that of orally administered erythromycin estolate.

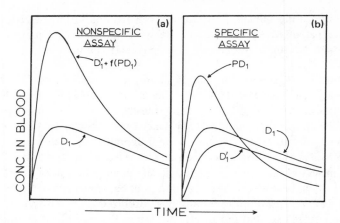

Fig. 15   (a) The molar concentration time course for drug in the blood following extravascular administration of drug itself (curve D_1) and the data using a nonspecific assay following an equimolar dose of its prodrug. The assay measures both the drug from the prodrug (D'_1) and a fraction (f) of the circulating prodrug (PD_1). Without a knowledge of this error it would appear that the prodrug has greatly increased bioavailability. (b) The prodrug data in Fig. 15(a) have been analyzed by an assay that can differentiate drug (D'_1) from prodrug (PD_1). Administration of prodrug has reduced the bioavailability of the drug (D'_1) relative to an equimolar dose of the drug itself (D_1). Prodrug kinetics are described by Scheme III wherein $k'_1 = 2.7\,k'_1$, $F' = 0.8F$ and $k_c = 0.75\,k'_1$.

While these data do not show a reversal of the order of magnitude of the plasma levels, they do show the importance of assay specificity when intact prodrug is present in plasma. The dashed line in Fig. 16 compares erythromycin estolate plasma levels to those obtained from the salt, erythromycin stearate [173]. This assay was not completely specific for free drug alone. Some of the estolate apparently hydrolyzed during the culture workup. The solid line shows the same set of data where a specific assay was designed to differentiate between total erythromycin as estolate and as free drug [174]. It can be seen that the free drug from the estolate is still higher than the free drug from the stearate. However, the degree of difference is not nearly as pronounced as would appear from the original curve shown as a dashed line.

    c. Conversion of Prodrug in the Intestines. Scheme IV illustrates a second mechanism for increased absorption. In this case, prodrug is converted to drug prior to the absorption step. This would apply to poorly soluble drugs or those that are unstable at the site of administration, such as a drug which undergoes hydrolysis in the stomach but is sufficiently stable for absorption in the intestine. The prodrug would stabilize the drug during passage through the stomach

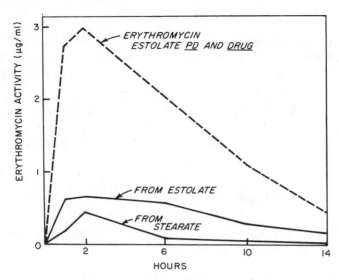

Fig. 16 Erythromycin activity in blood as a function of time following oral administration of either the estolate prodrug or the stearate salt. The assay used for the dashed line was nonspecific with regard to drug and prodrug. The solid lines represent an assay that was specific for erythromycin. Data are averages for 10 nonfasting human subjects after the fifth dose (250 mg) as given in Ref. 173.

into the intestine where reversal of prodrug to drug would occur followed by absorption of the drug itself. These pharmacokinetics are not complicated by the presence of circulating prodrug. Evaluation methods are identical to those employed for comparison of drug bioavailability from various dosage forms. Since prodrug is not absorbed the pharmacokinetics describe only the drug without the problem of assay specificity. The prodrug would affect only the rate of absorption or the fraction of drug absorbed. Direct comparisons of plasma levels of drug from various prodrugs can be made without misinterpretation. In the case of a solubility problem, reversal of prodrug to drug in the intestine might be based on either enzymatic or hydrolytic reversal immediately after dissolution.

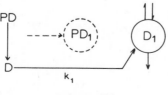

Scheme IV

3. Increase in Duration

a. The Rate-Determining Step. Prodrugs designed to increase duration may require the presence of circulating prodrug in contrast to those designed for bioavailability. Scheme V illustrates the two rate processes by which a prodrug may serve to extend the duration of the drug in the body:

1. The rate of input (or absorption) of prodrug from the site of administration to the blood
2. The subsequent conversion of prodrug to drug in the blood

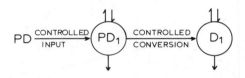

Scheme V

This latter conversion rate would be influenced by both the conversion constant and the fraction of prodrug in the blood. If the prodrug has a large distribution volume into nonreversing compartments, it could result in slow conversion due to the low concentration in the blood. This assumes that the primary conversion sites are located in the plasma and the liver, or other easily perfused tissues.

In any chain of events, such as those in Scheme V, there can be only one rate-determining step (RDS). This is further illustrated in Scheme VI. In the first case we have two consecutive first-order processes: $A \rightarrow B \rightarrow C$. This is a well-known case in chemical kinetics and could also represent first-order absorption with first-order loss in a one-compartment model. The rate-determining constant may be either k_1 or k_2 depending upon which one is slower. A similar model is shown for a two-compartment model drug. In this case the rate-determining step may be either the absorption constant, k_1, or the elimination constant of the drug from the body, β.

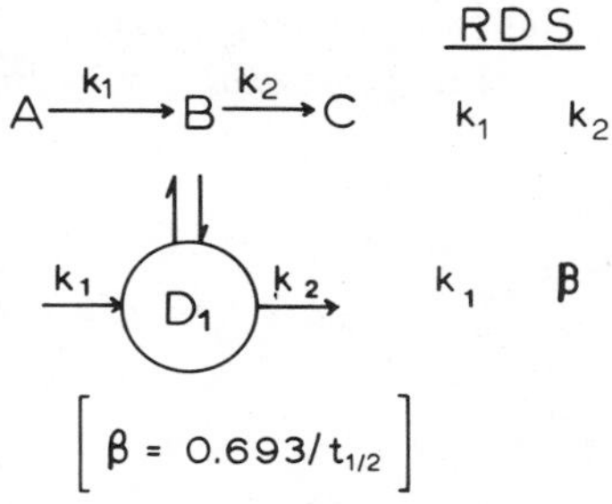

RDS

$$A \xrightarrow{k_1} B \xrightarrow{k_2} C \qquad k_1 \quad k_2$$

$$\xrightarrow{k_1} D_1 \xrightarrow{k_2} \qquad k_1 \quad \beta$$

$$\left[\beta = 0.693/t_{1/2} \right]$$

Scheme VI

If one step is to be rate determining, how much slower must it be in order that the kinetics may be said to be controlled by a slower step? This question has been examined in detail by Byron and Notari [175]. Terminal log-linear slopes (S) following first-order administration were compared with the terminal log-linear values after I.V. administration by computer simulation. Surprisingly, many of the systems described in Scheme VI were found to behave in a similar fashion. When the terminal slope of I.V. data provides a reliable estimate for β, then most cases examined (including the one-compartment model) can be summarized by a single "rule of thumb" for the numerical limits governing the rate-determining step. Allowing a 3% error, then a k_1/β ratio $\geqslant 3$ means that the slope (S) provides a good estimate for β. When $k_1/\beta \leqslant 0.3$, the slope provides a reasonable estimate for the absorption constant. Thus, a factor of 3:1 for the ratio of the two constants is minimal in order to assume that one of the two steps is rate controlling. If the value for β is three or more times larger than the value of the rate constant for absorption, it may be assumed that the terminal slope, which reflects the duration of the drug in the body, will approach k_1. If the absorption constant is three or more times larger than β, the terminal slope will estimate the β value for the drug itself. Exceptions to this rule are discussed elsewhere and occur primarily when I.V. injections fail to provide good estimates for β [175].

Scheme VII is an extension of this theory showing how administration of prodrug can give rise to three potential rate-determining constants: (1) the value of β (which is the property of the drug itself, (2) the prodrug absorption constant k_1', and (3) the overall prodrug conversion and elimination constant β'. If, for example, the absorption constant for prodrug was less than one-third the value for β but β' was three times the value of β, the terminal slope for drug loss in the body would be described by the absorption constant, k_1'. Similarly, the β' constant could become rate determining if absorption were rapid and β' were less than one-third the value of β. Thus, the terminal negative linear slope for $\ln D_1$ versus t may be k_1, β', or β. Only one step can be rate determining, however, and an extension of duration may be effectively controlled either by absorption of prodrug or conversion of prodrug but not both. The fraction, fr, of prodrug converted to drug is controlled by the ratio fr = $k_c'/(k_c' + k_2')$.

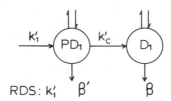

Scheme VII

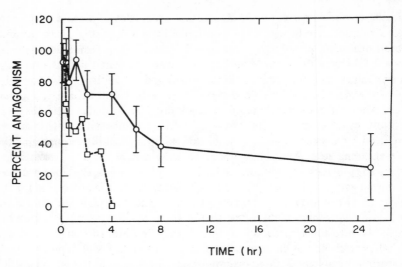

Fig. 17   Data of Malspeis and Reuning (personal communication) for the percent of morphine antagonism in mice (tail flick test) following an I.V. injection of the antagonist itself (□) or an equimolar dose of its prodrug (○).

The data from Malspeis and Reuning provide an example of the change in the rate-limiting step from prodrug conversion to absorption.* Figure 17 compares the percentage of narcotic antagonism following I.V. administration of the drug with I.V. administration of the prodrug in mice. The prodrug extends the duration of activity, indicating that conversion of prodrug to drug is sufficiently slow to extend the lifetime of the drug. Note that the time scale in this figure is in hours. Figure 18, however, shows a time scale in days. In this case the same prodrug and drug are compared following I.M. injections of aqueous suspensions. The prodrug behaves as a depot injection and the extension in the duration may be attributed to the slow release from the muscle. If a poorly soluble salt of the original drug could be made into a depot injection it would negate the necessity for the prodrug. However, attempts by other workers to increase duration through poorly soluble salts for depot injections were not successful. Thus, the increase in duration due to depot action is a unique characteristic for this particular prodrug.

   b. *The Optimum Rate-Determining Input Constant.* The ideal input rate for maintaining constant drug plasma levels is zero-order (see Sec. 4 of Chap. 4). A decreasing exponential supply rate (apparent first-order) is theoretically

*L. Malspeis and R.H. Reuning, College of Pharmacy, The Ohio State University, personal communication.

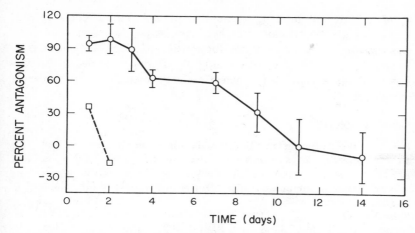

Fig. 18 Data of Malspeis and Reuning (personal communication) for the percent of morphine antagonism in mice (tail flict test) following an I.M. injection of the antagonist itself (□) or an equimolar dose of its prodrug (○).

possible for either rate-determining release of prodrug from the site of administration (i.e., I.M. injection) or the nonsaturated enzymatic postdistribution conversion of prodrug to drug. Assuming that one of two steps in Scheme V is a rate-controlling first-order process leads to the following observation. For a given drug of known minimum effective concentration (M.E.C.) in plasma there is only one optimum rate-determining first-order input constant (k_{opt}) which will provide the maximum duration of therapeutic levels for a defined dose [176,177]. The optimum ratio, $R_{opt} = k_{opt}/\beta$, which provides the maximum duration following a single dose, T_{max}, or the maximum dosage interval during the multiple-dose steady state, τ_{max}, may be estimated from

$$R_{opt} \approx \frac{e}{Q} \tag{13}$$

provided $Q \geqslant 8$. When $F = 1$,

$$Q = \frac{A_{max}}{[MEC]\ [Vd]} \tag{14}$$

where A_{max} is the maximum amount of *drug* in the depot immediately following the administration of a dose of prodrug [176,177]. We can define the dose, D_o, in terms of the *drug* itself by adjusting for the increased molecular weight (MW) of the prodrug using

$$D_o = \frac{(\text{prodrug dose}) (MW)_D}{(MW)_{PD}} \tag{15}$$

278   6. Pharmacokinetic Aspects of Drug Modification

For an I.M. injection of prodrug, where absorption is rate determining and circulating prodrug concentration is insignificant, A_{max} represents the maximum mass of *drug* in the muscle in the form of its prodrug. Thus, when n = 1, A_{max} is defined as a single dose of the drug, D_0. During multiple-dose steady state (n $=\infty$), $A_{max}^{\infty} = D_0/(1 - f)$ where f = fraction remaining in the depot $= e^{-k_1 \tau}$ (see Chap. 5).

Sample Problem 6

Estimate the optimum rate-limiting first-order input constant for an I.M. injection of a prodrug wherein the $t_{0.5}$ for the drug is 8.8 hr, the M.E.C. = 0.01 $\mu g/ml$, the Vd = 50 liters, and the maximum desirable accumulation of prodrug in the muscle is equivalent to 50 mg of drug.
Solution: $Q^{\infty} = A_{max}^{\infty}/(M.E.C.)(Vd) = (50$ mg)$/(0.01$ $\mu g/ml)(50$ liters) = 100. Since $Q^{\infty} > 8$, then $R_{opt} \approx e/Q^{\infty} = 0.0272$. Therefore $k_{opt} \approx 2.14 \times 10^{-3}$ hr^{-1}.

The maximum time between doses may be estimated from

$$\tau_{max} = \frac{1}{k_{opt}} \ln\left[\frac{Q^{\infty}}{\tau_{opt} - 1}\right] \tag{16}$$

where $\tau_{opt} = 1/R_{opt}$. In Practice Problem 6 the value for τ_{max} would be 20 days. Thus, if an I.M. injection of a prodrug could be designed to provide an input constant of 2.14×10^{-3} hr^{-1}, it would maintain drug plasma levels above 0.01 $\mu g/ml$ if dosed every 20 days. The loading dose (D*) would be equal to A_{max}^{∞}, which is the amount of prodrug required to provide 50 mg of *drug* in the muscle. The maintenance dose can be calculated from $D_0 = A_{max}^{\infty}(1 - f)$. In this example, f = 0.358 and D_0 is therefore the amount of prodrug required to provide 32 mg of *drug*.

REFERENCES

1. A. M. Burkman, R. E. Notari, and W. K. VanTyle, Structural Effects in Drug Distribution: Comparative Pharmacokinetics of Apomorphine Analogs, *J. Pharm. Pharmacol. 26*, 493-507 (1974).
2. K. H. Spitzy and G. Hitzenberger, The Distribution Volume of Some Antibiotics, *Antibiot. Annu. (1957-1957)*, 996.
3. R. Pratt, Antibiotics 1956-1961, *J. Pharm. Sci. 51*, 1 (1964).
4. C. M. Kunin, Pharmacology of the Antimicrobials, *Mod. Treat. 1*, 829 (1964).
5. G. H. Warren, The Prognostic Significance of Penicillin Serum Levels and Protein Binding in Clinical Medicine, *Chemotherapia 10*, 339 (1966).

6. J. P. Hou and J. W. Poole, β-Lactam Antibiotics: Their Physicochemical Properties and Biological Activities in Relation to Structure, *J. Pharm. Sci. 60*, 503 (1971).

7. J. Fabre, E. Milek, P. Kalfopoulos, and G. Merier, *Schweig. Med. Wschr. 101*, 625 (1971).

8. E. P. Abraham, Advances in Pharmaceutical Sciences, Vol. 1, D. Perlman, ed., John Wiley and Sons, N.Y., 1967, pp. 1-31.

9. K. E. Price, A. Gourevitch, and L. C. Cheney, Biological Properties of Semisynthetic Penicillins: Structure-Activity Relationships, *Antimicrob. Ag. Chemother.*, 670 (1966).

10. E. Kaczka and K. Folkers, in *The Chemistry of Penicillin*, H. T. Clarke, J. R. Johnson, and B. Robinson, eds., Princeton University Press, Princeton, N.J., 1949, pp. 243-268.

11. M. A. Schwartz and F. H. Buckwalter, Pharmaceutics of Penicillin, *J. Pharm. Sci. 51*, 1119 (1962).

12. Z. Modr and K. Dvoracek, in *Advances in Biosciences*, G. Raspe, ed., Pergamon Press, Elmsford, N.Y., 1970, p. 219.

13. J. E. Rosenblatt, A. C. Kind, J. L. Brodie, and W. M. M. Kirby, Mechanisms Responsible for the Blood Level Differences of Isoxazolyl Penicillins, *Arch. Int. Med. 121*, 345 (1968).

14. C. F. Gravenkemper, J. V. Bennett, J. L. Brodie, and W. M. M. Kirby, Dicloxacillin. *In Vitro* and Pharmacologic Comparisons with Oxacillin and Cloxacillin, *Arch. Internal. Med. 116*, 340 (1965).

15. L. W. Dittert, W. O. Griffin, J. C. LaPiana, F. J. Shainfeld, and J. T. Doluisio Pharmacokinetic Interpretation of Penicillin Levels in Serum and Urine After Intravenous Administration, *Antimicrob. Ag. Chemother.*, p. 42 (1969).

16. H. C. Standiford, M. C. Jordan, and W. M. M. Kirby, Clinical Pharmacology of Carbenicillin Compared with Other Penicillins, *J. Infect. Dis. 122*, 9 Suppl. (1970).

17. J. H. C. Nayler, Structure Activity Relationships in Semi-synthetic Penicillins, *Proc. Royal Soc. Lond. 179*, 357 (1971).

18. E. H. Nauta and H. Mattie, Dicloxacillin and Cloxacillin: Pharmacokinetics in Healthy and Hemodialysis Subjects, *Clin. Pharmacol. Ther. 20*, 98-108 (1976).

19. W. J. Jusko and G. P. Lewis, Comparison of Ampicillin and Hetacillin Pharmacokinetics in Man, *J. Pharm. Sci. 62*, 69 (1973).

20. D. Zarowny, R. Ogilvie, D. Tamblyn, C. MacLeod, and J. Reudy, Pharmacokinetics of Amoxicillin, *Clin. Pharmacol. Ther. 16*, 1045 (1974).

21. A. Philipson, L. D. Sabath, and B. Rosner, Sequence Effect on Ampicillin Blood Levels Noted in an Amoxicillin, Ampicillin and Epicillin Triple Crossover Study, *Antimicrob. Ag. Chemother. 8*, 311 (1975).

22. R. D. Libke, J. T. Clarke, E.D. Ralph, R. P. Luthy, and W. M. M. Kirby, Ticarcillin vs. Carbenicillin: Clinical Pharmacokinetics, *Clin. Pharmacol. Ther. 17*, 441 (1975). *

23. K. Roholt, Pharmacokinetic Studies With Mecillinam and Pivmecillinam, *J. Antimicrob. Chemother. 3,* (Suppl. B), 71 (1977).

24. L. J. Leeson, J. E. Krueger, and R. A. Nash, Concerning the Structural Assignments of the Second and Third Acidity Constants of the Tetracycline Antibiotics, *Tetrahedron Lett. 18,* 1155 (1963).

25. W. H. Barr, J. Adir, and L. Garrettson, Decrease in Tetracycline Absorption in Man by Sodium Bicarbonate, *Clin. Pharmacol. Ther. 12,* 779 (1971).

26. M. Barza, R. B. Brown, C. Shanks, C. Gamble, and L. Weinstein, Relation Between Lipophilicity and Pharmacological Behavior of Minocycline, Doxycycline, Tetracycline and Oxytetracycline in Dogs, *Antimicrob. Ag. Chemother. 8,* 713 (1975).

27. J. Scheiner and W. A. Altemeir, Experimental Study of Factors Inhibiting Absorption and Effective Therapeutic Levels of Declomycin, *Surgery 114,* 9 (1962).

28. L. A. Mitscher, A. C. Bonacci, and T. D. Sokoloski, Circular Dichroism and Solution Conformation of the Tetracycline Antibiotics, *Tetrahedron Lett. 51,* 5361 (1968).

29. N. A. Baker and P. M. Brown, Metal Binding in Tetracyclines — Cobalt (II) and Nickel (II) Complexes, *J. Amer. Chem. Soc. 88,* 1314 (1966).

30. L. Z. Benet and J. E. Goyan, Thermodynamics of Chelation by Tetracyclines, *J. Pharm. Sci. 55,* 1184 (1966).

31. J. E. Rosenblatt, J. E. Barrett, J. L. Brodie, and W. M. M. Kirby, Comparison of *in Vitro* Activity and Clinical Pharmacology of Doxycycline with Other Tetracyclines, *Antimicrob. Ag. Chemother.* 134 (1966).

32. P.G. Welling, P. A. Koch, C. C. Law, and W. A. Craig, Bioavailability of Tetracycline and Doxycycline in Fasted and Nonfasted Subjects, *Antimicrob. Ag. Chemother. 11,* 462 (1977).

33. C. M. Kunin, Blood Level Measurements and Antimicrobial Agents, *Clin. Pharmacol. Ther. 16,* 251 (1974).

34. W. J. Jusko and M. Gretch, Plasma and Tissue Protein Binding of Drugs in Pharmacokinetics, *Drug Metab. Rev. 5,* 43 (1976).

35. J. Koch-Weser and E. M. Sellers, Binding of Drugs to Serum Albumin, *Med. Intell. 294,* 311 and 526 (1976).

36. R. C. Batterman, L. F. Tauber, and M. E. Bell, Long-acting Sulfonamides: *In Vivo* Correlation in Man of Protein Binding, Serum Concentration and Antimicrobial Activity, *Curr. Ther. Res. 8,* 75 (1966).

37. C. M. Kunin, Clinical Pharmacology of the New Penicillins. 1. The Importance of Serum Protein Binding in Determining Antimicrobial Activity and Concentration in Serum, *Clin. Pharmacol. Ther. 7,* 166 (1966).

38. M. C. Meyer and D. E. Guttman, The Binding of Drugs by Plasma Proteins, *J. Pharm. Sci. 57,* 895 (1968).

39. M. Schach von Wittenau and T. M. Twomey, The Disposition of Doxycycline by Man and Dog, *Chemotherapy 16,* 217 (1971).

40. H. MacDonald, R. G. Kelly, E. S. Allen, J. F. Noble, and L. A. Kangis, Pharmacokinetic Studies on Minocycline in Man, *Clin. Pharmacol. Ther. 14,* 852 (1973).

41. P. G. Welling, W. R. Shaw, S. J. Uman, F. L. S. Tse, and W. A. Craig, Pharmacokinetics of Minocycline in Renal Failure, *Antimicrob. Ag. Chemother.* 8, 532 (1975).

42. J. T. Doluisio and L. W. Dittert, Influence of Repetitive Dosing of Tetracyclines on Biologic Half-life in Serum, *Clin. Pharmacol. Ther.* 10, 690 (1969).

43. M. Gibaldi and H. Weintraub, Some Considerations as to the Determination and Significance of Biological Half-life, *J. Pharm. Sci.* 60, 624 (1971).

44. M. Barza and R. T. Scheife, Drug Therapy Reviews: Antimicrobial Spectrum, Pharmacology and Therapeutic Use of Antibiotics. Part 4. Aminoglycosides, *Amer. J. Hosp. Pharm.* 34, 723 (1977).

45. F. C. Luft, Netilmicin: A Review of Toxicity in Laboratory Animals, *J. Int. Med. Res.* 6, 286 (1978).

46. P. J. S. Chiu, A. Brown, G. Miller, and J. F. Long, Renal Extraction of Gentamicin in Anesthetized Dogs, *Antimicrob. Ag. Chemother.* 10, 277 (1976).

47. R. Nedden, T. Fuchs, K. Schroder, and W. Wundt, Die Renale Ausscheidung Von Gentamicin beim Menschen, *Dtsch. Med. Wochenschr.* 97, 1496 (1972).

48. P. J. S. Chiu, G. H. Miller, A. D. Brown, J. F. Long, and J. A. Wartz, Renal Pharmacology of Netilmicin, *Antimicrob. Ag. Chemother.* 11, 821 (1977).

49. J. J. Schentag and W. J. Jusko, Renal Clearance and Tissue Accumulation of Gentamicin, *Clin. Pharmacol. Ther.* 22, 364 (1977).

50. J. J. Schentag, G. Lasezkay, T. J. Cumbo, M. E. Plaut, and W. J. Jusko, Accumulation Pharmacokinetics of Tobramycin, *Antimicrob. Ag. Chemother.* 13, 649 (1978).

51. J-C. Pechere, R. Dugal, and M-M. Pechere, Kinetics of Netilmicin in Man, *Clin. Pharmacol. Ther.* 23, 677 (1978).

52. J. A. Jahre, K. P. Fu, and H. C. Neu, Kinetics of Netilmicin and Gentamicin, *Clin. Pharmacol. Ther.* 23, 591 (1978).

53. G. Kahlmeter and C. Kamme, Prolonged Excretion of Gentamicin in a Patient with Unimpaired Renal Function, *Lancet*, Feb. 1, 286 (1975).

54. H. Wahlig, G. Langenberg, and D. von Kobyletzki, Erganzende Untersuchungen zur Pharmakokinetik von Gentamicin, *Infection 3*, 217 (1975).

55. J. J. Schentag, W. J. Jusko, M. E. Plaut, T. J. Cumbo, J. W. Vance, and E. Abrutyn, Tissue Persistence of Gentamicin in Man, *JAMA.* 238, 327 (1977).

56. G. Kahlmeter, S. Jonsson, and C. Kamme, Longstanding Post-Therapeutic Gentamicin Serum and Urine Concentrations in Patients With Unimpaired Renal Function: A Pharmacokinetic Evaluation., *J. Antimicrob. Chemother.* 4, 143 (1978).

57. F. Follath, P. Spring, M. Wenk, L. Z. Benet, and L. Dettli, Comparative Pharmacokinetics of Sisomicin and Netilmicin in Healthy Volunteers, *Proc. 10th Int. Contr. Chemotherap.* Vol. 2, Zurich, p. 979 (1977).

58. G. Kahlmeter, S. Jonsson, and C. Kamme, Multiple-Compartment Pharmaco-

282 6. Pharmacokinetic Aspects of Drug Modification

kinetics of Tobramycin, *Proc. 10th Int. Congr. Chemotherap.* Vol. 2, Zurich, p. 912 (1977).

59. C. Q. Edwards, C. R. Smith, K. L. Baughman, J. F. Rogers, and P. S. Lietman, Concentrations of Gentamicin and Amikacin in Human Kidneys, *Antimicrob. Ag. Chemother. 9,* 925 (1976).

60. B. R. Meyers and S. Z. Hirschman, Pharmacologic Studies on Tobramycin and Comparison with Gentamicin. *J. Clin. Pharmacol. 12,* 321 (1972).

61. H. Lode, B. Kemmerich, and P. Koeppe, Comparative Clinical Pharmacology of Gentamicin, Sisomicin and Tobramycin, *Antimicrob. Ag. Chemother. 8,* 396 (1975).

62. J. Levy and J. Klastersky, Correlation of Serum Creatinine Concentration and Amikacin Half-life, *J. Clin. Pharmacol. 15,* 705 (1975).

63. J. T. Clarke, R. D. Libke, C. Regamey, and W. W. Kirby, Comparative Pharmacokinetics of Amikacin and Kanamycin, *Clin. Pharmacol. Ther. 15,* 610 (1974).

64. M. Barza, R. B. Brown, D. Shen, M. Gibaldi, and L. Weinstein, Predictability of Blood Levels of Gentamicin in Man, *J. Inf. Dis. 132,* 165 (1975).

65. B. M. Orme and R. E. Cutler, The Relationship Between Kanamycin Pharmacokinetics: Distribution and Renal Function, *Clin. Pharmacol. Ther. 10,* 543 (1969).

66. J. T. Doluisio, L. W. Dittert, and J. C. LaPiana, Pharmacokinetics of Kanamycin Following Intramuscular Administration, *J. Pharmacokin. Biopharm. 1,* 253 (1973).

67. B-S. Yap, D. Stewart, and G. P. Bodey, Clinical Pharmacology of Netilmicin, *Antimicrob. Ag. Chemother. 12,* 717 (1977).

68. G. Humbert, A. Leroy, J. P. Fillastre, and G. Oksenhendler, Pharmacokinetics of Netilmicin in the Presence of Normal or Impaired Renal Function, *Antimicrob. Ag. Chemother. 14,* 40 (1978).

69. I. Trestman, J. Parsons, J. Santoro, G. Goodhart, and D. Kaye, Pharmacology and Efficacy of Netilmicin, *Antimicrob. Ag. Chemother. 13,* 832 (1978).

70. B. R. Meyers, S. Z. Hirschman, G. Wormser, and D. Siegel, Pharmacokinetic Study of Netilmicin, *Antimicrob. Ag. and Chemother. 12,* 122 (1977).

71. F. Meunier-Carpentier, M. Staquet, and J. Klastersky, Comparative Study of Three Routes of Administration of Sisomicin, *J. Clin. Pharmacol. 16,* 625 (1976).

72. B. R. Meyers, S. Z. Hirschman, S. Yancovitz, and B. Ribner, Pharmacokinetic Parameters of Sisomicin, *Antimicrob. Ag. Chemother 10,* 25 (1976).

73. E. H. Flynn, ed., *Cephalosporins and Penicillins, Chemistry and Biology,* Academic Press, N.Y., 1972.

74. G. H. Constantine, Antibiotic Chemotherapy, *Pharm. Index 18,* No. 9, 13 (1976).

75. C. H. Nightingale, D. S. Greene, and R. Quintiliani, Pharmacokinetics and Clinical Use of Cephalosporin Antibiotics, *J. Pharm. Sci. 64,* 1899 (1975).

76. B. E. Cabana. D. R. Van Harken, G. H. Hottendorf, J. T. Doluisio, W. O. Griffin, D. W. A. Dourne, and L. W. Dittert, The Role of the Kidney in the Elimination of Cephapirin in Man, *J. Pharmacokin. Biopharm. 3,* 419 (1975).

77. D. A. Spyker, B. L. Thomas, M. A. Sande, and W. Kline Bolton, Pharmacokinetics of Cefaclor and Cephalexin: Dosage Nomograms for Impaired Renal Function, *Antimicrob. Ag. Chemother. 14,* 172 (1978).

78. O. M. Korzeniowski, W. M. Scheld, and M. A. Sande, Comparative Pharmacology of Cefaclor and Cephalexin, *Antimicrob. Ag. Chemother. 12,* 157 (1977).

79. P. Actor, D. H. Pitkin, G. Lucyszyn, J. A. Weisbach, and J. L. Bran, Cefatrizine (SKF 60771), A New Oral Cephalosporin: Serum Levels and Urinary Recovery in Humans After Oral or Intramuscular Administration: Comparative Study with Cephalexin and Cefazolin, *Antimicrob Ag. Chemother. 9,* 800 (1976).

80. M. Pfeffer, A. Jackson, J. Zimenes, and J. P. DeMenezes, Comparative Human Oral Clinical Pharmacology of Cefadroxil, Cephalexin and Cephradine, *Antimicrob. Ag. Chemother. 11,* 331 (1977).

81. R. J. Fuss and R. B. Prior, Comparative *In Vitro* Activities of Oral Cephalosporins and Competitive Antibiotics Against Recent Clinical Isolates, *Curr. Ther. Res. 24,* 352 (1978).

82. R. Bloch, J. J. Szwed, R. S. Sloan, and F. C. Luft, Pharmacokinetics of Cefaclor in Normal Subjects and Patients with Chronic Renal Failure, *Antimicrob. Ag. Chemother. 12,* 730 (1977).

83. M. Barza, S. Melethil, S. Berger, and E. C. Ernst, Comparative Pharmacokinetics of Cefamandole, Cephapirin, and Cephalothin in Healthy Subjects and Effect of Repeated Dosing, *Antimicrob. Ag. Chemother. 10,* 421 (1976).

84. R. E. Polk, G. L. Archer, and R. Lower, Cefamandole Kinetics During Cardiopulmonary Bypass, *Clin. Pharmacol. Ther. 23,* 473 (1978).

85. H-E. Mellin, P. G. Welling, and P. O. Madsen, Pharmacokinetics of Cefamandole in Patients with Normal and Impaired Renal Function, *Antimicrob. Ag. Chemother. 11,* 262 (1977).

86. E. S. Rattie and L. J. Ravin, Pharmacokinetic Interpretation of Blood Levels and Urinary Excretion Data for Cefazolin and Cephalothin After Intravenous and Intramuscular Administration in Humans, *Antimicrob. Ag. Chemother. 7,* 606 (1975).

87. J. B. deMaine and W. M. M. Kirby, Clinical Pharmacology of Cephalexin Administered Intravenously, *Antimicrob. Ag. Chemother. (1970)* p. 190.

88. L. A. Pagliaro and L. Z. Benet, Critical Compilation of Terminal Half-Lives, Percent Excreted Unchanged and Changes in Half-Life in Renal and Hepatic Dysfunction for Studies in Humans with References, *J. Pharmacokin. Biopharm. 3,* 333 (1975).

89. A. I. Hartstein, K. E. Patrick, S. R. Jones, M. J. Miller, and R. E. Bryant, Comparison of Pharmacological and Antimicrobial Properties of Cefadroxil and Cephalexin, *Antimicrob. Ag. Chemother. 12,* 93 (1977).

90. I. W. Fong, E. D. Ralph, E. R. Engelking, and W. M. M. Kirby, Clinical Pharmacology of Cefamandole as Compared with Cephalothin, *Antimicrob. Ag. Chemother. 9*, 65 (1976).
91. B. R. Meyers, B. Ribner, S. Yancovitz, and S. Z. Hirschman, Pharmacological Studies with Cefamandole in Human Volunteers, *Antimicrob. Ag. Chemother. 9*, 140 (1976).
92. J. K. Seydel, in *Drug Design* Vol. 1, E. J. Ariens, ed., Academic Press, N.Y., 1971, p. 368.
93. M. A. Krupp and M. J. Chatton, *Current Diagnosis and Treatment*, Lange Medical Publications, Los Altos, Cal., 1972, p. 491.
94. J. K. Seydel, Sulfonamides, Structure-Activity Relationship, and Mode of Action, *J. Pharm. Sci. 57*, 1455 (1968).
95. C. L. Fox and H. M. Rose, Ionization of Sulfonamides, *Proc. Soc. Exp. Biol. Med. 50*, 142 (1942).
96. A. A. Lindberg, H. Bucht, and L. O. Kallings, Treatment of Chronic Urinary Tract Infections with Gentamicin, *Gentamicin First Intl. Symp.*, Paris, January 1967, pp. 75-83.
97. W. H. Hughes and H. C. Stewart, *Concise Antibiotic Treatment*, Appleton-Century-Crofts, N.Y., 1970, pp. 27-29.
98. C. M. Kunin, *Detection, Prevention and Management of Urinary Tract Infections*, Lea & Febiger, Philadelphia, 1972, p. 183.
99. B. B. Brodie, Displacement of One Drug by Another From Carrier or Receptor Sites, *Proc. Roy. Soc. Med. 58*, 946 (1965).
100. L. E. Hollister, Measuring Measurin: Problems of Oral Prolonged-Action Medications, *Clin. Pharmacol. Ther. 13*, 1-5 (1972).
101. H. Halkin, P. Meffin, K. Melmon, and M. Rowland, Influence of Congestive Heart Failure on Blood Levels of Lidocaine and Its Active Monodeethylated Metabolite, *Clin. Pharmacol. Ther. 17*, 669 (1975).
102. J. M. Strong, D. E. Mayfield, A. W. Atkinson, B. C. Burris, F. Faymond, and L. T. Webster, Pharmacological Activity, Metabolism, and Pharmacokinetics of Glycinexylidide, *Clin. Pharmacol. Ther. 17*, 184 (1975).
103. R. N. Boyes, D. B. Scott, P. J. Jebson, M. J. Godman, and D. G. Julian, Pharmacokinetics of Lidocaine in Man, *Clin. Pharmacol. Ther. 12*, 105 (1971).
104. G. Hollunger, Some Characteristics of an Amide-Hydrolyzing Microsomal Enzyme Before and After Its Solubilization, *Acta Pharmacol. Toxicol. 17*, 384 (1960).
105. D. Lalka, M. B. Meyer, B. R. Duce, and A. T. Elvin, Kinetics of the Oral Antiarrythmic Lidocaine Congener, Tocainide, *Clin. Pharmacol. Ther. 19*, 757 (1976).
106. N. F. H. Ho, J. Y. Park, W. Morozowich, and W. I. Higuchi, Physical Model Approach to the Design of Drugs with Improved Intestinal Absorption, in *Design of Biopharmaceutical Properties Through Prodrugs and Analogs*, E. B. Roche, ed., A.Ph.A., Washington, D.C., 1977, p. 136.
107. L. S. Schanker, Mechanisms of Drug Absoroption and Distribution, *Ann. Rev. Pharmacol. 1*, 29 (1961).

108. L. S. Schanker, Passage of Drugs Across Body Membranes, *Pharmacol. Rev. 14,* 501 (1962).
109. R. R. Levine and E. W. Pelikan, Mechanisms of Drug Absorption and Excretion, *Ann. Rev. Pharmacol. 4,* 69 (1964).
110. W. G. Crouthamel, G. H. Tan, L. W. Dittert, and J. T. Doluisio, Drug Absorption. IV. Influence of pH on Absorption Kinetics of Weakly Acidic Drugs, *J. Pharm. Sci. 60,* 1160 (1971).
111. R. R. Levine and E. W. Pelikan, The Influence of Experimental Procedures and Dose on the Intestinal Absorption of an Onium Compound, Benzomethamine, *J. Pharmacol. and Exp. Therap. 131,* 319 (1961).
112. R. H. Reuning, B. L. Ross, B. J. Shoemaker, and S. S. Watson, Positive Influence of an Acidic Medium on the Intestinal Absorption of a Quaternary Ammonium Compound in the Rat, *Pharmacologist 13,* 195 (1971).
113. A. R. DiSanto and J. G. Wagner, Pharmacokinetics of Highly Ionized Drugs. 2) Methylene Blue: Absorption, Metabolism and Excretion in Man and Dog after Oral Administration, *J. Pharm. Sci. 61,* 1086 (1971).
114. J. L. Colaizzi and P. R. Klink, pH-Partition Behavior of Tetracyclines, *J. Pharm. Sci. 58,* 1184 (1969).
115. J. T. Doluisio and J. V. Swintosky, Drug Partitioning. II. *In Vitro* Model for Drug Absorption, *J. Pharm. Sci. 53,* 597 (1964).
116. C. M. Kunin and M. Finland, Clinical Pharmacology of the Tetracycline Antibiotics, *Clin. Pharmacol. Ther. 2,* 51 (1961).
117. R. R. Levine, Factors Affecting Gastrointestinal Absorption of Drugs, *Dig. Dis. 15,* 171 (1970).
118. T. Fujita, J. Iwasa, and C. Hansch, A New Substituent Constant, π, Derived from Partition Coefficients, *J. Amer. Chem. Soc. 86,* 5175 (1964).
119. C. Hansch and W. J. Dunn, Linear Relationships Between Lipophilic Character and Biological Activity of Drugs, *J. Pharm. Sci. 61,* 1 (1972).
120. E. Miller and C. Hansch, Structure-Activity Analysis of Tetrahydrofolate Analogs Using Substituent Constants and Regression Analysis, *J. Pharm. Sci. 56,* 92 (1967).
121. Corwin Hansch, in *Drug Design,* Vol. 1, E. J. Ariens, ed., Academic Press, New York, 1971, p. 289.
122. G. L. Flynn, Structural Approach to Partitioning: Estimation of Steroid Partition Coefficients Based Upon Molecular Constitution, *J. Pharm. Sci., 60,* 345 (1971).
123. A. E. Bird and A. C. Marshall, Correlation of Serum Binding of Penicillins with Partition Coefficients, *Biochem. Pharmacol. 16,* 2275 (1967).
124. E. J. Lien and C. Hansch, Correlation of Ratios of Drug Metabolism by Microsomal Subfractions with Partition Coefficients, *J. Pharm. Sci. 57,* 1027 (1968).
125. C. Hansch and S. M. Anderson, The Structure-Activity Relationship in Barbiturates and Its Similarity to That in Other Narcotics, *J. Med. Chem. 10,* 745 (1967).
126. D. J. Curie, C. E. Lough, R. F. Silver, and H. L. Holmes, Partition Co-

efficients of Some Conjugated Heteroenoid Compounds and 1,4-Naptho-quinones, *Can. J. Chem. 44,* 1035 (1966).

127. W. P. Purcell, J. G. Bensley, R. P. Quintana, and J. A. Singer, Application of Partition Coefficients, Electrical Movements, Electronic Structures and Free-energy Relationships to the Interpretation of Cholinesterase Inhibition, *J. Med. Chem. 9,* 297 (1966).

128. J. Iwasa, T. Fujita, and C. Hansch, Substituent Constants for Aliphatic Functions Obtained from Partition Coefficients, *J. Med. Chem. 8,* 150 (1965).

129. C. Hansch and S. M. Anderson, The Effect of Intramolecular Hydrophobic Bonding on Partition Coefficients, *J. Org. Chem. 32,* 2583 (1967).

130. A. H. Beckett, R. N. Boyes, and E. J. Triggs, Kinetics of Buccal Absorption of Amphetamines, *J. Pharm. Pharmacol. 20,* 92 (1968).

131. A. H. Beckett and E. J. Triggs, Buccal Absorption of Basic Drugs and Its Application as an *In Vivo* Model of Passive Drug Transfer Through Lipid Membranes, *J. Pharm. Pharmacol. 19,* 315 (1967).

132. A. H. Beckett and A. C. Moffat, The Influence of Alkyl Substitution in Acids on Their Performance in the Buccal Absorption Test, *J. Pharm. Pharmacol. 20,* 2395 (1968).

133. A. H. Beckett and A. C. Moffat, Correlation of Partition Coefficients in n-Heptane-Aqueous Systems with Buccal Absorption Data for a Series of Amines and Acids, *J. Pharm. Pharmacol. 21,* 1445 (1969).

134. A. H. Beckett and A. C. Moffat, The Influence of Substitution in Phenyl-acetic Acids on Their Performance in the Buccal Absorption Test, *J. Pharm. Pharmacol. 21,* 1395 (1969).

135. A. H. Beckett and A. C. Moffat, Kinetics of Buccal Absorption of Some Carboxylic Acids and the Correlation of the Rate Constants and n-Heptane-Aqueous Phase Partition Coefficients, *J. Pharm. Pharmacol. 22,* 15 (1970).

136. M. J. Taraszka, Absorption of Clindamycin from the Buccal Cavity, *J. Pharm. Sci. 59,* 873 (1970).

137. R. G. Stehle, Diffusional Model for Transport Rate Studies Across Membranes, *J. Pharm. Sci. 56,* 1367 (1967).

138. N. F. H. Ho and W. I. Higuchi, Quantitative Interpretation of *In Vivo* Buccal Absorption of n-Alkanoic Acids by the Physical Model Approach, *J. Pharm. Sci. 60,* 537 (1971).

139. K. R. M. Vora, W. I. Higuchi, and N. F. H. Ho, Analysis of Human Buccal Absorption of Drugs by Physical Model Approach, *J. Pharm. Sci. 61,* 1785 (1972).

140. A. Suzuki, W. I. Higuchi, and N. F. H. Ho, Theoretical Model Studies of Drug Absorption and Transport in the Gastrointestinal Tract I, *J. Pharm. Sci. 59,* 644 (1970).

141. A. Suzuki, W. I. Higuchi, and N. F. H. Ho, Theoretical Model Studies of Drug Absorption and Transport in the Gastrointestinal Tract II, *J. Pharm. Sci. 59,* 651 (1970).

142. H. Nogami, M. Hanano, and H. Yamada, Studies on Absorption and Excretion of Drugs. 11. Relation Between Chemical Structure and Absorption

Rate, Intramolecular Interaction Constant, Additivity Rule and Prediction for Intestinal Absorption Rate Coefficient, *Chem. Pharm. Bull. 16,* 586 (1968).

143. H. Nogami, M. Hanano, and H. Yamada, Studies on Absorption and Excretion of Drugs. 10. Relation Between Chemical Structure and Absorption Rate. Substituent Constant for Absorption Rate Coefficient of Foreign Organic Compounds, *Chem. Pharm. Bull. 16,* 580 (1968).

144. G. L. Flynn and S. H. Yalkowsky, Correlations and Predictions of Mass Transport Across Membranes. 1. Influence of Alkyl Chain Length on Flux-determining Properties of Barrier Diffusant, *J. Pharm. Sci. 61,* 838 (1972).

145. J. T. Penniston, L. Beckett, D. L. Bentley, and C. Hansch, Passive Permeation of Organic Compounds Through Biological Tissue: A Non-steady-state Theory, *Mol. Pharmacol. 5,* 333 (1969).

146. T. Higuchi and S. S. Davis, Thermodynamic Analysis of Structure Activity Relationships of Drugs: Prediction of Optimal Structure, *J. Pharm. Sci. 59,* 1376 (1970).

147. J. W. McFarland, On the Parabolic Relationship Between Drug Potency and Hydrophobicity, *J. Med. Chem. 13,* 1192 (1970).

148. C. Hansch and J. M. Clayton, Lipophilic Character and Biological Activity of Drugs. 2. The Parabolic Case, *J. Pharm. Sci. 62,* 1 (1973).

149. E. J. Lien, Physicochemical Properties and Gastrointestinal Absorption of Drugs, *Drug Intell. 4,* 7 (1970).

150. W. Morozowich, M. J. Cho, and F. J. Kezdy, Application of Physical Organic Principles to Prodrug Design, in *Design of Biopharmaceutical Properties Through Prodrugs and Analogs,* E. B. Roche, ed., A.Ph.A., Washington, D.C., 1977, p. 344.

151. H. P. Fletcher, H. M. Murray, and T. E. Weddon, Absorption of Lincomycin and Lincomycin Esters from Rat Jejunum, *J. Pharm. Sci. 57,* 2101 (1968).

152. C. Lee, R. C. Anderson, F. G. Henderson, H. M. Worth, and P. N. Harris, Pharmacology and Toxicology of Erythromycin Propionate, *Antibiot. Ann. (1958-1959),* p. 354.

153. K. Ikeda, Y. Kurono, and T. Tukamoto, Methanesulfonic Acid Derivative of Sulfonamides 1. Hydrolysis Rate *In Vitro* and Pharmacokinetics *In Vivo, Chem. Pharm. Bull. 20,* 863 (1972).

154. W. J. Jusko, G. P. Lewis, and G. W. Schmitt, Ampicillin and Hetacillin Pharmacokinetics in Normal and Anephric Subjects, *Clin. Pharmacol. Ther. 14,* 90 (1973).

155. J. C. K. Loo, E. L. Foltz, H. Wallick, and K. C. Kwan, Pharmacokinetics of Pivampicillin and Ampicillin in Man, *Clin. Pharmacol. Ther. 16,* 35 (1974).

156. A. Swahn, Ph.D. thesis, Department of Medicine and Clinical Pharmacology, Karolinska Institutet, Stockholm, 1974, p. 13.

157. W. J. Jusko and G.P. Lewis, Precaution in Pharmacokinetic Evaluation of Ampicillin Precursors, *Lancet 1,* 690 (1972).

288   6. Pharmacokinetic Aspects of Drug Modification

158. H. Bundgaard, Polymerization of Penicillins: Kinetics and Mechanisms of Di- and Polymerization of Ampicillin in Aqueous Solution, *Acta Pharm. Suec.* 13, 9 (1976).
159. A. Tsuji, Y. Itatani, and T. Yamana, Hydrolysis and Epimerization Kinetics of Hetacillin in Aqueous Solution, *J. Pharm. Sci.* 66, 1004 (1977).
160. B. Lund, J. P. Kampmann, F. Lindahl, and J. M. Hansen, Pivampicillin and Ampicillin in Bile, Portal and Peripheral Blood, *Clin. Pharmacol. Ther.* 19, 587 (1976).
161. M. Rozencweig, M. Staquet, and J. Klastersky, Antibacterial Activity and Pharmacokinetics of Bacampicillin and Ampicillin, *Clin. Pharmacol. Ther.* 19, 592 (1976).
162. N-O. Bodin, B. Ekstrom, U. Forsgren, L-P. Jalar, L. Magni, C-H. Ramsay, and B. Sjoberg, Bacampicillin: A New Orally Well-absorbed Derivative of Ampicillin, *Antimicrob. Ag. Chemother.* 8, 518 (1975).
163. J. P. Clayton, M. Cole, S. W. Elson, and H. Ferres, BRL. 8988 (Talampicillin): A Well Absorbed Oral Form of Ampicillin, *Antimicrob. Ag. Chemother.* 5, 670-671 (1974).
164. J. P. Clayton, M. Cole, S. W. Elson, H. Ferres, J. C. Hanson, L. W. Mizen, and R. Sutherland, Preparation, Hydrolysis and Oral Absorption of Lactonyl Esters of Penicillins, *J. Med. Chem.* 19, 1385 (1976).
165. Y. Shiobara, A. Tachibana, H. Sasaki, T. Watanabe, and T. Sado, Phthalidyl D-α-Aminobenzylpenicillinate Hydrochloride (PC-183): A New Orally Active Ampicillin Ester, *J. Antibiot.* 27, 665 (1974).
166. W. von Daehne, W. O. Godtfredsen, K. Roholt, and L. Tybring, Pivampicillin, A New Orally Active Ampicillin Ester, *Antimicrob. Ag. Chemother.* 431 (1970).
167. I. Isaka, K. Nakano, T. Kashiwagi, A. Koda, H. Horiguchi, H. Matsui, K. Takahashi, and M. Murakami, Lactol Esters of Ampicillin, *Chem. Pharm. Bull.* 24, 102 (1976).
168. J. Sjovall, L. Magni and T. Bergan, Pharmacokinetics of Bacampicillin Compared with those of Ampicillin, Pivampicillin and Amoxycillin, *Antimicrob. Ag. Chemother.* 13, 90 (1978).
169. T. Bergan, Pharmacokinetic Comparison of Oral Bacampicillin and Parenteral Ampicillin, *Antimicrob. Ag. Chemother.* 13, 971 (1978).
170. A. P. Ball, A. K. Viswan, M. Mitchard, and R. Wise, Plasma Concentrations and Excretion of Mecillinam After Oral Administration of Pivmecillinam in Elderly Patients, *J. Antimicrob. Chemother.* 4, 241 (1978).
171. K. Butler, A. R. English, A. K. Knirsch, and J. J. Korst, Metabolism and Laboratory Studies with Indanyl Carbenicillin, *Del. Med. J.* 43, 366 (1971).
172. J. F. Wallace, E. Atalus, D. M. Bear, N. K. Brown, H. Clark, and M. Turck, Evaluation of an Indanyl Ester of Carbenicillin, *Antimicrob. Ag. Chemother.*, 223 (1970).
173. V. C. Stephens, C. T. Pugh, N. E. Davis, M. M. Hoehn, S. Ralston, M. C. Sparks, and L. Thompkins, A Study of the Behavior of Propionylerythromycin in Blood by a New Chromatographic Method, 8th Intersci. Conf.

Antimicrob. Ag. Chemother., N.Y., October 21-23. (1968). Data are summarized in *New Studies Reaffirm Consistent Absorption, Dependable Antibacterial Activity of Ilosone, Erythromycin Estolate,* Eli Lilly and Co., Indianapolis, 1968.

174. V. C. Stephens, C. T. Pugh, N. E. Davis, M. M. Hoehn, S. Ralston, M. C. Sparks, and L. Thompkins, A Study of the Behavior of Propionylerythromycin in Blood by a New Chromatographic Method, *J. Antibiot. 22,* 551 (1969).

175. P. R. Byron and R. E. Notari, Critical Analysis of "Flip-Flop" Phenomenon in Two-Compartment Pharmacokinetic Model, *J. Pharm. Sci. 65,* 1140-(1976).

176. P. R. Byron, R. E. Notari, and M-Y. Huang, Pharmacokinetic Predictions of Optimum Drug Delivery Rates From Prodrugs Designed for Maximum Duration, *Int. J. Pharmaceut. 1,* 219 (1978).

177. R. E. Notari, M-Y. Huang, and P. R. Byron, Calculations of Optimum Pharmacokinetic Drug Supply Rates for Maximum Duration During Multiple Dose Therapy by Prodrug Administration, *Int. J. Pharmaceut. 1,* 233 (1978).

Chapter 7

AN OVERVIEW OF PHARMACOKINETIC APPLICATIONS
IN CLINICAL PRACTICE

I. INTRODUCTION   291
   A. Applications of Pharmacokinetic Research   291
   B. Drug Product Selection   292

II. PHARMACOKINETIC DRUG INTERACTIONS   294
   A. Oral Absorption   295
      1. Instability   296
      2. Complexation   296
      3. Dissolution Rate   297
      4. Physiology   298
   B. Elimination   298
      1. Renal Excretion   299
         a. Glomerular Filtration   299
         b. Tubular Resorption   299
         c. Tubular Secretion   302
      2. Metabolism   302
         a. Enzyme Induction   302
         b. Enzyme Inhibition or Competition   302
         c. Dosage Adjustment in Drug Interactions   303
   C. Distribution   304
      1. Binding   304
   D. Improper Product Use   306

III. CLINICAL PHARMACOKINETICS   308
   A. Introduction   308
   B. Selected Problems in Clinical Pharmacokinetics   309
      1. Phenytoin   309
         a. Nonlinear Kinetics   310
         b. Bioavailability   310
         c. Drug Interactions   311
         d. Compliance   311

  e. Dosage Adjustment with Nonlinear Kinetics   311
   Practice Problem 1   312
   Practice Problem 2   313
   Practice Problem 3   313
  f. Constructing a Linear Dosage Nomogram with
   Nonlinear Kinetics   314
   Practice Problem 4   317
 2. Gentamicin   317
  a. Therapeutic and Toxic Plasma Levels   317
  b. Pharmacokinetics   318
  c. The Need for Monitoring   319
   Practice Problem 5   320
  d. Further Complications in Establishing Standardized
   Dosage Regimens   321
 3. Lidocaine   322
  a. Pharmacokinetics and Actions   322
  b. Dosage Regimen Adjustment   323
   Practice Problem 6   324
 4. Theophylline   324
  a. Why Monitor?   325
  b. Pharmacokinetics   325
  c. Dosage Regimen Complications   326
  d. Loading Dose   327
  e. Maintenance Dose   328
  f. Oral Administration   328
  g. Dosage Forms   329
 5. Digoxin   329
  a. Introduction   329
  b. Steady-State Plasma Levels   330
  c. Bioavailability   330
  d. Individualized Dosage Regimens   331
REFERENCES   333

I. INTRODUCTION

A. Applications of Pharmacokinetic Research

Both the methodology and published results of pharmacokinetic research hold potential for the improvement of three areas of drug therapy:

1. *Product* design and evaluation
2. *Drug* design and evaluation
3. Clinical practice

The practicality of pharmacokinetic research was initially realized in the area of product design and evaluation. Here optimum bioavailability has become a well-recognized goal for quality products. Specialized products, such as sustained release dosage forms, illustrate how the application of kinetic principles can improve the clinical efficacy of a known drug. Progress in the application of biopharmaceutics to product development is reviewed in Chap. 4.

Chemical modification of drugs has been successfully employed to improve pharmacokinetic properties and, in turn, efficacy. Kinetic considerations play a major role in determining the relative potency and effectiveness of structural analogs. Pharmacokinetic aspects of drug design and evaluation are reviewed in Chap. 6.

This chapter provides an overview of the contributions of pharmacokinetics to the improvement of drug therapy at the clinical level. The degree of success achieved in therapy with any drug is measured by the degree to which the observed results approach the expected results. Given that a good choice of drug has been made, the observed results may fall short of the expected results for a number of reasons:

1. Drug-drug interactions
2. Drug-food interactions
3. Improper dosage regimen
4. Improper product use
5. Inappropriate route of administration
6. Poor formulation
7. Toxicity

Pharmacokinetics provides the foundation for two elements which can be significant in clinical practice:

1. Product evaluation
2. Rational choice and use of drug products

A single drug may be available in several dosage forms from many manufacturers. What type of information is necessary to evaluate product efficacy? Once a drug and a dosage form have been chosen it must then be rationally used. This includes establishing the correct mode of administration, avoiding drug and food interactions, and adjusting the dosage regimen. The influence of biopharmaceutics and pharmacokinetics in achieving clinical success is the subject of this chapter.

B. Drug Product Selection

It is well recognized that the route of administration and the formulation can affect drug bioavailability. *Bioavailability* refers to both the amount of drug absorbed as well as its rate of absorption whereas *bioavailable dose* refers only to the amount absorbed. It is therefore possible to have drug products which are absorbed to the same extent (have equivalent bioavailable doses) but which provide different therapeutic results because of differences in their rates of absorption. The areas under the plasma level time profiles (AUC) are indicative only of the *amount* absorbed when comparing products containing a *single* drug. Conversely, the onset and the height of the plasma curve at its peak are affected by both the amount and by the rate. As discussed in Chap. 4, there are many reasons why the dosage form can alter the time course for drug in the blood. Since *bioavailable dose* does not take into account the shape of the profile, *bioequivalency* provides a more rigorous test for product comparison.

An acceptable product should either be superior or bioequivalent to the reference product. But what is the reference product? The answer is not simple. It is often the first marketed product (sometimes called the innovator's product) containing that particular drug. This is especially evident in literature comparing antibiotic products. An example may be found in Practice Problem 8, Chap. 4, where comparison to the original product, A, resulted in the recall of over 200 million capsules of nonbioequivalent formulations. However, the original or first marketed dosage form cannot be categorically assumed to have the ideal plasma profile.

One definition for the optimum bioavailability pattern is that which provides the longest duration per unit mass [1]. If the minimum effective concentration (M.E.C.) is known, then the optimum formulation would be that which exceeded this value for the longest duration of time without the sacrifice of bioavailable fraction or side effects. Comparisons based on duration are more difficult (if not impossible) when M.E.C. values are not known. The criteria for optimum profiles may change with the drug and/or disease in question. While it is generally agreed that the efficacy of an antimicrobial agent depends upon its ability to reach a given area of inflammation it is often debated as to whether high peak or extended effective levels are more desirable. High peak blood levels may aid diffusion into relatively avascular areas such as in the treatment of pneumococcal meningitis with penicillin [2]. In gonorrhea sustained high concentrations are required to destroy relatively insensitive organisms [2]. It is not yet clear as to how the mechanism of bacterial kill may alter the optimum time course for antibiotic therapy. For drugs wherein blood levels are not related to the clinical response the ideal pattern must be determined using clinical endpoints. This is not to say that bioavailability is no longer important since absorption is still prerequisite to reaching the site of action.

When two products exceed the M.E.C. for equal duration but differ significantly in F values, the one with the greater bioavailable fraction should be considered superior. In the author's opinion, the argument that both will work is not sufficient for clinical equivalence. The product that is less bioavailable will be more variable in performance and will therefore have a greater risk. The one which exceeds the M.E.C. to a greater extent and has the larger F value will be more predictable and more likely to successfully withstand some negative effect on its absorption. If side effects due to high plasma levels are a consideration then a smaller dose of a more bioavailable product is still better than a large dose of a poorly absorbed product.

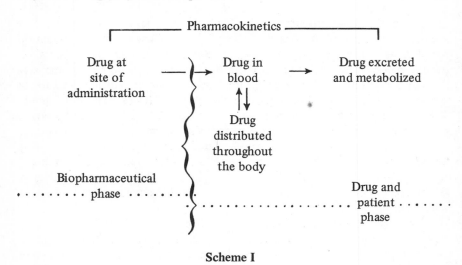

Scheme I

Scheme I reviews the rate processes involved in biopharmaceutics and pharmacokinetics. Biopharmaceutics includes all of the processes leading up to the arrival of drug in the bloodstream. The *biopharmaceutical phase* may be influenced by the manufacturing methods of the dosage form, the foods eaten by the patient, the route of administration, the effect of the disease state on the absorption process, the age of the patient, and the chemistry of the drug. The fate of the absorbed drug is determined by the *drug and patient phase.* For example, a patient in renal failure may elicit a reduction in the elimination of certain drugs that are excreted in the urine. Pharmacokinetics includes all of the rate processes, namely, absorption, distribution, metabolism, and excretion. Molecular modification may effect any or all of the processes. Thus, selection of a particular analog or prodrug for clinical use should include pharmacokinetic considerations. Those are reviewed in Chap. 6. Clinical results are best assured when the predictability of the processes in Scheme I is at its maximum. It is the responsibility of the clinician to pursue this goal.

II. PHARMACOKINETIC DRUG INTERACTIONS

Drug interactions may be classified under two categories:

1. Pharmacological interactions
2. Pharmacokinetic interactions

Table 1

Pharmacokinetic Drug Interactions

A. Absorption
    1. Stability
    2. Complexation
    3. Dissolution
    4. Physiology

B. Elimination
    1. Excretion
    2. Metabolism

C. Distribution
    1. Binding

The number and types of pharmacological reactions are both numerous and diverse. In general they are learned through experience and are often difficult to predict. The multiplicity of pharmacological interactions which have been observed and their ever increasing numbers make this problem best controlled by the aid of computers. In such an approach the patient's individual drug therapy is entered into the computer, which could then warn of drug interactions and suggest alternatives based on a vast memory of stored information. It is impossible for any member of the health team to be responsible for memorizing all of the possible pharmacological drug-drug interactions and to effectively deal with this problem. Conversely, to some degree pharmacokinetic drug interactions can be predicted from a knowledge of physical chemistry of the drugs and the interplay of the physical chemical characteristics with the pharmacokinetic behavior. Table 1 lists the three primary mechanisms by which pharmacokinetic drug interactions might be expected to alter an otherwise successful course of therapy.

In simple terms, one drug may decrease the absorption of a second drug. One drug may change the distribution pattern of a second drug. Finally, a drug may alter the elimination of a second drug in such a way as to increase or decrease its biological half-life depending on the circumstances. Theoretical [3] and clinical [4,5] aspects have been reviewed.

A. Oral Absorption

The absorption of a drug may be altered by other drugs or foods in four ways. Drugs which are unstable may be caused to undergo increased degradation. Some drugs may undergo complexation (as with heavy metals) and may not be well absorbed. A drug may fail to undergo dissolution due to the ingestion of food or other drug substances. The gastrointestinal physiology may be altered such as to interfere with an active absorption process or alter gastrointestinal motility.

In addition to drug interactions, absorption may be altered due to disease states or physiological changes accompanying aging. Nimmo [6] has discussed the factors which can alter gastric emptying and their potential influence on the absorption of orally administered drugs. Parsons [7] has reviewed the effects of gastrointestinal diseases on bioavailability with particular emphasis on mal-absorption syndromes. Welling [8] has reviewed the influence of food on the gastrointestinal absorption of drugs. A few examples are discussed here to illustrate the concepts.

1. Instability

Consider the problem of acid instability, as in the case of penicillins, erythromycin, cephalosporins, etc., wherein the stomach represents a prime area for drug degradation. Drugs which undergo hydrolysis in the stomach have a decreased possibility for absorption. Since this degradation is acid-catalyzed, the pH of the stomach can influence the degree of hydrolysis. Stomach pH varies from roughly 1 to 3.5 and the pH of the duodenum is 5-6. These regions are more acidic during mealtimes since acid is secreted for the digestion of foods. Table 1 in Chap. 4 summarizes the half-lives for some of the common penicillins in an acid pH at 35°C. Methicillin, with a half-life of 2.3 min, is so unstable in the gastrointestinal tract as to be suitable for use only by the parenteral route. More recent penicillins (such as oxacillin, penicillin V, amoxicillin, and ampicillin) have increased stability in stomach acid. In spite of this, it has been observed that penicillins in general are better absorbed on a fasting stomach than they are just after meals. For optimum oral penicillin therapy, one should always be advised to take penicillins at least 30 min before or 2 hr after mealtime.

The effect of food on erythromycin absorption has been somewhat varied. In the case of those dosage forms which readily present erythromycin base to stomach fluids there is usually a decrease in bioavailability with meals. Suspension dosage forms, coated tablets, and prodrugs all appear less sensitive to this effect. The effect of food on the bioavailability of the ethyl succinate or the estolate is probably clinically insignificant.

2. Complexation

The tetracyclines provide the most well-known example for decreased absorption due to complexation. This problem has been widely publicized and it is known that all tetracyclines undergo such complexation with resultant decrease in oral absorption in the presence of aluminum, calcium, and magnesium. This complexation is known to yield inactive species which are unable to penetrate biological membranes. In the case of demeclocyclin, it has been shown that only 13% is absorbed when taken with 8 oz of whole milk as compared to that absorbed with an equal dose taken after 7 hr of fasting (Practice Problem 7, Chap. 4). On co-administration with 20 ml of aluminum hydroxide gel, only 22% was absorbed compared to the fasting state. Doxycycline has been shown to be less sensitive than demeclocyclin to nondairy foods and to skim milk. While doxycycline absorption is decreased somewhat in the presence of whole milk, it appears to be the least sensitive tetracycline in current clinical use. However, all tetracyclines (including doxycycline) undergo decreased bioavailability if ingestion of antacids containing divalent or trivalent cations occurs simultaneously. When doxycycline was administered orally with aluminum hydroxide gel, observed plasma concentrations were reduced to 10% of normal (see Chap. 6). Rational oral tetracycline therapy should include precautions against concomitant administration of dairy products or aluminum-, magnesium- or calcium-containing antacid preparations. Certainly, the patient cannot be expected to realize this without being counseled by the clinician.

3. Dissolution Rate

As might be expected, the dissolution of poorly soluble drugs is often rate limiting in the absorption process. It is therefore important to keep those factors in mind which govern dissolution rates (see Chap. 4).

With weak base drugs, which require protonation for good dissolution characteristics, the bioavailability may be decreased if the stomach is buffered to an alkaline pH. This phenomenon has also been observed in the case of tetracycline which behaves as a zwitterion [9]. Tetracycline hydrochloride capsules resulted in decreased oral absorption when administered with an aqueous solution of sodium bicarbonate. Since the hydrochloride salt of tetracycline is meant to aid in the dissolution rate, it might have been anticipated that co-administration with sodium bicarbonate would tend to neutralize the acid salt and either decrease dissolution rate or precipitate tetracycline which had dissolved in the stomach.

A logical extension of this observation is the hypothesis that achlorhydria accompanying disease states, aging, or certain drug therapy might also reduce the bioavailability of tetracycline. The most widely used trade name capsules were compared to solutions in normal volunteers and elderly achlorhydric patients [10]. The capsules were also administered to the normal subjects with concurrent administration of sodium bicarbonate solution. Contrary to the previous study [9], neither alkalinization nor achlorhydria decreased absorption which was equivalent for both the capsules and the solutions [10]. Since the products which had previously been shown to be decreased by sodium bicarbonate were only 61.5% as bioavailable as the capsules used in the latter study, it was suggested that the pH effect was significant only to a product with less than optimum dissolution characteristics. If the formulation is sufficiently rapid in its dissolution pattern, the increase in stomach pH may not significantly inhibit its dissolution.

This supports the suggestion made earlier in the section on drug product selection. A product that achieves therapeutic blood levels but has decreased bioavailability will have an increased risk in clinical use where less than ideal circumstances may further compromise its potential.

4. Physiology

More complex phenomena include the alteration of gastrointestinal absorption due to changes in active mechanisms for absorption (enzyme transport systems) or in gastrointestinal motility. One rather complex example involves phenytoin (diphenylhydantoin) and folic acid. It has been reported that phenytoin inhibits folic acid absorption. A patient on phenytoin therapy may therefore experience folic acid deficiency. One such patient, who was adequately controlled for 18 months without a seizure, was given 5 mg of folic acid in addition to the regular dosage for phenytoin and phenobarbital. Although no significant effect was observed on the phenobarbital plasma levels, the phenytoin level fell and the patient experienced the first grand mal seizure in 18 months. When the phenytoin dose was doubled the plasma level soared from 5 to 80 μg/ml with severe intoxication. However, when the folic acid dose was reduced to 2 mg and the phenytoin dosage returned to 300 mg daily, the patient again showed normal plasma levels of phenytoin without side effects [11]. Admittedly, such complicated interactions are unfortunately learned from experience. However, the potential exists for drugs that are actively absorbed to interfere with other compounds which can compete for the same enzyme systems. Individualization of phenytoin dosage is complicated by other factors and is covered separately in this chapter.

Drugs which show "site-specific" absorption may be influenced by gastrointestinal motility which can determine the time available for absorption. Digoxin appears to be best absorbed from the upper intestine. Higher steady-state plasma levels of digoxin have been reported after treatment with propantheline, presumably due to increased residence time in the upper intestine. Conversely, propantheline has been reported to decrease the plasma concentrations obtained with paracetamol.

B. Elimination

The second category of pharmacokinetic-based drug interactions is that of alteration of elimination. This may be considered in terms of drugs which influence *excretion* by the kidneys or *metabolic* processes. At this time the first is better understood and more easily predicted. Drugs that are eliminated solely by glomerular filtration tend to show less inter-patient variation in elimination half-life than those which are wholly metabolized. The adjustment of dosage in renal failure by considering glomerular filtration rate (GFR) has further reduced interpatient variability. Attempts to accommodate changes in liver function based on clinical tests have not been successful.

How can one look at drugs from the standpoint of relative *susceptibility* to drug-drug interaction due to changes in renal excretion? Basically, two considerations have to be brought into this question. One is the percent of elimination of a drug attributed to the kidney. The second is the mechanism by which the kidney excretes drug.

1. Renal Excretion

a. Glomerular Filtration. Chapter 3 provides a discussion of renal clearance. If we consider the mechanisms by which the kidney eliminates drugs, we can roughly categorize compounds according to their renal clearance values. Table 2 presents typical normal renal clearance values. The elimination of compounds by glomerular filtration can be reduced by plasma protein binding. The biological half-lives for sulfonamides, for example, have been shown to correlate with degree of plasma protein binding. However, compounds which undergo active tubular secretion (such as penicillins with renal clearance values in the range 200-500 ml/min) are not affected by the percentage which is plasma protein bound. In fact, all penicillins have half-lives in the range of 30 min to 1 hr regardless of the wide range of their protein binding from 20% to greater than 90%. The effect that displacement of one protein-bound drug by another has on renal clearance and duration is therefore somewhat predictable.

b. Tubular Resorption. Renal clearance values significantly less than 120 ml/min indicate tubular resorption (or reabsorption). Tubular reabsorption of drugs is a passive process. Figure 1 illustrates tubular reabsorption of acidic and basic drugs. The concepts are analogous to those of the pH partition considerations in gastrointestinal absorption. A neutral species is preferentially reabsorbed in comparison to a charged form. For a weak acid drug, passive reabsorption would be increased if the urine is acidic enough to cause an increase in the concentration of neutral species. This would result in increased biological half-life. Notable examples are sulfonamides and salicylates. The

Table 2

Renal Clearance[a] (ml/min)

1.	Glomerular Filtration	$C_R = 120\text{-}130$
2.	Tubular Resorption	$C_R < 120$
3.	Tubular Secretion	$C_R \geqslant 130$

[a]Average values based on $(C_R) \times 1.73/\text{surface area in } m^2$.

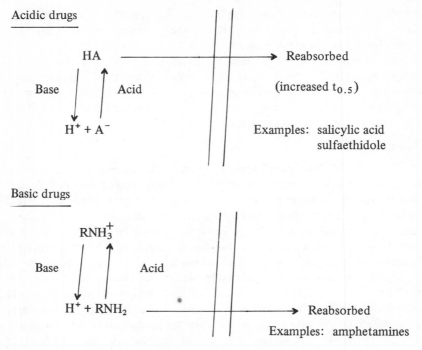

Fig. 1 Passive tubular reabsorption of acidic and basic drugs in the kidney.

effect is opposite with weakly basic drugs. Here the uncharged species is formed in alkaline urine and its reabsorption would be expected to increase. Amphetamines have been shown to be reabsorbed when alkaline urine increases the concentration of the noncharged base species.

Tetracyclines are zwitterions which are generally thought to have their maximum lipid solubility at their isoelectric points. Doxycycline has an isoelectric point of 5.6 which is presumably its pH of maximum tubular reabsorption. Thus, alkalinization of the urine (mean pH range 7.4-8.0) decreased the apparent $t_{0.5}$ of doxycycline from 13 hr in the control group (mean pH range 5.3-6.3) to 9 hr following administration of a single oral dose of 200 mg. During multiple-dose steady state the apparent $t_{0.5}$ decreased from 17 hr in the control (pH 5.6-6.7) to 12 hr in the alkaline urine (pH 7.7-8.4) [12].

The narcotic analgesic, methadone, is an amine base of pK_a 8.62. Lowering the urinary pH should therefore increase formation of the charged protonated species and promote renal excretion. A study of 12 male patients attributed nearly a 3-fold increase in renal clearance to decreased urinary pH [13]. This

Table 3

Control Of Urinary pH

Acid (daily)	Alkaline (daily)
$NH_4 Cl$ (8-12 g)	$Na_2 HPO_4$ (2 g)
Methionine (8-12 g)	$NaHCO_3$ (12-24 g)
Ascorbic Acid (2 g)	Acetazolamide (0.5-1.5 g)
$NaHSO_4$ (2 g)	

was accompanied by a reduction in the excretion ratio of metabolite to intact methadone.

Urinary pH is often controlled in the clinic for a variety of therapeutic reasons. Typical compounds which are used are shown in Table 3. In addition to the desired therapeutic effect of controlling urinary pH, the half-life of drugs which have been administered to the patient may be altered. For example, the half-life of salicylic acid may be increased by acidifying the urine with oral doses of $NH_4 Cl$. Conversely, alkalinization of the urine with sodium bicarbonate will decrease the half-life of salicylic acid. It has been demonstrated that adjustment of the pH of the urine during sulfonamide excretion can change the half-life from 11 hr at a urinary pH of roughly 5 to only 4 hr after alkalinization of the urine to a pH of roughly 7.5 [14]. The half-life of dl-amphetamine is roughly 4 hr at pH 5.3 ($NH_4 Cl$) and 13 hr at pH 7.8 ($NaHCO_3$) [15].

It is also possible to inadvertently increase urinary pH by repetitive administration of oral antacids. Although the potential for pH variation in the distal tubules ranges from pH 4.5 to 8.0 the observed increase due to antacid was only about 1 pH unit. A suspension of magnesium and aluminum hydroxides was the most effective of those tested in increasing the pH of the urine [16]. Similar results were obtained with either 15 or 30 ml of suspension given four times daily (8-1-6-11), which increased the average pH (seven normal subjects) from ~5.8 to approximately 6.2-6.9. Although the change in pH is small, it could significantly change ionization if the pK_a of the drug is in the range 5-7.

It is easily recognized that two types of therapeutic problems can result from unexpected changes in drug reabsorption. If the half-life of a drug is decreased, then its duration of action may decrease and therapeutic failure may result. Since the dosage regimen has been based on the normal or average half-life it can be inadequate for the patient experiencing an increased rate of elimination due to alteration of urinary pH. Conversely, an increase in half-life could result in undesirable accumulation of drug with resultant toxicity or side effects.

   c. *Tubular Secretion.* The kidneys are able to actively secrete many organic carboxylic acids by a somewhat nonspecific active tubular secretion process. A drug which is normally secreted in this fashion can accumulate when co-administered with a second drug competing for the same mechanism. Renal clearance tests such as PAH may be altered by such drugs if the sum of their concentrations in the plasma is sufficient to exceed the capacity for the system.

   An interesting example of a toxic drug interaction of this type has been reported in the literature. The antidiabetic agent acetohexamide is converted in the body to hydroxyhexamide which is an active metabolite. Phenylbutazone, given concurrently with the parent drug, competes with hydroxyhexamide for tubular secretion. Although the half-life of acetohexamide remains constant, phenylbutazone was shown to increase the half-life of hydroxyhexamide from 5 hr to 22 hr [17]. In the presence of phenylbutazone, the hypoglycemia following administration of acetohexamide is therefore greatly prolonged due to the inability of the body to eliminate the active metabolite hydroxyhexamide.

   The intentional interference with penicillin tubular secretion by co-administration of probenecid has long been recognized as a means of increasing the duration of penicillin body levels.

2. Metabolism

   Alteration of drug metabolism may either increase or decrease the biological half-life depending on the mechanism. Certain drugs are enzyme inducers which can result in increased metabolism of other drugs. Conversely, a drug may inhibit enzymatic activity with the opposite result. These are difficult to predice a priori but once observed appear to be rather general.

   a. *Enzyme Induction.* Several drugs are known enzyme inducers [4,18]. Rifampicin, glutethimide, phenytoin, and nearly all barbiturates. are known to increase the rate of drug metabolism in man. The effect of barbiturates on oral anticoagulant plasma levels is of particular clinical significance. Phenobarbital induces the metabolic rate of coumarin anticoagulants, phenytoin, antipyrine, desmethylimipramine, and others. Pretreatment of either mother or the newborn with phenobarbital leads to a significant reduction of diazepam half-life in the newborn from 35 hr to 15 hr. Antipyrine is often used in man as a model for metabolic hydroxylation kinetics. However, it has not been successful as a means to predict an individual's ability to metabolize other drugs.

   b. *Enzyme Inhibition. or Competition.* Agents which either compete with a drug for an enzyme system or inhibit the enzyme activity can produce an increase in the duration of drug. Competition for the glucuronidation pathways appears to be responsible for extended half-lives of both drugs when paracetamol and salicylates are administered together. Tolbutamide elimination is reduced in the presence of concomitant therapy with dicoumarol, phenylbutazone, sulfa-phenazole, or phenyramidol, presumably due in part to inhibition of oxidation to hydroxytolbutamide. Sulfaphenazole has been reported to increase the tolbutamide half-life from roughly 4-8 hr to 24-70 hr. The clinical pharmaco-kinetics of phenytoin are discussed in a later section where it is shown that nonlinear kinetics are observed at therapeutic dosage levels. Although the half-life is dose-dependent, the apparent phenytoin half-life has been observed to increase from roughly 9 hr to 30 hr on co-administration of dicoumarol. Table 4 summarizes a few of the reported changes in $t_{0.5}$ attributed to drug interactions.

   c. *Dosage Adjustment in Drug Interactions*. Theoretically it might be possible to adjust the dosage regimen in order to accommodate drug-drug interactions which change the biological half-lives of the drugs. Adjustment of dosage regimen during renal impairment is becoming commonplace. However, there is little information on half-lives of drugs during combined therapy and no procedure for accommodating intersubject variability. It would be safest to avoid co-administration of drugs which can be expected to alter drug elimination especially if one has low margin of safety.

Table 4

Reported Changes in Biological Half-Lives of Drugs Observed
After Initiating Therapy with a Second Agent[a]

Agent causing interaction	Drug affected	Half-life (hr)		
		Before	After	Reason
Rifampicin	Tolbutamide	6.0	2.8	Induction
	Hexobarbital	5.2	2.8	Induction
	Digitoxin	288	76	Induction
Phenobarbital	Antipyrine	17	9	Induction
Dicoumarol	Tolbutamide	5	17	Inhibition
	Phenytoin[b]	9	40	Inhibition
Phenylbutazone	Phenytoin[b]	14	22	Inhibition
	Tolbutamide	4.5	10	Inhibition
Sulfaphenazole	Tolbutamide	4	27	Inhibition[c]
Sulfadimethoxine	Tolbutamide	5	2.8	Displacement from plasma protein

[a]From Refs. 4 and 18.
[b]Apparent values since kinetics are nonlinear. See Sec. III.B.1.
[c]Also increases free tolbutamide in vitro.

C. Distribution

1. Binding

The potential for changes in pharmacokinetics by alteration in plasma and tissue protein binding due to age, disease, or displacement by other agents is widely recognized. Two excellent reviews summarize a great cross-section of the literature [19,20]. The displacement of one protein-bound drug by another can increase the body levels of free drug resulting in increased biological activity, distribution into tissues, and in some instances elimination. The clinical significance and the prediction and management of these phenomena has not been systematically developed.

There is a common misconception that drugs which have a high degree of binding to plasma proteins are therefore amenable to displacement by other drugs which will result in increased free-drug levels. While such drugs may be displaced, the plasma level need not rise. The meaning of the data generally used to describe protein binding of drugs is not always understood. If a drug is said to be 98% protein-bound, this does not mean that 98% of the drug in the body is protein-bound. It means that 98% of the drug contained in the blood is protein-bound and 2% is free. Since free drug undergoes distribution throughout the rest of the body (Fig. 2), the fraction of total drug which is protein bound is dependent on the total volume in which the free drug is distributed. If the volume of distribution is small, then a large fraction of the drug may be stored on plasma protein. Displacement of this drug from the protein might

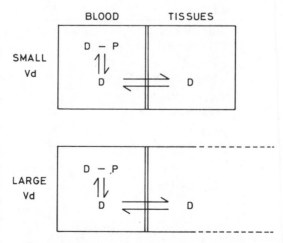

Fig. 2 Equilibria between plasma protein-bound drug (D-P) and free drug (D), where the volume of distribution of D is small and where it is large.

be expected to increase the concentration of the free drug which must be distributed between blood and tissue. However, if the volume of distribution is exceedingly large, so that the total drug stored on the protein is a very small fraction of drug in the body, then displacement of the drug from the protein would not notably increase the concentration of free drug. In other words, if free drug must be distributed to a very large volume, then any increase that one might observe in the blood due to displacement from plasma protein would be diluted to the point where it would have no clinical significance.

Several orally active anticoagulants apparently fulfill the criteria required to present a danger due to displacement from plasma protein. These criteria are

1. A high percentage bound
2. A small volume of distribution

One such example which is well known is that of warfarin. It has been shown that concomitant administration of warfarin and phenylbutazone can result in increased loss of warfarin from plasma. This reduced half-life is presumably due to the increased access to metabolic destruction of warfarin resulting from displacement of bound warfarin to form free warfarin. As would be expected, this increase in free warfarin in the blood caused not only an increased rate of loss but an increase in pharmacological activity. The peak prothrombin time was increased from roughly 25 to 50 sec. Thus, the duration of warfarin in circulating plasma decreased while prothrombin time was seen to roughly double. It is easily appreciated that a patient who was normally well controlled by warfarin may suddenly be out of control upon administration of phenylbutazone.

It has been emphasized that this displacement of bound warfarin by phenylbutazone is probably an oversimplification of the clinical situation [5]. Warfarin in clinical use is a mixture of R(+) and S(-) enantiomers. These two forms differ in pharmacokinetic behavior, potency, and biotransformation [21]. Phenylbutazone and metronidazole increase the hypothrombinemic activity of S(-) but not R(+) warfarin. It has been suggested that the potential for drug interactions might be reduced if R(+)-warfarin replaced the commonly used racemic mixture in therapy.

Patients receiving anticoagulants should be carefully and continuously checked so that any change in prothrombin time can be rapidly diagnosed. Many drugs have been observed to cause such interactions with coumarin anticoagulants. Among those reported are chloral hydrate, several analgetics, barbiturates, several diuretics, and some antibiotics. It is well known that both sulfonamide drugs and vitamin K are able to interact at plasma protein binding sites with subsequent release of bilirubin. This effect was originally discovered in a clinical trial comparing tetracycline and penicillin-sulfonamide mixture in the treatment of premature infants. The higher rate of kernicterus found in the sulfonamide-penicillin treatment lead to the realization that displaced bilirubin in the premature infant passed into the brain causing kernicterus which is often fatal.

D. Improper Product Use

The pharmacist often takes for granted his understanding of drug products, which is unique in the health professions. The pharmacist is the single health professional who studies (in detail) drug products, the physical chemistry of drugs, and biopharmaceutics. One cannot expect patients or professionals to rationally make use of drug products without regard for their design. A simple example is the grinding of sustained release or enteric coated products into a powder to be administered in food or drink for patients who have difficulty in swallowing. While the long-acting form may produce an overdose, the enteric-coated form may fail to produce adequate blood levels or may cause gastric side effects. The following example is taken from a clinical practice experience.

Methenamine mandelate is a urinary tract anti-infective agent. The usual dose is 250 mg-1.0 g taken two to four times a day. If methenamine itself is administered orally, 10-30% may be degradated in the stomach. This degradation is responsible for its mechanism of action in urine. Methenamine may be considered a prodrug. Methenamine itself is not a drug but in the presence of acid it is converted to the antibacterial agent formaldehyde. Since the stomach is acid, orally administered methenamine may be prematurely converted to formaldehyde.

The use of methenamine mandelate in an enteric-coated preparation is an attempt to prevent premature conversion. Upon reaching the intestine the enteric coating is removed and methenamine undergoes dissolution. Since the intestinal tract is not sufficiently acidic to convert the methenamine to formaldehyde the absorption of the prodrug follows. A pH of 5.5 or less is required for conversion of methenamine to formaldehyde. Upon arriving in the blood, methenamine is in an environment at pH of 7.4, which is insufficient acidity for conversion and it is highly cleared into the urine. Scheme II represents conversion of methanamine into formaldehyde in the urine. This rate of conversion is proportional to hydrogen ion concentration. If the pH is less than 5.5, sufficient formaldehyde may be formed for antibacterial treatment. This should be ensured by administration of a urinary acidifier (Table 3). Table 5 represents some selected aspects of a patient's medication record. It can be seen that the patient was receiving sodium bicarbonate to aid in uric acid excretion. However, the sodium bicarbonate simultaneously aided uric acid excretion while preventing conversion of the methenamine to the active antibacterial agent formaldehyde.

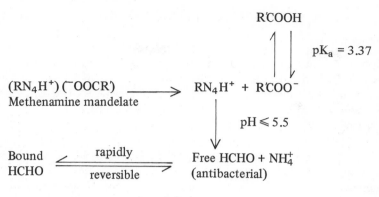

Scheme II

Lack of success in treating the urinary tract infection with mandelamine lead to the use of furadantin. When furadantin failed to help, macrodantin (which is a form of furadantin) was employed.

This well illustrates the potential significance of knowledge that the pharmacist often takes for granted. The study of drug products is unique to pharmacy. It would have been a simple matter for the pharmacist to predict the failure of methenamine by considering the chemistry required for it to be effective. In addition, the choice of furadantin under conditions of alkaline pH was not rational (see Chap. 6). Neither was the change from furadantin to macrodantin since it is macrocrystals of the same drug.

Table 5

Selected Excerpts from a Patient's Medication Record[a]

Drug	Days: 1-2	3-14	15-18	19-23	24	25-26	27-33
Sodium bicarbonate (I.V.)	X						
Allopurinol (300 mg/day)	X	X	X	X	X	X	X
Sodium bicarbonate (P.O. 6 g/day)			X	X	X	X	X
Mandelamine (2 g/day)				X	X		
Furadantin (400 mg/day)					X	X	
Macrodantin (400 mg/day)							X

[a]The author is indebted to Dr. James Visconti for suggesting this example and for supplying the necessary information.

III. CLINICAL PHARMACOKINETICS

A. Introduction

By necessity drug therapy represents a gamble wherein optimization of the benefit-to-risk ratio is the reward. What we refer to as our knowledge of drug action is really a statement based on population averages. The initial dosage regimen and its expected results are generally a statistical best guess which we term "usual dosage" and "actions and adverse reactions." Clinicians recognize that each individual patient is different and the practice of medicine attempts to anticipate and avoid "nonaverage" complications or to adjust therapy based on observations made a posteriori.

Individual patients can be expected to differ with respect to both drug disposition (pharmacokinetics) and drug sensitivity (pharmacology). Many factors are potentially capable of influencing the drug-patient interaction including age, sex, disease state, weight, personal habits such as smoking, other drugs, foods, etc. Obviously the modification of drug therapy based on the quantitative prediction of these effects for every drug is not possible nor is it always necessary. However, there are a growing number of drugs for which consideration of the overriding characteristics of the drug-patient interaction can increase the likelihood of a more favorable benefit-to-risk ratio. This section will present five drugs selected to illustrate the clinical use of pharmacokinetics in improving the prospects for successful drug therapy. Individual pharmacokinetic variations may occur in absorption, distribution, excretion, and metabolism. These may be effected by disease, age, drugs, etc. The use of kinetic methods to counteract these influences by individualization of drug therapy is called clinical pharmacokinetics.

Review on pharmacokinetics in the aged [22,23] and two published symposia, *Clinical Pharmacokinetics* [24] and *The Effect of Disease States on Drug Pharmacokinetics* [25], contain excellent examples together with an abundance of literature references. Although it is not reviewed here, it should be kept in mind that pharmacological response is also potentially affected by these same factors.

The safe and effective management of drug therapy in individual patients represents one of the most dramatic means by which pharmacokinetics has contributed to improved medical practice. While the dosage regimens for many drugs can be adjusted safely using symptomatic endpoints, there are important agents for which this is not ideal. Some agents require individual blood level determinations and adjustment of the dosage schedule to "titrate" the patient with the drug. Typical drug characteristics calling for this approach are (1) the drug is critically needed, (2) the response is better related to plasma concentration than to drug dosage, (3) a narrow range exists between minimum required blood level and that which is likely to produce adverse effects, and (4) wide variability occurs in interpatient blood levels resulting from identical dosage regimens. An effective course of therapy with such an agent thus necessitates the determination of the dosage regimen required to provide the desired blood levels for each individual patient.

There has been a great deal of research on the problem of individual dosage regimens (see also Chap. 5). The number of publications and dosage nomograms is too large to allow citation. One should also realize that it is a dynamic area. The future will bring further refinements. Today's "state of the-art" with regard to a given drug therapy is just that. Therefore, the selected drugs which follow are presented to illustrate the *concepts* involved in individualization of dosage and not to recommend treatments since tomorrow's answer may be different. The problems presented by each of these examples differ and therefore their clinical solutions differ as well. In each case the author's goal is to define the problem and to review the kinetic approaches to its solution.

B. Selected Problems in Clinical Pharmacokinetics

1. Phenytoin

Phenytoin (diphenyhydantoin) is one of the most widely used anticonvulsants. The control of seizures is more reliably correlated with anticonvulsant plasma levels than with dose. Average dosage regimens do not take into account individual patient variability. Plasma level monitoring of anticonvulsant drugs is widely recognized as the recommended approach to establishing the optimum dosage regimen for each patient. The range of optimal plasma concentrations has been established for several anticonvulsant drugs (Table 6).

Table 6

Optimum Therapeutic Plasma Levels for
Anticonvulsant Drugs[a]

Drug	Range (amount/ml)
Carbamazepine	4-10; 6-12 μg
Clonazepam	~30-60; 15-50 ng
Ethosuximide	40-80; 40-100 μg
Diazepam	>400-500; >600 ng
N-Desemethylmethsuximide[b]	10-40 μg
Phenobarbital	10-30; 10-25 μg
Phenytoin	10-20 μg
Primidone	5-10 μg
Valproic Acid	~60-80; >50 μg

[a]As reviewed in Refs. 26 and 27.
[b]Active metabolite of methsuximide.

The clinical evaluation of phenytoin pharmacokinetics has been extensively reported and references may be found in the reviews [26,29]. The problems associated with individual patient variation in phenytoin plasma levels has necessitated this research activity.

Individual patient variability in phenytoin plasma concentration may be attributed to one or more of several reasons:

1. Nonlinear kinetics
2. Bioavailability
3. Drug interactions
4. Noncompliance

a. Nonlinear Kinetics. Less than 2% of the administered dose is excreted as intact phenytoin in the urine. The primary metabolite, parahydroxyphenyl-phenyhydantoin (HPPH), accounts for 70-80% of the dose [30]. In most patients phenytoin elimination is nonlinear following therapeutic doses due to partial saturation of the p-hydroxylation metabolic pathway. A dose of 300 mg given once daily is often recommended for adequate seizure control with minimum side effects. While this was found to provide a mean of 10.8 μg/ml in 38 patients the range was roughly 1-53 μg/ml [28]. A dose of 400 mg daily showed a mean nearly twice as high (18 μg/ml, 19 patients) and a similar wide range. This is due to the fact that the therapeutic range (10-20 μg/ml) approaches the maximum rate at which phenytoin can be eliminated [30]. Thus, minor changes in dosage (or enzyme activity) have relatively dramatic effects on steady-state phenytoin levels. Since the therapeutic range is close to that for both toxicity and saturation, the resulting wide variability indicates the need for individual patient dosage adjustment and plasma monitoring of drug concentration.

b. Bioavailability. Phenytoin is a cyclic imide of $pK_a \approx 9$ that is practically insoluble in water. The sodium salt dissolves to the extent of 1 g in 66 ml of water but the solution is turbid until the pH is adjusted to > 11.7. Thus, the drug presents a solubility problem at physiological pH. It is mainly absorbed from the proximal portion of the small intestine where the rate is slow and variable with t_{max} varying from 4 to 24 hr [29]. In a single-dose study of 100-mg capsules containing phenytoin sodium the elimination phase was considered first-order, thus allowing the comparison of AUC values which varied from 92 to 131% of the innovator's product [31]. These results are surprisingly uniform when compared to previous reports of bioavailability from tablets which varied from 20 to 90% [29]. Steady-state phenytoin blood levels are significantly affected by absorption rates. Differences in manufacturing processes for various dosage forms can result in different dissolution and absorption rates. Most capsules of phenytoin sodium should be administered several times a day with the possible exception of Dilantin sodium which might be given once a day due to its slow release characteristics [32,33]. Differences in bioavailability characteristics do not appear to be due to faulty manufacturing processes but seem instead to be a problem inherent to phenytoin dosage forms. In general, the behavior of a single product from a single source appears consistent. Thus, a patient whose dosage has been adjusted to provide suitable plasma levels should not be switched to alternate dosage forms or brands without re-establishing the optimum dosage regimen.

c. Drug Interactions. A great number of pharmacokinetic drug interactions involving phenytoin may be found in the literature. Only a few have been shown to be clinically significant [27]. Some of these have been reviewed in the section on pharmacokinetic drug interactions and additional references are given elsewhere [27,28]. It should be kept in mind that drugs may elevate or depress phenytoin levels and some of the variability reported in patients may be attributed to differences in their drug therapy.

d. Compliance. Compliance, while always a problem, is especially difficult when patients do not understand the prophylactic nature of the treatment. Absence of seizures often provides a basis for noncompliance in the patient's mind. This is a well-documented problem with phenytoin.

Results reported by Lund [29] are typical showing that 52% of 276 patients had levels below 10 μg/ml at prescribed doses of 5.6 ± 1.8 (S.D.) mg/kg per day. Only 36.6% had values in the 10.0-20 μg/ml range while 11.6% (35 patients) were higher than 20 μg/ml and 6 of these patients had side effects (nystagmus, ataxia, or somnolence). Compliance was tested in low plasma level patients, one of which had reported a seizure. Drug administration was supervised over a 7-day period and an increase of 25% or more in the plasma concentration was taken as evidence for previous lack of compliance. Of the 48 patients tested, 16 showed a positive test and admitted to noncompliance.

e. Dosage Adjustment with Nonlinear Kinetics. Phenytoin elimination can be described by Michaelis-Menten kinetics (discussed in Chap. 2) where elimination velocity (V in mg/kg per day) may be defined:

$$V = \frac{V_{max} [P]}{K_m + [P]} \tag{1}$$

where V_{max} is the maximal rate and K_m is numerically equal to the value for [P] that provides $V = (V_{max}/2)$. During multiple-dose steady state the dose administered is equal to the amount eliminated during each dosage interval, τ. It follows that the daily drug intake must equal the daily output. If R is defined as the daily administration rate (e.g., mg/day) then at steady state:

$$R = \frac{V_{max} [\bar{P}_{ss}]}{K_m + [\bar{P}_{ss}]} \tag{2}$$

which may be solved for the average steady-state concentration $[P_{ss}]$ from:

$$[\bar{P}_{ss}] = \frac{RK_m}{V_{max} - R} \tag{3}$$

Dividing by R gives

$$\frac{[\bar{P}_{ss}]}{R} = \frac{K_m}{V_{max} - R} \tag{4}$$

which may be inverted to the linear form:

$$\frac{R}{[\bar{P}_{ss}]} = \frac{V_{max}}{K_m} - \left(\frac{1}{K_m}\right)R \tag{5}$$

A plot of $R/[\bar{P}_{ss}]$ versus R should be linear with slope $(-1/K_m)$ and intercept (V_{max}/K_m). Practice Problem 1 illustrates how these estimates are obtained.

Chapter 3 illustrated that clearance (C) equals (rate/concentration). Since the input rate (R) is equal to the elimination rate (V) during the steady state, then $C_T = R/[\bar{P}_{ss}]$. Thus, Eq. (5) is a clear demonstration of how total body clearance $(R/[\bar{P}_{ss}])$ decreases with increased dose (R) for Michaelis-Menten elimination kinetics. The plot based on Eq. (5), as shown in the following problem, may be thought of as C_T versus dose and it illustrates this point.

Practice Problem 1

The following steady-state data were obtained from a single patient as a function of the total daily dose of phenytoin given approximately every 8 hr.

Table 7

Average Phenytoin Steady-State Plasma Levels $(\bar{P}_{ss})$ as a Function of Total Daily Dose in a Single Patient (90 kg)

Dose (mg/day)	$\bar{P}_{ss}$ (mg/liter)
90	1.20
210	3.36
300	5.41
390	8.13
540	15.4
600	20.3

Estimate the value for K_m (in mg/liter) and V_{max} (in mg/day) for this patient.

Answer: A plot of $(R/\bar{P}_{ss})$ versus R is linear with slope = -0.0874 = $1/K_m$ and intercept = 82 = V_{max}/K_m making K_m = 11.4 mg/liter and V_{max} = 935 mg/day.

The approach used in the previous problem can be applied to the adjustment of dose for an individual patient. If the $\bar{P}_{ss}$ values associated with two dosing rates (R) are known for a patient, then V_{max} and K_m may be estimated and R can be calculated for the desired $\bar{P}_{ss}$ using Eq. (2). If additional sets of $\bar{P}_{ss}$ and R values are obtained in the process of adjusting for that patient then the line of best fit for a plot based on Eq. (5) can be used to graphically determine the dosage rate to obtain a desired steady-state plasma level.

Practice Problem 2

Using the figure constructed for Practice Problem 1, predict the dose required to provide a steady-state plasma level of 12 mg/liter. *Answer:* Since the plot is linear for $(R/\bar{P}_{ss})$ versus R, then the dose may be read from the graph by finding the R value that represents (12) $(R/\bar{P}_{ss})$ or approximately (12) $(40) = 480$ mg/day. This may also be calculated directly from Eq. (2) using the V_{max} and K_m estimates in Practice Problem 1.

A similar approach has been reported [34] based on the following rearrangement of Eq. (5):

$$R = V_{max} - K_m \left(\frac{R}{\bar{P}_{ss}} \right) \tag{6}$$

where a linear plot of R versus $(R/\bar{P}_{ss})$ has an intercept, V_{max}, and a negative slope, K_m. Therapy is initiated at a dosage rate (R) of 3-4 mg/kg per day using phenytoin sodium (for phenytoin use R/1.09). In accordance with Mawer et al. [35] dosage may be increased by 50-100 mg/day increments if the average steady-state plasma levels are less than 6 mg/liter. If the levels exceed this value then more conservative increments of 25-50 mg/day are suggested. Once two pairs of R and $\bar{P}_{ss}$ values are available, a two-point plot based on Eq. (6) may be used to estimate V_{max}, K_m, and—if necessary—the third dosage rate. As additional data become available the assessment of V_{max} and K_m may be done on a statistical basis.

Practice Problem 3

A trial dosage regimen of 250 mg/day of phenytoin is found to produce a $\bar{P}_{ss}$ value of 4.16 mg/liter. The dose is increased to 350 mg/day and the resultant $\bar{P}_{ss}$ value is 6.82 mg/liter. Using the method of Ludden et al. [34], estimate V_{max} and K_m by making a two-point plot based on Eq. (6). Using Eq. (2), recommend a dose rate to provide a $\bar{P}_{ss}$ value of 12 mg/liter in this patient. *Answer:* These data represent the patient in the two previous problems wherein $V_{max} = 935$ mg/day and $K_m = 11.4$ mg/liter. Solving

Eq. (2) provides R = (935 mg/day) (12 mg/liter)/[(11.4 mg/liter) + (12 mg/liter)] = 480 mg/day.

f. Constructing a Linear Dosage Nomogram with Nonlinear Kinetics. A nomogram may be defined as a graph that by using a straight edge allows the estimation of a dependent variable from the known values for two or more independent variables. It has the advantage of providing a rapid estimate without solving complex equations. If the equations for a system are solved once and represented in an effective nomogram, it should be possible to make future estimates without the need for repeatedly solving the equations. Phenytoin dosage adjustment provides an excellent example wherein nonlinear pharmacokinetics make simple dosage adjustment decisions difficult especially since K_m and/or V_{max} may vary. It would be convenient to construct a nomogram which would use the known values for the two independent variables (daily dose and observed plasma concentration) to determine what adjustment, if any, should be made in order to obtain the desired plasma concentration.

The following approach, taken from Martin et al. [30], illustrates how a convenient nomogram was developed and employed. The experimental values are for normal volunteers taking a suspension of phenytoin as the free acid. However, while the resulting nomogram provided satisfactory estimates when applied to literature data, further testing is required to establish its applicability. The extent of utility of this specific nomogram is not the reason for its inclusion here. Rather, the method of construction of this linear dosage nomogram for nonlinear kinetics is considered a useful technique.

The method of Ludden et al. [34] allowed the calculation of the third dose based on the results for the first and second estimates. But how can one estimate the second dosage adjustment, given nonlinear kinetics, when the first dosage schedule (R) chosen for a patient does not provide the desired P_{ss}? One approach is by use of a nomogram suggested by Martin et al. [30]. Dividing Eq. (5) by R provides the linear form

$$\frac{1}{\overline{P}_{ss}} = \frac{-1}{K_m} + \left(\frac{V_{max}}{K_m} \right) \left(\frac{1}{R} \right) \tag{7}$$

A plot of $1/\overline{P}_{ss}$ versus $1/R$ should be linear with positive slope (V_{max}/K_m) and intercept $(-1/K_m)$. While a nomogram based on reciprocals could be made, it is more convenient to read the dose and plasma concentration directly. This is achieved by using full reciprocal scales wherein the relative distances on both the ordinate and abscissa are based on the reciprocals of the values. The method of construction follows.

Assume that two or more doses are given daily for a total range of 2-10 kg per day (X axis) with a $\overline{P}_{ss}$ range of 4-40 mg/liter (Y axis). Table 8 shows how the difference (Δ) between the reciprocals (1/n) decreases with increasing values for n.

Table 8

Construction of Reciprocal Scales (1/n)
Between the Limits of $2 \leqslant n \leqslant 40$

n	1/n	Δ	Rel. dist.
2	0.500	—	—
3	0.333	0.167	20.00
4	0.250	0.0833	10.00
5	0.200	0.0500	6.00
6	0.167	0.0333	4.00
7	0.143	0.0238	2.86
8	0.125	0.0178	2.14
9	0.111	0.0139	1.67
10	0.100	0.0110	1.32
12	0.0833	0.0167	2.00
15	0.0667	0.0167	2.00
20	0.0500	0.0167	2.00
30	0.0333	0.0167	2.00
40	0.0250	0.00833	1.00

If the smallest distance (n = 30, n = 40) is chosen as the reference the relative distances between successive n values are shown in the final column. Both axes in Fig. 3 are based on these relative distances; the absolute distances on the Y axis are twice that of the X axis. The factional distances between individual numbers are assigned relative values in a similar manner. For example, the space between 3.0 and 3.1 is 1.677 times the space between 3.9 and 4.0. A line described by Eq. (7) may be drawn directly on this full reciprocal paper. The reported average values, V_{max} = 10.3 mg/kg per day and K_m = 11.5 mg/liter [30], have been used to directly plot the reference line (darkest line) in Fig. 3. This nomogram is based on data representing the average steady-state phenytoin concentration achieved during the administration of phenytoin acid three times a day.

The recommended test dose is 4.3 mg/kg per day given in two or more divided doses. (A minimum of two doses per day is recommended [30].) If the average values apply to the patient, then the $\overline{P}_{ss}$ value will be approximately 8.2 mg/liter as shown by the reference line in Fig. 3. The adjusted dosage to achieve a therapeutic level may then be taken directly from this reference line. For example, a dose of 5.8 mg/kg per day would be required to achieve 15 mg/liter. Once two doses are tried and their resulting $\overline{P}_{ss}$ values are known, the patient's K_m and V_{max} may be estimated. Further adjustments, if necessary, can be made using Eq. (2).

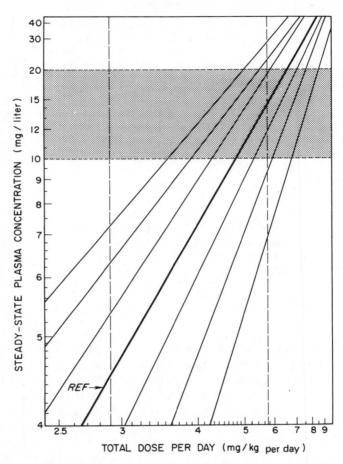

Fig. 3 Full reciprocal scales have been constructed as shown in Table 8. The reference line was drawn using V_{max} = 10.3 mg/kg per day and K_m = 11.5 mg/liter [30] in Eq. (7). If a trial dose of 4.3 mg/kg day-1 of phenytoin (in two or more doses) provides a $\overline{P}_{ss}$ near this line (∼ 8.2 mg/liter), then the reference line may be used to predict the corrected dosing rate (R) to achieve the therapeutic range (shaded). If the trial dose provides a $\overline{P}_{ss}$ closer to one of the other lines, then that line should be used. The additional lines have been constructed by estimating the V_{max} and K_m values used in the nomogram of Martin et al. For the complete nomogram see Ref. 30. The region of applicability for the initial dose is shown by the two horizontal lines.

If the $\overline{P}_{ss}$ is not on the reference line, then K_m and/or V_{max} may be different for that patient. The additional lines in Fig. 3 represent other estimates for K_m and V_{max}. The mathematical technique by which the additional lines were calculated is complex. It involves an acceptable fit to this single observation so that the new K_m and V_{max} estimates are jointly a minimum scaled distance from the original population averages. The lines represent a statistical best estimate for that individual based on the single data point and a knowledge of the population values. The use of the nomogram is simple. (Figure 3 has been constructed from values in the original report. For the complete nomogram see Ref. 30.) The line which is closest to the observed $\overline{P}_{ss}$ value at a given dose is used to make an estimate of the adjusted dose for the desired $\overline{P}_{ss}$.

Practice Problem 4

A dose of 4 ml of phenytoin suspension (125 mg phenytoin acid per 5 ml) is administered to a 70-kg patient every 8 hr and the resultant steady-state plasma level was found to be 4.1 mg/liter. Using the portion of the dosage nomogram of Martin et al. [30] reconstructed in Fig. 3., recommend a regimen to provide a $\overline{P}_{ss}$ of 11 mg/liter.

Answer: The total daily dose being given is (3) (100 mg)/70 kg or 4.3 mg/kg per day. After locating the appropriate line in Fig. 1, one can estimate that a dose rate of 7.1 mg/kg per day or 497 mg/day would provide the desired $\overline{P}_{ss}$. The recommended second trial dose rate would be 5 ml every 6 hr or 10 ml every 12 hr. Once this dose is given and the resultant $\overline{P}_{ss}$ determined, a final adjustment (if necessary) may be made by estimating K_m and V_{max} for this patient and using Eq. (2) (or the graphical approach shown in Practice Problem 2).

2. Gentamicin

a. Therapeutic and Toxic Plasma Levels. Survival rates for patients with nosocomial infections caused by gram-negative organisms are significantly improved by aminoglycoside therapy. This success is realized in spite of their known oto- and nephrotoxicity. While there is general agreement that a narrow margin exists between therapeutic and toxic blood levels, the optimum therapeutic range is uncertain. In addition to variations in bacterial sensitivity which alter the minimum effective concentration of antibiotic required for various infections, there is also the difficulty of relating plasma concentration to potential for toxicity. The therapeutic peak levels for gentamicin are generally regarded as 6-10 μg/ml. Peak levels above 12-15 μg/ml and prolonged maintenance of trough (or nadir) levels above 2 μg/ml have been associated with increased incidence of toxicity [36,37]. Goodman et al. [38] reported that a gentamicin nadir level greater than 4 μg/ml was the only variable among those tested that correlated significantly with nephrotoxicity.

The aminoglycosides are used parenterally to treat systemic infections since bioavailability by the oral route is inadequate. Treatment failures may be due to resistant organisms or subtherapeutic serum levels. Serum concentrations following calculated doses are highly unpredictable even when creatinine renal clearance values are used as a guide. The $t_{0.5}$ values show wide intersubject variation even with normal renal function.

b. *Pharmacokinetics.* Literature references for the clinical pharmacokinetics of aminoglycoside antibiotics may be found in the review in Chap. 6, where it was suggested that an equation of the type

$$P = Ae^{-S_1 t} + Be^{-S_2 t} + Ce^{-S_3 t} \tag{8}$$

might be generally applicable. The exponents S_1, S_2, and S_3 were suggested instead of the usual α, β, and γ to avoid confusion since literature reports have used one-, two-, or three-compartment models to describe different segments of the time course for the same aminoglycoside. Because of differences in the sampling schedules and the duration studied, reports of two-compartment models have described phases associated with S_1 and S_2 or S_2 and S_3 assigning the symbols α and β to the exponentials in both instances (see Table 12 in Chap. 6). One notable exception is the three-compartment analysis of sisomicin and of netilmicin [39] where the percentage contribution of each term in Eq. (9) to the total area under the curve, defined as

$$AUC = \frac{A}{S_1} + \frac{B}{S_2} + \frac{C}{S_3} \tag{9}$$

is approximately 18%, 71%, and 11% respectively. The dominant half-life, which is associated with S_2, is roughly 2 hr. This is the $t_{0.5}$ value most widely quoted for aminoglycosides, (see Table 12 in Chap. 6). The relatively small contributions of the S_1 and S_3 phases to the total AUC, in addition to the great interpatient variability, has probably obscured any discrepancies which might have been attributed to the use of an inappropriate model. In some cases one- or two-compartment models have been intentionally applied with a knowledge of their inadequacy in order to simplify dosage calculations. In general 75% or more of the dose is excreted unchanged in the urine within 24 hr (Chap. 6, Table 12). Therefore, the dominant half-life, $0.693/S_2$, is very sensitive to renal function. While dosage adjustment based on creatinine clearance values has undoubtedly reduced the incidence of toxicity, it has not provided a reliable means for predicting gentamicin plasma levels. The simple methods for dosage adjustment described in Chap. 5 have not been adequate for aminoglycoside antibiotics.

c. The Need for Monitoring. The narrow therapeutic index and wide patient variability make plasma level monitoring a necessity in aminoglycoside antibiotic therapy. A large number of dosage adjustment calculations and nomograms have been suggested. One proposal for gentamicin dosage based on the pharmacokinetic analysis of the drug in each individual patient [40] cited eleven earlier methods, nine of which had previously been critically reviewed [41]. The earlier methods were based on the relationship between gentamicin half-life and either creatinine renal clearance or plasma values using one-compartment model kinetics. These recommendations have been beneficial but not ideal. Predictability of gentamicin plasma levels was improved but still uncertain.

Since the use of creatinine renal clearance does not result in reliable dosage adjustments, it has been suggested that gentamicin itself be used to calibrate the patient [40,42]. In this method an initial dose must be administered in order to determine the gentamicin time course and calculate subsequent doses. The test dose (and subsequent doses) is given by constant-rate infusion over a 1-hr period and a minimum of three blood samples are analyzed during the postinfusion phase usually shortly after termination and 1 and 3 hr later. In renal failure the creatinine clearance or creatinine plasma values may be used a priori to estimate the $t_{0.5}$ and adjust the sampling time. The three or more data points are fitted by nonlinear regression to a simple first-order function, $P_t = P_{max}e^{-kt}$, where t is the time since cessation of the infusion. The initial rapid distribution is ignored but the 1-hr infusion decreases the error so that k should approximate S_2. The volume of distribution is estimated from

$$Vd = \frac{k_o (1 - e^{-kt'})}{k(P_{max} - P_o e^{-kt'})} \qquad (10)$$

where k_o is infusion rate (mg/hr), t' is the infusion period (usually 1 hr), P_o is the preinfusion serum gentamicin (mg/liter), and P_{max} and k have been obtained from the above data. The dosing interval required to maintain the desired $(P_{min}^{\infty}/P_{max}^{\infty})$ ratio is calculated in the usual way by correcting for the infusion period (t') so that

$$(\tau - t') = \frac{-\ln f}{k} \qquad (11)$$

where $(\tau - t')$ is the length of the postinfusion phase and f is the fraction of the maximum value remaining or $(P_{min}^{\infty}/P_{max}^{\infty})$. This is similar to the one-compartment calculations in Chap. 5 except that the monoexponential phase begins at t'.

The infusion rate required to produce P_{max}^{∞} may be calculated from

$$k_o = kVdP_{max}^{\infty} \left(\frac{1 - e^{-k\tau}}{1 - e^{-kt'}} \right) \tag{12}$$

or for P_{min}^{∞} from

$$k_o = kVdP_{min}^{\infty} \left(\frac{e^{k\tau} - 1}{e^{kt'} - 1} \right) \tag{13}$$

Practice Problem 5 (taken from Ref. 42)

A 60-kg patient received a 1-hr infusion of gentamicin. The post-infusion data provided a half-life estimate of 2.7 hr and Vd = 0.21 liter/kg. Recommend a dosage interval and an infusion rate to achieve a steady-state maximum of 6 mg/liter and a minimum of 1 mg/liter assuming that each infusion period is 1 hr.
Answer: From Eq. (11): $\tau = t' - (\ln f/k) = 1$ hr + 6.97 hr = 8 hr. From Eq. (12): $k_o = (0.257$ hr^{-1}) (0.21 liter/kg) (60 kg) (6 mg/ liter) [(0.872)/0.227)] = 74.6 mg/hr.

This method was assessed in burn patients [42,43] and in surgical, medical, obstetric, and gynecology patients receiving gentamicin for gram-negative infections [40]. In the latter study desired peak and nadir levels ranged from 6 to 10 and 0.5 to 2 μg/ml depending on the diagnosis and clinical condition. To assess the predictability of the method 63 pairs of peak and nadir levels were determined at least five half-lives after the regimen was initiated. Sixty percent of the P_{max}^{∞} and 56% of P_{min}^{∞} values were within 1 μg/ml of that predicted. Some bias was implied in the model in that predicted steady-state nadir values tended to be lower than observed. Patients with serum creatinine values below 1.2 mg% had $t_{0.5}$ and total body clearances (C_T) (means: $t_{0.5} = 2.25$ hr; $C_T = 0.082$ liter/hr per kg) significantly different from those with levels above 1.2 mg% (means = 5.3 hr and 0.21 liter/hr per kg). Distribution volumes were similar (means = 0.22 and 0.21 liter/kg). The variability in Vd, $t_{0.5}$, and C_T values was significant even with normal renal function. Although the maximum recommended dose is considered to be 5 mg/kg per day for life-threatening infections with normal renal function, the average doses for patients under 40 years of age was 6.78 mg/kg per day. Those with serum creatinine levels less than 1.2 mg% required 6.14 mg/kg per day.

It was recognized that a multicompartment model might be more accurate in fitting the postinfusion data. Although the difference was regarded as clinically insignificant, determination of postdistribution data was suggested as a means of further minimizing the error.

   d. Further Complications in Establishing Standardized Dosage Regimens. In a study of 14 burn patients the recommended maximum dose of 5 mg/kg per day was found to be subtherapeutic (peak concentrations < 4 mg/liter) [43]. The $t_{0.5}$ values in the younger patients ($\leqslant$ 20 years) were significantly different from the older patients (31-64 years) with means and standard deviations of 1.1 ± 0.44 hr and 3.3 ± 1.1 hr respectively. The average doses required to obtain average peaks were 12.8 mg/kg per day for 7.6 mg/liter (younger) and 7.2 mg/kg per day for 7.7 mg/liter (older). No renal or ototoxicity was observed. The study suggests that burn patients may require increased dosage of gentamicin and that the measurement of serum gentamicin levels is required to individualize the regimen since additional factors, such as age, are significant.

   The methods outlined by Sawchuk et al. [40,42] use the individual patient as his or her own control. They argue that with proper management, the time required to evaluate the patient's individual pharmacokinetic parameters using a test dose can be less than that required to determine creatinine clearance. It also has the advantage of representing a direct determination of Vd and $t_{0.5}$ for that patient.

   Quite aside from the methods of Sawchuk et al. there exists controversy with regard to the potential for improving the calculations of dosages based on renal function. This simple approach would be especially advantageous if the patient's creatinine clearance value was already known prior to the need for gentamicin therapy. It has been suggested that aminoglycosides are primarily distributed throughout extracellular fluid so that dosing on a body weight basis can result in overdoses in obesity. Hull and Sarubbi [44] have published an improved method for gentamicin dosage adjustment based on lean body weight and renal function. Bryan [45] criticized the approach arguing that the dose size has been corrected for distribution but the frequency, which is dependent on both renal clearance and distribution, has only been corrected for renal function. A small patient would tend to be underdosed and a large patient overdosed. Spyker and Guerrant [46] reach a similar conclusion and advocate the use of a "corrected creatinine clearance" to account for the fact that a single clearance value may be operating on different Vd values. Thus, if the initial concentration and creatinine clearance values are equal, the fraction of drug cleared per dosing interval will increase as Vd decreases. Hull and Sarubbi [47] applied this recommendation retrospectively and found that ignoring this resulted in an overprediction of 0.7 μg/ml at 40 kg and an underprediction of 1.2 μg/ml at 95 kg. The clinical significance was questionable.

   The determination of the optimum basis for body weight has also caused debate [48]. Tobramycin concentration was 28% higher and gentamicin was 22% greater in obese subjects given doses equal to that of normal volunteers

[49]. The adjustment of Vd based on ideal weight plus 40% of excess weight provided values similar to those for the normals. It was suggested that this reflects some distribution into adipose tissue.

Further refinements in dosage regimen adjustments will no doubt occur. In the case of drugs like gentamicin, the use of population averages to make adjustments for obesity, renal function, burns, age, and other variables will be likely to remain a compromise that is not without risk. Perhaps the narrow margin between life-saving therapeutic blood levels and toxic side effects justifies the individualization based on the pharmacokinetics of the drug itself.

3. Lidocaine

   a. Pharmacokinetics and Actions. The clinical pharmacokinetics of lidocaine have been reviewed [50,51]. Rowland [50] has recommended an approach to dosage adjustment of lidocaine based on the clinical endpoint of suppression of arrythmias. The following discussion is based on those recommendations.

Lidocaine is widely employed for treating ventricular arrhythmias accompanying myocardial infarction and heart surgery. As mentioned in Chap. 6, lidocaine is not administered orally due to extensive "first-pass" metabolism. Following I.V. injections only a small percentage of intact lidocaine (3-10%) can be recovered from the urine. It is recommended that an I.V. bolus *not* be administered faster than 1 mg/kg per min. Lidocaine is rapidly taken up by highly perfused organs such as heart, brain, lungs, liver, and kidney, leaving only an estimated 15% of the dose in the blood [50]. A biphasic time course follows with the distribution (or α) phase lasting approximately 30 min, $t_{0.5}(\alpha) \approx 4$ min, and an elimination half-life, $t_{0.5}$ (β), of roughly 1.6 hr. Up to 30% of the administered dose may be eliminated during the distribution phase. Total body clearance, C_T, is roughly 10 ml/kg per min.

Lidocaine undergoes successive N-de-ethylation to form monoethylglycinexylidide (MEGX), which is approximately equal to lidocaine in half-life and potency. This is further metabolized to glycinexylidide (GX) with decreased antiarrythmic effect but increased $t_{0.5}$ of 10 hr, making its contribution to toxicity likely due to its accumulation.

The onset of antiarrythmic and central nervous effects following I.V. bolus is 1-2 min. The maximum rate of injection should *not* exceed 1 mg/kg per min for safety [50]. The majority of patients respond to 1.2-6.9 μg/ml blood (or plasma) levels. Normally plasma levels are linear with dose and show an initial level of 2 μg/ml per 1 mg/kg dose. Duration is often 20-30 min and effects are minimal below 1.2 μg/ml. Toxicity (usually central nervous depression, hypotension, convulsions) generally occurs above 6 μg/ml. However, the M.E.C. must be determined for each patient and levels in excess of 6 μg/ml have been reportedly required to suppress premature ventricular beats in some patients while central nervous symptoms have been observed within the 1.2-6.0 μg/ml range in some cases.

  b. Dosage Regimen Adjustment. It is only practical to monitor plasma levels during extended treatment to check predictions or to distinguish between low levels and refractory patients. Rowland [50] has pointed out that the emergency use of lidocaine does not provide time for dose adjustments based on plasma assays and has recommended the following method based on clinical response.

  Since onset is immediate, the dosage adjustment period begins with the very first dose and does not refer only to the steady state as was the case with previous discussions in Chap. 5. An I.V. bolus of 1 mg/kg (infused no faster than 1 mg/kg per min) is often used as an initial dose. If suppression is achieved, then the dose is repeated each time arrythmias return. In this regimen the value for τ increases with each succeeding dose as the tissue levels increase until the steady state is achieved. It is only in the steady state that the duration following each dose will become uniform.

  If the first dose fails to achieve acceptable results, a dose of 0.5 mg/kg every 5 min up to three times should be administered until suppression is achieved. After the third dose the total administered is 2.5 μg/kg which if given as a bolus would provide an initial level of 5 μg/ml. Neglecting the fact that levels would be lower due to elimination and distribution, the lack of suppression at this dose suggests a refractory patient and the potential for toxicity. An alternative agent might be considered in this event.

  If suppression is achieved at 1 mg/kg followed by 0.5 mg/kg (every 5 min up to three doses), then the observed duration may be used to estimate how high the plasma levels are above the M.E.C. If duration is 15 min, then plasma levels are sufficiently high and an infusion rate may be calculated based on the plasma level expected from a bolus of the total administered lidocaine. If duration is short, such as 5 min, then another bolus of 0.5 kg/mg is recommended and the contribution of this dose to the expected plasma level should be included in the infusion rate calculation. The infusion is then started to maintain this estimated blood level.

  An infusion steady state will require approximately four half-lives or 6 hr. During the first hour the rapid decline following the initial loading doses may not be offset by the slow infusion and symptom breakthrough may occur. A single 0.5 mg/kg bolus is recommended while maintaining the infusion rate.

  If arrythmias reappear during a stabilized infusion, then a 0.5 mg/kg bolus is recommended together with an increase in infusion rate. A transient duration following this supplemental bolus suggests that the infusion is too slow and should be increased by an increment of 10-15 μg/kg per min. A relatively long duration indicates that a smaller increase in infusion would be appropriate. As the need for lidocaine decreases the infusion rate should be slowly reduced in increments of 10 μg/kg per min since the time to achieve a new steady-state plateau is also four half-lives. If arrythmias reappears, a 0.5 mg/kg bolus should be given and the duration again used to estimate the relationship of plasma levels to M.E.C. Loss of control within an hour suggests returning to the previous rate whereas control lasting several hours implies that the adjusted rate is adequate. During steady state each increase of 10 μg/kg per min of constant-rate infusion increases the plasma level approximately 1 μg/ml.

During congestive heart failure the lidocaine clearance is reduced. In the range of cardiac output (C.O.) equal to 35-90 ml/kg per min the clearance may be approximated by

$$C_T(\text{ml/min per kg}) \simeq 0.14\text{C.O.} - 1.7 \tag{14}$$

The recommended procedure is similar to that previously described except that the C_T value used to calculate the infusion rate is estimated from Eq. (14).

Practice Problem 6

A 60-kg patient is given an initial dose of 1 mg/kg by I.V. bolus (at 1 mg/kg per min), which fails to suppress arrythmias. A second bolus of 0.5 mg/kg is given with adequate results for 15 min.
(a) Recommend an infusion rate for this patient.
Answer: The initial plasma concentration estimate is 3 μg/ml. The infusion rate, k_o, is $[P_o][C_T] = 30$ μg/min per kg = 1800 μg/min.
(b) After 30 min the arrythmias are found to return. Recommend a course of action.
Answer: A single dose of 0.5 mg/kg (30 mg) is given while maintaining the infusion. If the relief is transient the infusion rate should be increased.
(c) If a 70-kg patient suffered from congestive heart failure and had a cardiac output of 40 ml/kg per min, how would this change the estimates in part (a) assuming the same history regarding the bolus doses?
Answer: The estimated clearance, Eq. (14), is $C_T = (0.14)(40) - 1.7 = 3.9$ ml/min per kg. Therefore $k_o = (3$ μg/ml)(3.9 ml/min per kg) = 12 μg/kg per min or 840 μg/min.

4. Theophylline

Theophylline was isolated in 1885 and first introduced as a diuretic near the turn of the century. Its value in treating bronchial asthma has been recognized since at least 1941 [Lamson and Bacon, JAMA 116, 915 (1941)]. In the United States alone, nearly 9 million people are asthmatics [52]. Theophylline overdosage can result in anorexia, headache, nausea, diarrhea, vomiting, seizures, and cardiac arrythmias [52-54]. Deaths have generally been preceeded

by seizures wherein high blood levels (a mean of 54 μg/ml in one study [54])
have been reported. No serious adverse effects were reported when patients
averaged less than 20 μg/ml [54]. Degree of toxicity in 17 patients with elevated
blood levels was reported as mild at 28 μg/ml (averages); potentially serious at
41 μg/ml and severe at 47 μg/ml. However, in one report seven out of eight
deaths occurred without apparent adverse effects prior to the seizure [54].
A great deal of clinical research has been directed toward effective and safe
theophylline dosage regimens. Only in recent years has theophylline therapy
become dependent on pharmacokinetic management. The reports on which
the following section is based are cited in the references [52-56]. Although
progress has been made, it is likely that further refinements will become
available.

   a. Why Monitor? Theophylline pharmacokinetics are well behaved with
the exception of the intersubject variability in biological half-life. This is somewhat surprising since its pharmacokinetics are generally linear in adults within
the dosage ranges encountered in therapy. It might be anticipated that genetic
factors would play an important role since only 7% of the I.V. dose is excreted
intact in the urine. In general, highly metabolized drugs appear predisposed
toward wide $t_{0.5}$ variation. In addition, age, weight, diet, disease, and cigarette
smoking can influence theophylline elimination.

   The exact mechanisms and enzymes by which the liver metabolizes theophylline are not known. Since cigarette smoking increases elimination, cyto-
chrome P_{448} which can be induced by substances in the smoke has been
implicated. The proposed metabolic products are 3-methylxanthine (36%),
1,3-dimethyluric acid (40%), and 1-methyluric acid (17%), the remaining 7%
being excreted as theophylline.

   The effective plasma concentration range for theophylline is rather narrow.
Although improvement in pulmonary function was reported at blood levels of
5, 10, and 20 μg/ml, it is generally agreed that 10-20 μg/ml is the desirable
range. Despite considerable variation in the individual tolerance to theophylline,
steady-state minimum levels above 20 μg/ml are generally associated with
adverse effects and those below 5 μg/ml are considered subtherapeutic.

   The observations that theophylline toxicity and efficacy are related to
serum levels, the therapeutic index is low, and a high degree of interpatient
half-life variability exists all combine to make individual patient blood level
monitoring a necessity.

   b. Pharmacokinetics. Theophylline blood levels following I.V. injections
have been described by a two-compartment open model. The α phase is completed within roughly 30 min and is very rapid relative to the β phase, which
has an average $t_{0.5}$ of 5-6 hr. Typical reported ratios for α/β (average values)
vary from 24 to 46. Therefore, for most clinical decisions theophylline may
be regarded practically as a one-compartment drug. Although Michaelis-Menten

kinetics might be expected, dose-dependent kinetics have not been reported in adults in the usual dosage range. In children, where the $t_{0.5}$ is reduced to an average of 3-4 hr, steady-state levels as a function of infusion rate were characteristic of saturation kinetics [57].

In spite of normally linear kinetics, the $t_{0.5}$ varies from roughly 3.0 to 20.7 hr (usually stated 3 to 10 hr) in healthy adults and 1.4-7.9 in asthmatic children [53]. In premature primary apnoea a range of 12.6-29 hr has been reported [53]. The $t_{0.5}$ was decreased in adults who smoked (from roughly 7 hr to 4 hr) and increased in the case of liver disease. Reduced clearance and increased toxicity have been reported in congestive heart failure. Mean half-life values increased slightly in obese patients while Vd was not altered when based on total body weight (TBW) [58], making TBW more useful than ideal weight for calculating loading doses. Mean values for C_T increased from 52 ml/kg hr-1 in nonsmokers to 74 ml/kg per hr in either marihuana or tobacco smokers [59].

In contrast to elimination, the absorption and distribution parameters are relatively stable. Theophylline is quickly and nearly completely absorbed (> 90%) from solutions and rapid-release tablets. Plasma peak concentrations are reached within 1-2 hr and absorption is generally predictable. Displacement problems are not considered significant since only 55-63% is plasma protein bound in the therapeutic range [52]. The apparent volume of distribution is approximately 0.5 liter/kg and is relatively constant in comparison to the $t_{0.5}$ values. Since the α/β ratios are so large, there is no significant difference between Vd_{area} and Vd_{inf}.

Thus, absorption is dependable, Vd is relatively constant, and displacement from bound protein is insignificant whereas the $t_{0.5}$ is extremely variable and the steady-state desirable range is narrow.

   c. *Dosage Regimen Complications.* In addition to genetic factors the plasma clearance of theophylline is altered by age, obesity, hepatic cirrhosis, congestive heart failure, cigarette and marihuana smoking, troleandomycin, erythromycin, and possibly other dietary, disease, and drug influences [53]. In comparison, the Vd is relatively constant with an average of roughly 0.5 liter/kg and a range of 0.3-0.7 liter/kg. Since absorption is rapid and complete the loading dose equation for I.V. administration, $D^* = [P] [Vd]$, is useful for either route [54]. This equation is generally employed without individualization. In contrast, the initial estimation of maintenance dose is dependent on $t_{0.5}$, making it nearly impossible to proceed with certainty. Hendeles et al [54] have stated that "variability in plasma clearance among patients is so great that no constant infusion can be recommended that can reasonably predict both optimum therapeutic efficacy and safety." Literature recommendations do not always agree on the details of approaching this problem [60]. There is general agreement on dosage philosophy; cautiously attempt to steady-state the patient without exceeding 20 μg/ml by using average values for guidelines. The plasma theophylline levels must then be determined and the dose adjusted accordingly.

Determination of steady-state plasma values is a good example of differences among recommendations. Levy [52] emphasized that the shape of the plasma concentration curve between doses makes single time point determinations risky. He recommended taking four to six samples followed by the calculation $\bar{P}_{ss}$ = [AUC/dose]. He noted that the use of saliva samples in place of plasma represents a potential solution to the problems of pain and trauma associated with multiple blood sampling during a short (typically 6 hr) dosage interval. Hendeles et al [54] recommended the determination of P_{max}^{∞} assuming t_{max} values of 2 hr (solutions and rapid tablets) and 4 hr (prolonged release tablets) after 3 or more days of a stable regimen. They criticize the use of only P_{min}^{∞} values using the following example. Suppose P_{max}^{∞} = 18 μg/ml and P_{min}^{∞} = 8 μg/ml and the patient experiences symptom breakthrough near the end of each dosage interval. Since $P_{min}^{\infty} < 10\,\mu$g/ml one might be tempted to increase the dosage. Realizing that P_{max}^{∞} is nearly 20 μg/ml, it would be better to keep the total daily dose constant but decrease the dosing interval and dose size. This would increase P_{min}^{∞} and decrease P_{max}^{∞}. According to Ogilvie [53], P_{min}^{∞} is the single most useful value if only one sample is to be taken since it is known to occur at $t = \tau$ whereas t_{max} is variable. The divergence in opinion reflects the problem of obtaining the best appraisal of the patient's situation with the minimum pain and cost. It is well accepted that initial doses should be low and the increases small to reduce patient risk. The adjustment of dosage with a knowledge of an adult patient's steady-state values is done by simple proportion assuming linear kinetics and has been discussed in Chap. 5. The process requires added caution in children where nonlinear kinetics have been reported [57]. The difficult question is how to begin when interpatient $t_{0.5}$ values are so variable. The recommendations as reviewed by Hendeles et al. [54], which illustrate one rational approach to the problem, will be discussed.

d. Loading Dose. The average Vd of 0.5 liter/kg allows one to estimate that each (1 mg/kg) dose results in a (2 μg/ml) increase in plasma concentration using D* = [P] [Vd]. To avoid overestimates due to Vd values that are smaller than average, it is recommended that 10-15 μg/ml be used as the target value. In patients having no residual theophylline levels prior to initiating therapy, the loading dose based on this range would be 5-7.5 mg/kg. This can be administered as an oral solution, as uncoated tablets, or as a 30-min infusion of aminophylline wherein the dosage must be adjusted for theophylline content. (Each 100 mg of aminophylline contains 78-86 mg of theophylline.) If the treatment is an emergency and the patient has been taking theophylline previously, it is recommended that the initial plasma level be rapidly determined and the dose be calculated to make up the difference. If this is not possible, then a reduced dose should be estimated (e.g., 2.5 mg/kg).

  e. *Maintenance Dose.* The initial estimation of a maintenance dosage regimen represents a best guess in consideration of all possible factors followed by cautious drug administration and finally correction of the regimen based on plasma theophylline level. An early estimate which was often reviewed recommended 0.9 mg/kg per hr of aminophylline (approximately 0.75 mg/kg per hr of theophylline) as a constant infusion to provide 10 μg/ml. Using the equation $P_{ss} = k_o/\beta Vd$, the $t_{0.5}$ value which corresponds to this estimate is roughly 4.6 hr. Since this $t_{0.5}$ value is near the lower end of the adult range the input rate would tend to be high for many patients. This recommendation was found to be more likely to produce an average of 20 μg/ml in hospitalized adults and some of those above the average approached the seizure range [54]. Using average doses corresponding to 0.7 mg/kg per hr of theophylline resulted in 20 of 49 patients exceeding 20 μg/ml and 17 patients experiencing various degrees of toxicity [54].

  The initial estimated infusion rate following the loading dose must be modified to include those factors which influence $t_{0.5}$ [53,54]. Examples in mg/kg per hr are children < 9 years, 0.85; children > 9 years, 0.75; smoking adults, 0.75; nonsmoking adults, 0.5; cardiac decompensation, 0.3; liver dysfunction and cardiac decompensation, 0.1 [54].

  The loading dose and infusion rates discussed above are only first approximations. The resulting blood levels must be determined and the dosage adjusted for each patient. Hendeles et al. [54] have suggested that samples be drawn just prior to and 4-8 hours after beginning the maintenance infusion. The concentrations are then compared to determine the direction taken by the serum concentrations and their values relative to the therapeutic range. Empirical adjustments followed by repeated serum measurements are employed to achieve the final steady-state desired values. An alternative approach is to employ a conservative infusion rate over a 24-hr period and determine the resulting plasma concentration, which should begin to approach the steady-state value for most patients. Adjustments are then made and plasma concentrations monitored until a satisfactory stable condition is achieved. When the emergency has passed, the satisfactory infusion rate can then be converted to an oral maintenance dose regimen.

  f. *Oral Administration.* In order to minimize patient intolerance it is recommended that the dosage be slowly increased with a minimum of 3 days between each adjustment [54]. The initial dose should be 16 mg/kg per day up to a 400 mg/day maximum. If tolerated, this is to be increased slowly up to the average which for adults is 900 mg/day. For children the averages are age-dependent: < 9 years, 24 mg/kg day-1; 9-12, 20 mg/kg day-1; 12-16, 18 mg/kg per day. It is estimated that 10-20% of the patients will be at risk of toxicity due to peak levels exceeding 20 μg/ml when using the average dosage regimens. Plasma monitoring and adjustment of dose (if indicated) are therefore appropriate. It is cautioned that small increments in dosage changes are prudent especially in children where dose dependent elimination has been implicated [57]. Determination of plasma levels during the process of attaining steady state will help to prevent the potential for high levels due to a patient being at the long end of the half-life range.

g. Dosage Forms. The wide variety of dosage forms containing varying amounts of theophylline has contributed to the confusion surrounding dosage calculations. Kern and Lipman [55a] have listed more than 50 theophylline products including the chemical analog dyphylline [7-(2,3-dihydroxypropyl) theophylline], which is not a theophylline salt and whose theophylline reference point has been challenged [55b]. Some typical examples of products and their approximate theophylline contents are aminophylline (theophylline ethylenediamine), 85%; theophylline sodium glycinate, 50%; oxtriphylline (choline theophyllinate) 65%; theophylline ethanolamine, 75%; and theophylline as the monohydrate, 91%.

There appears to be little difference in oral bioavailability of various dosage forms with the exception of the longer duration in the case of sustained release products. While sustained release oral dosage forms appear to be generally well absorbed (there are notable exceptions), their absorption rate characteristics vary widely. Some of these products show very slow drug input rates. Such products are not interchangeable with the normal rapidly bioavailable tablets without careful monitoring of the patient and the readjustment of the dosage regimen. The same degree of caution should be exercised in interchanging sustained release products since bioequivalency cannot be assumed due to the wide variability in absorption rates. A well-designed sustained release product can afford a clinical advantage. One study documents the maintenance of therapeutic blood levels, with a peak-trough difference of 5 μg/ml, by administration of sustained release oral tablets every 12 hr [60]. For the interested reader, that report also provides an excellent bibliography on the biopharmaceutics of theophylline sustained-release products.

When parenteral use is indicated, the I.V. route is preferred over the I.M. route, which is painful. Rectal solutions are well absorbed but suppositories appear to be absorbed slowly, erratically, and with irritation.

5. Digoxin

a. Introduction. In 1967 Jelliffe published a mathematical approach to digitalis kinetics in patients with normal and impaired renal function [61]. In spite of the limited availability of clinical pharmacokinetic data at that time, this work led to reduced digitalis toxicity when the physician's dosage recommendations were kinetic-based. Although the pharmacokinetic parameters used for the nomograms are no longer regarded as dependable, the results of their use were most encouraging. In one report [62] the incidence of toxicity was reduced from 35 to 12%. These reports did much to foster the philosophy of individualization of dosage and of monitoring patient drug levels. Digoxin served as a case in point in the widespread acceptance of the role of clinical pharmacokinetics in therapy. Ironically, today there is less agreement on dosage recommendations for digoxin than there is for many other drugs wherein plasma monitoring and/or individualization of dosage is practiced. This is due to the fact that increased research has shown the effects of disease on digoxin pharmacokinetics to be increasingly unmanageable. Published opinions vary from the position that the approach will never be successful to the fact that it is already successful and future research will make it more so [63]. In this resume the various facets of the problem will be presented. For the reader interested in more details, most of the literature cited here is heavily referenced e.g., Ref. 63 has 169 citations).

   b. *Steady-State Plasma Levels.* While there is ample evidence that monitoring patients' steady-state digoxin levels can lead to decreased toxicity, there is no assurance that such precautions will be preventative. This information must be combined with the best clinical judgment and is not meant to replace it. There remains uncertainty with regard to ideal digoxin plasma levels. Most patients exhibit a satisfactory inotropic effect at steady-state digoxin levels of 0.7-1.5 ng/ml [64]. Toxicity, especially life-threatening arrhythmias, are most likely at levels that exceed 3 ng/ml. But there is an undefined range from 1.5 to 3 ng/ml regarding potential toxicity. In a study of 109 patients treated with digitalis preparations, 16 patients developed arrhythmias potentially due to digitalis intoxication. When subjected to further testing 5 were nontoxic and showed levels less than 1.6 ng/ml. The remaining 11 all exceeded 1.6 ng/ml and were categorized as either definitely or possible toxic [65].

   c. *Bioavailability.* Just as success in digoxin dosage adjustment provided a major incentive for clinical pharmacokinetics, so did the variability in bioavailability from oral tablets cause an unprecedented interest in the question of generic bioequivalency. This is understandable because in both cases the risks were high. A patient who is underdosed may die from the disease; overdose may result in death from the drug. And the range between these limits is narrow. It has been estimated that a 50% difference in bioavailability can make a well-digitalized patient either toxic or nontreated [66].

   In 1971, Lindenbaum et al. [67] provided the basis for international concern when they discovered significant differences in bioavailability from different products with peak levels from one tablet being seven times those resulting from tablets of another manufacturer. The dissolution rate has been shown to be a key factor in the absorption of digoxin from tablets [66,68], with rapidly dissolving tablets approaching the absorption obtained from a solution. In one review the range of percentage absorbed and their dissolution rates for commercial tablets was 38% (dissolving at 44% in 2 hr) to more than 90% (wherein more than 90% dissolved in 2 hr). Since 1973 (beginning with the United States Pharmacopoeia) official compendia have required dissolution rates aimed at producing tablet bioavailability equivalent to the elixir. The most rigorous test appears to be the Dutch Pharmacopoeia (a minimum of 90% dissolution in 1 hr) whereas the British Pharmacopoeia required 75% (1975) and the United States Pharmacopoeia 65% (1975) [66]. Results show that marketed products have clinically satisfactory bioavailability and variations in absorption are primarily due to patient factors [68].

Reported mean values for absolute bioavailability of digoxin from solutions ranged from 65 to 89% [66,68]. There are several nonformulation factors that can interfere with digoxin absorption. Digoxin is nearly completely hydrolyzed after 2 hr at pH 1 and gastric acidity combined with delayed stomach emptying could result in degradation [63]. However, neither rate nor amount absorbed was influenced by food when the elixir was administered [68]. Absorption from tablets was decreased in patients receiving metoclopramide (which increases motility) and increased with propantheline (which reduces motility) [68]. The reduction may be due to reduced time for dissolution since these tablets were slow to dissolve and the effect was not seen with the elixir or rapidly dissolving tablets. The effect of various malabsorption syndromes on digoxin bioavailability is a subject of some controversy. Jejunoileal bypass for morbid obesity severely limited absorption surface and decreased fat absorption, but digoxin bioavailability from rapidly dissolving tablets was 87% of that prior to surgery [63]. Intrasubject variation in bioavailability is well recognized and appears to be an additional problem to that of dosage form effects [66]. While intersubject variation was partially connected to the dosage form, some subjects showed reduced absorption ability even with rapidly dissolving tablets [66].

d. *Individualized Dosage Regimens.* In spite of the role that digoxin itself has played in bringing about widespread interest in drug plasma monitoring and bioequivalency, it remains a drug of controversy with regard to the optimum approach to digitalization of a patient. The difficulty in defining the optimum drug plasma concentration has been discussed in Sec. b. This necessitates a careful individualization of the desired steady-state plasma levels based on clinical evaluation. The adjustment of steady state levels can be done empirically using the equation (see Chap. 5)

$$\overline{P}_{ss} = \frac{F(D_o)}{Vd\beta \tau} \tag{15}$$

where D_o/τ are the adjustable parameters. Average doses of 0.25 mg/day reportedly accommodate 75% of patients, 0.50 mg/day for 20%, and 0.75 mg/

day for 5% [69]. The use of nomograms and the calculation of loading doses represent areas of conflicting opinion. One of the problems is undoubtedly the observed decrease in distribution volume accompanying renal failure [70]. Dosage adjustment was normally based on the half-life (or β value) relationship to renal creatinine clearance, which assumes a constant Vd (see Chap. 5 for methods). It is possible to observe changes in both Vd and β which are not accommodated by this approach. Since (β) (Vd) is total body clearance, (C_T), it has been suggested that digoxin clearance be used instead of $t_{0.5}$ [71]. Rearranging Eq. (15) gives

$$(\bar{P}_{ss})(C_T) = \frac{FD_o}{\tau} \tag{16}$$

which states that the average steady-state plasma level times the clearance gives the dosing rate (D_o/τ) times F. To adjust for renal failure, clearance may be divided into its components [71]:

$$C_T = 1.101\ C_{Dig} + C_{Met} \tag{17}$$

where C_{Dig} is renal clearance and $C_{Met} = 36$ ml/min is metabolism. Since digoxin renal clearance was related to creatinine clearance (C_{Cr}), the equation was rewritten $C_T = 1.303\ C_{Cr} + C_M$, $C_M = 41$ ml/min. This approach, as yet insufficiently tested, satisfies one criticism, namely, the wide and unpredictable variation in steady-state distribution volume (Vd_{ss}) among renal failure patients. The range in normal adults has been reported as 580-777 liters [72] and 430-630 liters [70]. In a single study of only seven azotemic patients, the Vd_{ss} range was 195-489 liters/1.73 m^2 [71]. Half-life values in these patients ranged from 36 to 125 hr whereas values for normals had a mean of 44 hr [72] (range 33-52 hr) and 45 hr [73] based on the terminal slopes of two- [72] and three- [73] compartment models. Thus, the normal and renal failure half-life ranges overlap.

A specific point of controversy has been the suggested loading dose. One view is that the normal loading dose would be appropriate in renal failure while the opposing view is that one-half to two-thirds of the usual should be employed due to decreased Vd_{ss} values. A good discussion of the problem has been published by Aronson and Grahame-Smith [74]. The answer is by no means clear-cut, especially in view of the unpredictability of Vd_{ss}, which necessitates caution and close clinical observation in the digitalization process.

The complexity of digoxin clinical pharmacokinetics has limited the success of dosage nomograms. While they have proven useful it is understandable that agreement has not yet been reached regarding the final recommendations. There are many complications which can influence the choice of a digoxin regimen, some of which are well on the way to being solved and others which continue to resist simplification.

Bioavailability has been a problem which is greatly improved. Yet nondosage form absorption problems may be hard to predict. Assays have not always been specific. The potential for metabolite error in the assay has contributed to the confusion.

The original nomogram used an average $t_{0.5}$ value of 4.46 days for anephric patients. Ranges of 2.2-4.9 (four patients) and 1.5-5.2 (seven patients) days have been reported [71]. Correction for $t_{0.5}$ alone seems insufficient since Vd_{ss} can vary widely in renal failure. The lack of digoxin distribution into fatty tissue in obesity has prompted the suggestion that lean body weight be used in such cases and this has resulted in limited improvement [75]. Hyperthyroid patients have been reported to show increased digoxin metabolism whereas it is decreased in hypothyroidism [73,74]. Confusion exists regarding the clinical significance of malabsorption syndromes and drug interactions in the bioavailability of digoxin. In addition there remains some question as to the desired plasma concentration and its variability among patients.

In light of the problems one might allow that considerable progress has been made. There is little doubt that clinical pharmacokinetics has improved the course of digoxin therapy over approximately a decade. It will undoubtedly continue to do so.

REFERENCES

1. P. R. Byron, R. E. Notari, and M-Y. Huang, Pharmacokinetic Predictions of Optimum Drug Delivery Rates From Prodrugs Designed For Maximum Duration, *Int. J. Pharm. 1,* 219 (1978).
2. C. M. Kunin, Blood Level Measurements and Antimicrobial Agents, *Clin. Pharmacol. Ther. 16,* 251 (1974).
3. J. R. Gilette and S. Pang, Theoretical Aspects of Pharmacokinetic Drug Interactions, *Clin. Pharmacol. Ther. 22,* 623 (1977).
4. M. B. Kristensen, Drug Interactions and Clinical Pharmacokinetics, *Clin. Pharmacokin. 1,* 351 (1976).
5. M. Rowland and S. B. Matin, Kinetics of Drug-Drug Interactions, *J. Pharmacokin. Biopharm. 1,* 553 (1973).
6. W. S. Nimmo, Drugs, Diseases and Altered Gastric Emptying, *Clin. Pharmacokin. 1,* 189 (1976).
7. R. L. Parsons, Drug Absorption in Gastrointestinal Disease With Particular Reference to Malabsorption Syndromes, *Clin. Pharmacokin. 2,* 45 (1977).
8. P. G. Welling, Influence of Food and Diet on Gastrointestinal Drug Absorption, *J. Pharmacokin. Biopharm. 5,* 291 (1977).
9. W. H. Barr, J. Adir, and L. Garrettson, Decrease of Tetracycline Absorption in Man by Sodium Bicarbonate, *Clin. Pharmacol. Ther. 12,* 779 (1971).
10. P. A. Kramer, D. J. Chapron, J. Benson, and S. A. Mercik, Tetracycline

Absorption in Elderly Patients with Achlorhydria, *Clin. Pharmacol. Ther.* *23*, 467 (1978).

11. E. M. Baylis, J. M. Crowley, J.ᵒM. Preece, P. E. Sylvester, and V. Marks, Influence of Folic Acid on Blood Phenytoin Levels, *Lancet 1*, 62 (1971).

12. J. M. Jaffe, R. I. Poust, S. L. Feld, and J. L. Colaizzi, Influence of Repetitive Dosing and Altered Urinary pH on Doxycycline Excretion in Humans, *J. Pharm. Sci. 63*, 1256 (1974).

13. G. D. Bellward, P. M. Warren, W. Howald, J. E. Axelson, and F. S. Abbott, Methadone Maintenance: Effect of Urinary pH on Renal Clearance in Chronic High and Low Doses, *Clin. Pharmacol. Ther. 22*, 92 (1977).

14. H. B. Kostenbauder, J. B. Portnoff, and J. V. Swintosky, Control of Urine pH and Its Effect on Sulfaethidole Excretion in Humans, *J. Pharm. Sci. 51*, 1084 (1962).

15. M. Rowland and A. H. Beckett, The Amphetamines: Clinical Pharmaco-kinetic Implications of Recent Studies of An Assay Procedure and Urinary Excretion in Man, *Arzneimittel-Forschung 1*, 1369 (1966).

16. M. Gibaldi, B. Grundhofer, and G. Levy, Time Course and Dose Dependence of Antacid Effect on Urine pH, *J. Pharm. Sci. 64*, 2003 (1975).

17. J. B. Field, M. Ohta, C. Boyle, and A. Remers, Potentiation of Aceto-hexamide Hypoglycemia by Phenylbutazone, *New Eng. J. Med. 277*, 889 (1967).

18. D. D. Breimer and E. Richter, Pharmacokinetic Interactions With Rifam-picin, *Clin. Pharmacokin. 2*, 61 (1977).

19. W. J. Jusko and M. Gretch, Plasma and Tissue Protein Binding of Drugs in Pharmacokinetics, *Drug Metab. Rev. 5*, 43 (1976).

20. J. Koch-Weser and E. M. Sellers, Binding of Drugs to Serum Albumin, *Med. Intell. 294*, 311 and 526 (1976).

21. L. B. Wingard, Jr., R. A. O'Reilly, and G. Levy, Pharmacokinetics of Warfarin Enantiomers: A Search For Intrasubject Correlations, *Clin. Pharmacol. Ther. 23*, 212 (1978), and references therein.

22. J. Crooks, K. O'Malley, and I. H. Stevenson, Pharmacokinetics in the Elderly, *Clin. Pharmacokin. 1*, 280 (1976).

23. E. J. Triggs and R. L. Nation, Pharmacokinetics in the Aged, *J. Pharmaco-kin. Biopharm. 3*, 387 (1975).

24. G. Levy, ed., *Clinical Pharmacokinetics*, A.Ph.A., Washington, D.C., 1974.

25. L. Z. Benet, ed., *The Effect of Disease States on Drug Pharmacokinetics*, A.Ph.A., Washington, D.C., 1976.

26. M. J. Eadie, Plasma Level Monitoring of Anticonvulsants, *Clin. Pharmaco-kin. 1*, 52 (1976).

27. E. F. Hvidberg and M. Dam, Clinical Pharmacokinetics of Anticonvulsants, *Clin. Pharmacokin. 1*, 161 (1976).

28. A. J. Atkinson, Individualization of Anticonvulsant Therapy. *Med. Clinics N.A. 58*, 1037 (1974). (Symposium)

29. L. Lund, Effects of Phenytoin in Patients with Epilepsy in Relation to its Concentration in Plasma, in *Biological Effects of Drugs in Relation to Their*

Plasma Concentrations, S. S. Davies and B. N. C. Prichard, eds., University Park Press, Baltimore, 1973, p. 227.

30. E. Martin, T. N. Tozer, L. B. Sheiner, and S. Riegelman, The Clinical Pharmacokinetics of Phenytoin, *J. Pharmacokin. Biopharm. 5,* 579 (1977).

31. A. P. Melikian, A. B. Straughn, G. W. A. Slywka, P. L. Whyatt, and M. C. Meyer, Bioavailability of 11 Phenytoin Products, *J. Pharmacokin. Biopharm. 5,* 133 (1977).

32. R. E. Baars, R. P. Rapp, B. Young, and D. Canafax, Phenytoin 300 mg Daily—Not a Dose For Everyone, *Drug. Intel. Clin. Pharm. 12,* 584 (1978).

33. *FDA Drug Bulletin 8,* No. 4, Aug-Sept, 1978.

34. T. M. Ludden, J. P. Allen, W. A. Vatutsky, A. V. Vicuna, J. M. Nappi, S. F. Hoffman, J. E. Wallace, D. Lalka, and J. L. McNay, Individualization of Phenytoin Dosage Regimens, *Clin. Pharmacol. Ther. 21,* 287 (1977).

35. G. E. Mawer, P. W. Mullen, M. Rodgers, A. J. Robins, and S. B. Lucas, Phenytoin Dose Adjustment in Epileptic Patients, *Br. J. Clin. Pharmacol. 1,* 163 (1974).

36. A. M. Gyselynck, A. Forrey, and R. Cutler, Pharmacokinetics of Gentamicin: Distribution and Plasma and Renal Clearance, *J. Infect. Dis. Suppl. 124,* 570 (1971).

37. J. G. Dahlgren, E. T. Anderson, and W. L. Hewitt, Gentamicin Blood Levels: A Guide To Nephrotoxicity, *Antimicrob. Ag. Chemother. 8,* 58 (1975).

38. E. L. Goodman, J. VanGelder, R. Holmes, A. R. Hull, and J. P. Sanford, Prospective Comparative Study of Variable Dosage and Variable Frequency Regimens for Administration of Gentamicin, *Antimicrob. Ag. Chemother. 8,* 434 (1975).

39. F. Follath, P. Spring, M. Wenk, L. Z. Benet, and L. Dettli, Comparative Pharmacokinetics of Sisomicin and Netilmicin in Healthy Volunteers, *Proc. 10th Int. Congr. Chemotherap.,* Vol. 2, Zurich, p. 979 (1977).

40. R. Sawchuk, D. E. Zaske, R. J. Cipolle, W. A. Wargin, and R. G. Strate, Kinetic Model for Gentamicin Dosing With The Use of Individual Patient Parameters, *Clin. Pharmacol. Ther. 21,* 362 (1977).

41. G. E. Schumacher, Gentamicin Blood Level Versus Time Profiles of Various Dosage Regimens Recommended For Renal Impairment, *Amer. J. Hosp. Pharm. 32,* 299 (1975).

42. R. J. Sawchuk and D. E. Zaske, Pharmacokinetics of Dosing Regimens Which Utilize Multiple Intravenous Infusions: Gentamicin in Burn Patients, *J. Pharmacokin. Biopharm. 4,* 183 (1976).

43. D. E. Zaske, R. J. Sawchuk, D. N. Gerding, and R. G. Strate, Increased Dosage Requirements of Gentamicin in Burn Patients, *J. Trauma 16,* 824 (1976).

44. J. H. Hull and F. A. Sarubbi, Gentamicin Serum Concentrations: Pharmacokinetic Predictions, *Ann. Intern. Med. 85,* 183 (1976).

45. C. Bryan, Letter to the Editor, *Ann. Intern. Med. 86,* 358 (1977).

46. D. A. Spyker and R. L. Guerrant, Gentamicin Dosage, *Ann. Intern. Med. 86,* 357 (1977).

47. J. H. Hull and F. A. Sarubbi, In Comment, *Ann. Intern. Med. 86*, 358 (1977).
48. J. S. Raichlen, Calculating Gentamicin Doses, and J. H. Hull and F. A. Sarubbi, In Comment, *Ann. Intern. Med. 85*, 827 and 828 (1976).
49. C. S. Matkovic, G. J. Pazin, S. N. Schwartz, J. A. Lyon, and A. W. Pasculle, Aminoglycoside Pharmacokinetics in Obesity, *18th Interscience Conf. Antimicrob. Ag. Chemother.*, Atlanta, Abstract 387, 1978.
50. M. Rowland, Clinical Pharmacokinetics of Lidocaine, in *Clinical Pharmacokinetics*, G. Levy, ed., A.Ph.A., Washington, D.C., 1974, p. 53.
51. N. L. Benowitz and W. Meister, Clinical Pharmacokinetics of Lignocaine, *Clin. Pharmacokin. 3*, 177 (1978).
52. G. Levy, Pharmacokinetic Control of Theophylline Therapy, in *Clinical Pharmacokinetics*, G. Levy, ed., A.Ph.A., Washington, D.C., 1974, pp. 103-110.
53. R. I. Ogilvie, Clinical Pharmacokinetics of Theophylline, *Clin. Pharmacokin. 3*, 267 (1978).
54. L. Hendeles, M. Weinberger, and G. Johnson, Monitoring Serum Theophylline Levels, *Clin. Pharmacokin. 3*, 294 (1978).
55. (a) J. W. Kern and A. G. Lipman, Rational Theophylline Therapy, *Drug Intell. Clin. Pharm. 11*, 144 (1977); (b) M. Weinberger, "Rational Theophylline Therapy": Article Contents Questioned; J. W. Kern and A. G. Lipman, Authors' reply, *Drug Intell. Clin. Pharm.* 11, 624, 625 (1977).
56. L. Hendeles, L. Bighley, R. H. Richardson, C. D. Hepler, and J. Carmichael, Frequent Toxicity From I.V. Aminophylline Infusions in Critically Ill Patients, *Drug Intell. Clin. Pharm. 11*, 12 (1977).
57. M. Weinberger and E. Ginchansky, Dose-Dependent Kinetics of Theophylline Disposition In Asthmatic Children, *J. Ped. 91*, 820 (1977).
58. P. Gal, W. J. Jusko, A. M. Yurchak, and B. A. Franklin, Theophylline Disposition in Obesity, *Clin. Pharmacol. Ther. 23*, 438 (1978).
59. W. J. Jusko, J. J. Schentag, J. H. Clark, M. Gardner, and A. M. Yurchak, Enhanced Biotransformation of Theophylline in Marihuana and Tobacco Smokers, *Clin. Pharmacol. Ther. 24*, 406 (1978).
60. J. Dasta, J. M. Mirtallo, and M. Altman, Comparison of Standard and Sustained-Release Theophylline Tablets in Patients with Chronic Obstructive Pulmonary Disease, *Amer. J. Hosp. Pharm. 36*, 613 (1979).
61. R. W. Jelliffe, A Mathematical Analysis of Digitalis Kinetics in Patients with Normal and Reduced Renal Function, *Math. Biosci. 1*, 305 (1967).
62. R. W. Jelliffe, J. Buell, and R. Kalaba, Reduction of Digitalis Toxicity by Computer-Assisted Glycoside Dosage Regimens, *Ann. Intern. Med. 77*, 891 (1972).
63. F. I. Marcus, Current Status of Therapy with Digoxin, *Curr. Probl. Cardiol. 3*, No. 5 (Aug 1978).
64. W. J. Jusko, Clinical Pharmacokinetics of Digoxin, in *Clinical Pharmacokinetics*, G. Levy, ed., A.Ph.A., Washington, D.C., 1974, p. 31.
65. S. Waldorff and J. Buch, Serum Digoxin and Empiric Methods in Identification of Digitoxicity, *Clin. Pharmacol. Ther. 23*, 19 (1978).

66. L. Nyberg, Bioavailability of Digoxin in Man After Oral Administration of Preparations with Different Dissolution Rate, *Acta Pharmacol. Toxicol.* *40*, Supplement 3 (1977).
67. J. Lindenbaum, M. H. Mellow, M. O. Blackstone, V. P. Butler, Variation in Biologic Availability of Digoxin From Four Preparations, *N. Engl. J. Med.* *285*, (Dec 1971), 1344-1347.
68. D. J. Greenblatt, T. W. Smith, and J. Koch-Weser, Bioavailability of Drugs: The Digoxin Dilemma, *Clin. Pharmacokin 1*, 36 (1976).
69. H. F. Conn, *Current Therapy*, W. B. Saunders, Philadelphia, 1971.
70. R. H. Reuning, R. A. Sams, R. E. Notari, Role of Pharmacokinetics in Drug Dosage Adjustment; Pharmacologic Effect Kinetics and Apparent Volume of Distribution of Digoxin, *Clin. Pharmacol 13*, 127 (1973).
71. J. R. Koup, W. J. Jusko, C. M. Elwood, and R. K. Kohli, Digoxin Pharmacokinetics: Role of Renal Failure in Dosage Regimen Design, *Clin. Pharmacol. Ther. 18*, 9 (1975).
72. J. R. Koup, D. J. Greenblatt, W. J. Jusko, T. W. Smith, and J. Koch-Weser, Pharmacokinetics of Digoxin in Normal Subjects After Intravenous Bolus and Infusion Doses, *J. Pharmacokin. Biopharm 3*, 181 (1975).
73. W. G. Kramer, R. P. Lewis, T. C. Cobb, W. F. Forester, Jr., J. A. Visconti, L. A. Wanke, H. G. Boxenbaum, and R. H. Reuning, Pharmacokinetics of Digoxin: Comparison of a Two and a Three-Compartment Model in Man, *J. Pharmacokin. Biopharm 2*, 299 (1974).
74. J. K. Aronson and D. G. Grahame-Smith, Altered Distribution of Digoxin in Renal Failure — A Cause of Digoxin Toxicity?, *Br. J. Clin. Pharmacol. 3*, 1045 (1976).
75. J. G. Wagner, J. D. Yates, P. W. Willis, E. Sakmar, and R. G. Stoll, Correlation of Plasma Levels of Digoxin in Cardiac Patients With Dose and Measures of Renal Function, *Clin. Pharmacol. Ther. 15*, 291 (1974).

Appendix A

FICK'S LAW

I. PASSIVE TRANSPORT ENERGETICS: FICK'S LAW

In the discussion of reversible first-order rate processes, we have considered a system where the rate of drug transfer is governed by Fick's first law, which states that the flux (the quantity of substance diffusing per unit time through a unit area) through a plane perpendicular to the direction of diffusion is directly proportional to the concentration gradient.

In the case of a biological barrier, such as that illustrated in Fig. 1 (p. 7), the concentration gradient between the compartments is assumed to be due to the barrier itself. That is, we are defining the system such that the diffusion within a compartment is not rate-determining but that passage through the membrane itself is the slowest diffusion process. For the case represented by Figs. 1 and 2, the mass transport from compartment A to B through the rate-controlling barrier is described by

$$\frac{-da}{dt} = D'A \frac{dC}{dX} \tag{1a}$$

where $-da/dt$ equals the decrease in mass in the A compartment as a function of time, D' is the diffusion constant of the drug in the barrier, A is the area of the membrane, and dC/dX is the change in concentration as a function of distance. For a given drug and membrane the following may be stated: The diffusion constant, D', will be a constant; the area will remain constant; the thickness of the barrier (dX is sometimes referred to as h in the barrier case) is constant, and dC is the concentration gradient $(A_t - B_t)$ or the difference in concentration between the two compartments. The membrane–drug parameters, $D'A/h$, may be set equal to a constant, k, and Eq. (1a) may then be written as a rate process

$$\frac{-da}{dt} = k(A_t - B_t) \tag{2a}$$

338

In the case of equivalent compartments, the volume of $A(V_A)$ equals the volume of $B(V_B)$, so that $V_A = V_B = V$. The right side of Eq. (2a) may now be expressed in terms of mass:

$$\frac{-da}{dt} = k\left(\frac{a_t}{V} - \frac{b_t}{V}\right) \tag{3a}$$

where a_t and b_t represent the mass of a drug in compartments A and B, respectively. Letting $k/V = k'$,

$$\frac{-da}{dt} = k'(a_t - b_t) \tag{4a}$$

Since $b_t = a_0 - a_t$, substitution gives

$$\frac{da_t}{2a_t - a_0} = -k'\,dt \tag{5a}$$

which integrates directly to

$$\ln(2a_t - a_0) = -2k't + \ln a_0 \tag{6a}$$

between the limits of a_0 and a_t and $t = 0$ and t. Now, $a_\infty = b_\infty = (\tfrac{1}{2})a_0$, so Eq. (6a) may be expressed as

$$\ln(a_t - a_\infty) = -2k't + \ln a_\infty \tag{7a}$$

Equation (7a) has been derived from Fick's law, while Eq. (15) (p. 14) has been used to demonstrate the fact that a first-order plot will allow the calculation of the pseudo-first-order rate constants, k_1, which is the sum of k_f and k_r. Since both equations refer to the same system, the relationship between k' and $(k_f + k_r)$ will now be examined.

II. RELATIONSHIP OF FICK'S LAW TO $A \rightleftharpoons B$ REVERSIBLE FIRST-ORDER KINETICS

Equation (15) (p. 14) may be written in terms of mass as:

$$\ln\left(\frac{a_t}{V} - \frac{a_\infty}{V}\right) = -(k_f + k_r)t + \ln\frac{a_\infty}{V}$$

This reduces to

$$\ln(a_t - a_\infty) = -(k_f + k_r)t + \ln a_\infty \tag{8a}$$

which has the same form as Eq. (7a). We may therefore conclude that $2k' = k_f + k_r$. Since, in the present case where $A_\infty = B_\infty$ and $a_\infty = b_\infty$, $k_f = k_r$, then $k' = k_f = k_r$ and $k = k'V$ so that the rate constant, k, associated with the mass transport Eq. (3a) is related to the first-order constants by the expression

$$k = k_f V = k_r V = \frac{k_1 V}{2} \tag{9a}$$

This applies only to the simplest case where the compartments are identical and, therefore, the microconstants are equal. When, for example, V_A is not equal to V_B, the Fick's law equation may be written

$$\frac{-da_t}{dt} = k \left(\frac{a_t}{V_A} - \frac{b_t}{V_B} \right) \tag{10a}$$

$$\frac{-da_t}{dt} = k_1 a_t - k_2 b_t$$

This may be integrated to yield

$$\ln(a_t - a_\infty) = -(k_1 + k_2)t + \ln(a_0 - a_\infty) \tag{11a}$$

Equation (14) (p. 14) written in terms of mass is

$$\ln(a_t - a_\infty) = -(k_f + k_r)t + \ln(a_0 - a_\infty) \tag{12a}$$

which is comparable to Eq. (11a), allowing us to conclude that in this case $k_1 + k_2 = k_f + k_r$.

It is important to realize that only the concentration gradient between transferable species is described by Fick's law. The derivatives to compare the Fick's law expressions to the kinetic equations when $A_\infty \neq B_\infty$ are considerably more complex and will not be covered.

Appendix B

Vd

I. Volume of Distribution in the One-Compartment Open Model

a. *Mass Balance.* Equation (10) in Chap. 3 states that

$$Vd = \frac{D_t}{P_t} \tag{13a}$$

where D_t is the sum of the amount of drug in the central compartment, P', and in other tissues, T', so that

$$Vd = \frac{P' + T'}{P_t} \tag{14a}$$

This can be written

$$Vd = \frac{P'(1 + T'/P')}{P_t} \tag{15a}$$

For a one-compartment model, $T'/P' \rightarrow k_{12}/k_{21}$, so Vd becomes

$$Vd = \frac{P'(1 + k_{12}/k_{21})}{P_t} \tag{16a}$$

Since

$$V_p = \frac{P'}{P_t} \tag{17a}$$

where V_p is the volume of the central compartment,

$$Vd = V_p \left(1 + \frac{k_{12}}{k_{21}}\right) \tag{18a}$$

as discussed in Chap. 3.

The analogous expression for a two-compartment model is given by Eq. (40a), which, in contrast to (18a), is dependent upon elimination.

b. Volume of Distribution by Extrapolation. We know that Eq. (29), Chap. 2, $P = Be^{-\beta t}$, describes the concentration of drug in blood over virtually the entire time the drug is in the body if a one-compartment model applies. At time zero,

$$P_0 = B \tag{19a}$$

so Eq. (10) in Chap. 3 becomes

$$Vd = \frac{D_0}{B} \tag{20a}$$

which is Eq. (11), Chap. 3.

c. Volume of Distribution by Area. The area under the plasma concentration curve (AUC) is found by integrating Eq. 29 (Chap. 2), from $t = 0$ to $t = \infty$.

$$AUC = \int_0^\infty P_t \, dt = \int_0^\infty Be^{-\beta t} \, dt \tag{21a}$$

$$AUC = \frac{B}{\beta} \, e^{-\beta t} \Big|_0^\infty \tag{22a}$$

$$AUC = \frac{B}{\beta} \tag{23a}$$

Substituting into Eq. (20a),

$$Vd = \frac{D_0}{(AUC)\beta} \tag{24a}$$

which is Eq. 12, Chap. 3.

II. Volume of Distribution in the Two-Compartment Open Model

a. Volume of Distribution by Extrapolation. The plasma concentration of drug in a two-compartment model is given by

$$P_t = \frac{D_0(k_{21} - \alpha)e^{-\alpha t}}{Vp(\beta - \alpha)} + \frac{D_0(k_{21} - \beta)e^{-\beta t}}{Vp(\alpha - \beta)} \tag{25a}$$

After the distribution phase is complete, the first term becomes negligible and extrapolation of the second phase back to zero time yields

$$P = B = \frac{D_0(k_{21} - \beta)}{Vp(\alpha - \beta)} \tag{26a}$$

Substituting into Eq. (20a),

$$Vd = \frac{Vp(\alpha - \beta)}{(k_{21} - \beta)} \tag{27a}$$

By means of Eqs. (21) and (22) (pp. 21, 23) we can show that

$$\alpha - \beta = \sqrt{C_1^2 - 4C_2} \tag{28a}$$

and

$$k_{21} - \beta = \tfrac{1}{2}(k_{21} - k_{12} - k_2 + \sqrt{C_1^2 - 4C_2}) \tag{29a}$$

Therefore

$$Vd = \frac{Vp \sqrt{C_1^2 - 4C_2}}{\tfrac{1}{2}(k_{21} - k_{12} - k_2 + \sqrt{C_1^2 - 4C_2})} \tag{30a}$$

b. Volume of Distribution by Area. It can be shown that the area under the plasma concentration-vs-time curve (AUC) for a two-compartment model following I.V. injection is given by

$$AUC = \frac{P_0}{k_2} \tag{31a}$$

Substituting into Eq. (24a),

$$Vd = \frac{D_0 k_2}{P_0 \beta} \tag{32a}$$

and since $Vp = D_0/P_0$ then

$$Vd = \frac{Vp k_2}{\beta} \tag{33a}$$

Nagashima et al. (Chap. 3, Ref. 27) have shown that k_2 is related to β by the fraction of the total drug which is in the central compartment, fp, or

$$\beta = \frac{k_2(P')}{T' + P'} = k_2 fp \tag{34a}$$

344   **Appendix B**

Substituting into Eq. (33a),

$$Vd = \frac{Vp(T' + P')}{(P')} = \frac{Vp}{fp} \tag{35a}$$

or

$$Vd = Vp\left(1 + \frac{T'}{P'}\right) \tag{36a}$$

The ratio T'/P' can be obtained using the following equations

$$P' = \frac{D_0}{(\alpha - \beta)}\left[(k_{21} - \beta)e^{-\beta t} - (k_{21} - \alpha)e^{-\alpha t}\right] \tag{37a}$$

and

$$T' = \frac{k_{12}D_0}{(\alpha - \beta)}(e^{-\beta t} - e^{-\alpha t}) \tag{38a}$$

As $t \to \infty$, $e^{-\alpha t} \to 0$, and T'/P' in the β phase approaches the ratio

$$\frac{T'}{P'} = \frac{k_{12}}{k_{21} - \beta} \tag{39a}$$

Substituting this into Eq. (36a), we obtain

$$Vd = Vp\left[1 + \left(\frac{k_{12}}{k_{21} - \beta}\right)\right] \tag{40a}$$

as discussed in Chap. 3. This equation may also be derived by the method used for Eq. (18a).

    c. Steady-State Infusion Distribution Volume, Vd_{inf}. When the amount of drug in the plasma has reached a constant value during a zero-order infusion,

$$\frac{dP'}{dt} = 0 = k_0 + k_{21}T' - k_{12}P' - k_2P' \tag{41a}$$

At any time during an infusion, the plasma concentration is given by (Chap. 3, Ref. 8)

$$P_t = \frac{k_0}{Vpk_2}\left[1 + \frac{(k_2 - \beta)e^{-\alpha t}}{(\beta - \alpha)} - \frac{(k_2 - \alpha)e^{-\beta t}}{(\beta - \alpha)}\right] \tag{42a}$$

When a constant plasma concentration has been established, that is, at infinite time, this reduces to

$$P_{inf} \approx \frac{k_0}{Vpk_2} \tag{43a}$$

or

$$k_0 \approx k_2 P'$$ (44a)

Substituting Eq. (44a) into Eq. (41a),

$$\left(\frac{T'}{P'}\right)_{inf} = \frac{k_{12}}{k_{21}}$$ (45a)

Equation (10) in Chap. 3 can be rewritten as

$$Vd = \frac{P' + T'}{P_t}$$ (46a)

Substituting from Eq. (45a) for T'

$$Vd_{inf} = \frac{P'(k_{21} + k_{12})}{k_{21} P_{inf}}$$ (47a)

or

$$Vd_{inf} = Vp \frac{(k_{21} + k_{12})}{k_{21}} = V_p \left[1 + \frac{k_{12}}{k_{21}}\right]$$ (48a)

as discussed in Chap. 3, and also identical to Vd_{ss} as defined by Riggs (Chap. 3, Ref. 8). Notice that even in a two-compartment model, T'/P' equals the equilibrium ratio k_{12}/k_{21} after infusion has continued long enough for the plasma level to become constant.

Appendix C

AREA UNDER I.V. CURVES

I. ONE-COMPARTMENT OPEN MODEL

According to Eq. (29) in Chap. 2,

$$P = Be^{-\beta t} \tag{49a}$$

describes the plasma time course following a rapid I.V. injection of a drug distributed according to a one-compartment model. The area under a plot of P as a function of t would be

$$\int_0^\infty P = B \int_0^\infty e^{-\beta t} \tag{50a}$$

which upon integration yields

$$AUC = B \left(\frac{e^{-\beta\infty}}{-\beta} - \frac{e^{-\beta 0}}{-\beta} \right)$$

Thus the area under a blood level curve (AUC) following a rapid I.V. injection of a one-compartment drug can be calculated from the simple expression

$$AUC = \frac{B}{\beta} \tag{51a}$$

The area of such a curve from any time t to time ∞ may be calculated from

$$AUC = \frac{P_t}{\beta} \tag{52a}$$

where P_t is the blood concentration at time t.

II. TWO-COMPARTMENT OPEN MODEL

Equation (20) in Chap. 2 describes the time course for a rapid I.V. injection of a two-compartment model drug.

$$P = Ae^{-\alpha t} + Be^{-\beta t} \tag{53a}$$

Since it is the sum of two exponentials, the area under the curve may be derived as shown above with the results

$$AUC = \frac{A}{\alpha} + \frac{B}{\beta} \tag{54a}$$

Appendix D

MULTIPLE-DOSE EQUATIONS FOR THE
ONE-COMPARTMENT MODEL

In Chap. 5, "Dosage Regimens," several equations were presented without a formal derivation or explanation of how they were obtained. The following will give the interested student more insight into the nature of the equations and the system they describe.

The first-order equation for loss of drug from the body following a single rapid I.V. injection for a drug described by a one-compartment model is

$$D = D_0 e^{-\beta t} \tag{55a}$$

where D is the total amount of drug remaining in the body, D_0 is the dose, and t is the time elapsed after the administration of a dose. For the first dosage interval the maximum amount of drug in the body will be equal to the dose, D_0. The minimum amount will be equal to the amount remaining in the body when $t = \tau$. Thus from Eq. (55a),

$$D_{min}^1 = D_0 e^{-\beta \tau} \tag{56a}$$

where τ is the dosing interval. The value of D_{min}^1 is the amount of drug which has accumulated in the body before the administration of the second dose. When the second I.V. injection is given, the time course of the drug in the body is described by

$$D^2 = (D_0 + D_{min}^1) e^{-\beta t} \tag{57a}$$

or

$$D^2 = (D_0 + D_0 e^{-\beta \tau}) e^{-\beta t} \tag{58a}$$

The maximum amount of drug in the body during the second dosage interval will be that amount present when $t = 0$ and thus

$$D_{max}^2 = D_0 + D_0 e^{-\beta \tau} = D_0 + D_{min}^1 \tag{59a}$$

348

The minimum during the second interval will occur when $t = \tau$ as before, yielding

$$D_{min}^2 = D_0 e^{-\beta\tau} + D_0 e^{-2\beta\tau} \qquad (60a)$$

When a third dose is administered, the amount of drug in the body as a function of time will be given by

$$D^3 = (D_0 + D_0 e^{-\beta\tau} + D_0 e^{-2\beta\tau})e^{-\beta t} \qquad (61a)$$

or

$$D^3 = (D_0 + D_{min}^2)e^{-\beta t} \qquad (62a)$$

Using the same reasoning as was used previously, it can be shown that

$$D_{max}^3 = (D_0 + D_0 e^{-\beta\tau} + D_0 e^{-2\beta\tau}) = D_0 + D_{min}^2 \qquad (63a)$$

and

$$D_{min}^3 = (D_0 e^{-\beta\tau} + D_0 e^{-2\beta\tau} + D_0 e^{-3\beta\tau}) \qquad (64a)$$

It should be apparent by now that the amount of drug in the body after n doses will be described by the equations

$$D^n = (D_0 + D_{min}^{n-1})e^{-\beta t} \qquad (65a)$$

$$D_{max}^n = D_0 + D_{min}^{n-1} \qquad (66a)$$

$$D_{min}^n = D_0 e^{-\beta\tau} + D_0 e^{-2\beta\tau} + \cdots + D_0 e^{-n\beta\tau} \qquad (67a)$$

Expanding Eq. (65a) gives

$$D^n = D_0(1 + e^{-\beta\tau} + e^{-2\beta\tau} + \cdots + e^{-(n-1)\beta\tau})e^{-\beta t} \qquad (68a)$$

If we let the sum inside the parentheses equal X, then

$$Xe^{-\beta\tau} = e^{-\beta\tau} + e^{-2\beta\tau} + \cdots + e^{-n\beta\tau} \qquad (69a)$$

Subtracting Eq. (69a) from the equation for X gives

$$X - Xe^{-\beta\tau} = X(1 - e^{-\beta\tau}) = 1 - e^{-n\beta\tau} \qquad (70a)$$

Thus

$$X = \frac{1 - e^{-n\beta\tau}}{1 - e^{-\beta\tau}} \tag{71a}$$

which is a specific case of Eq. (11) in Chap. 5. Therefore (68a) may be written as

$$D^n = D_0 \left(\frac{1 - e^{-n\beta\tau}}{1 - e^{-\beta\tau}} \right) e^{-\beta t} \tag{72a}$$

Using similar arguments, Eqs. (65a) and (67a) may be rewritten

$$D^n_{max} = D_0 \left(\frac{1 - e^{-n\beta\tau}}{1 - e^{-\beta\tau}} \right) \tag{73a}$$

$$D^n_{min} = D_0 \left(\frac{1 - e^{-n\beta\tau}}{1 - e^{-\beta\tau}} \right) e^{-\beta\tau} \tag{74a}$$

The steady state will be reached when a sufficiently large number of doses have been given (i.e., as $n \to \infty$). Thus at the *steady state*,

$$D^\infty = \left(\frac{D_0}{1 - e^{-\beta\tau}} \right) e^{-\beta t} \tag{75a}$$

$$D^\infty_{max} = \frac{D_0}{1 - e^{-\beta\tau}} \tag{76a}$$

$$D^\infty_{min} = \frac{D_0 e^{-\beta\tau}}{1 - e^{-\beta\tau}} \tag{77a}$$

Recalling that we defined τ in terms of f as follows,

$$\tau = \frac{\ln(f)}{-\beta} \tag{78a}$$

Then

$$f = e^{-\beta\tau} \tag{79a}$$

Thus Eqs. (76a) and (77a) may be written

$$D^\infty_{max} = \frac{D_0}{1 - f} \tag{80a}$$

$$D^\infty_{min} = \frac{f D_0}{1 - f} = D^\infty_{max} - D_0 \tag{81a}$$

which are Eqs. (8) and (7) in Chap. 5.

LIST OF SYMBOLS OF GENERAL OCCURRENCE

A   the intercept of a semilog plot of slope $-\alpha$ in two-compartment analysis; $A = D_0(k_{21} - \alpha)/V_p(\beta - \alpha)$

AUC   the area under the curve for the concentration of drug in blood as a function of time

B   *compartmental schemes*—the central compartment or "blood" which may include well-perfused tissues
two-compartment analysis—the intercept of the first-order plot of slope $-\beta$; $B = D_0(k_{21} - \beta)/V_p(\alpha - \beta)$

β apparent first-order rate constant for elimination of drug from the body

β_e apprent first-order rate constant for *excretion* of drug from the body (intact drug)

β_m apparent first-order rate constant for loss of drug from the body by *metabolism*

C   general term for expressing a first-order rate process in terms of clearance where $C = (\text{rate})_t/(\text{concentration})_t$
in compartmental analysis—the compartment representing elimination from the body

C_{Cr} creatinine renal clearance

C_R renal clearance

C_T total body clearance; $C_T = \beta Vd = k_2 V_1$ (or $k_2 V_p$)

D   total amount of drug in the body $(D = P' + T')$

D_0 administered dose of a drug

D^* loading dose

D_{inf} the amount of drug in the body during steady state achieved by constant rate infusion

$\bar{D}_{ss}$ the average amount of drug in the body during steady state achieved by constant repetitive dosing at fixed time intervals

f   the fraction remaining in the case of a first-order process ($t_f = \ln f/-k$)

F   the fraction of a dose absorbed from the site of administration

K   an apparent equilibrium constant

k   a rate constant

k_0 a zero-order rate constant

k_1 *in modeling*—the first-order rate constant for absorption
        in general—a first-order rate constant

k_{12} first-order rate constant for transfer of drug from B (compartment 1) to T (compartment 2)

k_{21} first-order rate constant for transfer of drug from T (compartment 2) to B (compartment 1)

k_2 first-order rate constant for elimination of drug from the B compartment

k_m first-order rate constant for removal of drug from B by *metabolism*

K_m the Michaelis constant; K_m equals the concentration which results in a rate of $V_{max}/2$

k_e first-order rate constant for *excretion* of intact drug from B

M.E.C. minimum effective concentration of drug for desired effect (usually in blood)

P   concentration of drug in the B compartment at some specific time

P' the amount of drug in the B compartment at some specific time

P_{inf} the steady-state drug concentration in B achieved during constant-rate I.V. infusion (also called P_{ss})

P'_{inf} the amount of drug in the B compartment during steady state achieved by I.V. infusion

P^n_{max} the concentration of drug in B at its maximum following the n-th dose

P^n_{min} the concentration of drug in B at its minimum following the n-th dose

P_0 hypothetical value for drug concentration in blood at time zero if all drug remained in B compartment; $P_0 = A + B$ following a rapid I.V. dose

P_{ss} the steady-state drug concentration in B achieved during constant-rate I.V. infusion (also called P_{inf})

$\bar{P}_{ss}$ the average steady-state drug concentration in B during constant repetitive dosing at fixed time intervals

RDS (or rds)   the rate-determining step in a series of consecutive rate processes

T   the tissue compartment (all of the body except the central compartment)

T' the amount of drug in the tissue compartment (T) at some given time

t   time

$t_{1/2}$ half-life

t_f the time for a variable to decrease to the fraction, f, in a first-order process

t_{max} the time at which P_{max} is observed following a single extravascular dose

τ the time between doses

Vd   apparent volume of distribution

Vd_{inf} the apparent volume of distribution that applies to the steady state obtained by constant rate I.V. infusion (also called Vd_{ss})

V_p (or V_1)   the apparent volume of the B compartment; $V_p = D_0/P_0$

V_{max} the maximum rate in a system described by Michaelis-Menten kinetics

NATURAL LOG TABLES

Natural Logarithms

Natural Logarithms* 0.000 — 0.999

x	0.000	0.001	0.002	0.003	0.004	0.005	0.006	0.007	0.008	0.009
0.000	−∞	−6.90776	−6.21461	−5.80914	−5.52146	−5.29832	−5.11600	−4.96185	−4.82831	−4.71053
010	−4.60517	−4.50986	−4.42285	−4.34281	−4.26870	−4.19971	−4.13517	−4.07454	−4.01738	−3.96332
020	−3.91202	−3.86323	−3.81671	−3.77226	−3.72970	−3.68888	−3.64966	−3.61192	−3.57555	−3.54046
030	−3.50656	47377	44202	41125	38139	35241	32424	29684	27017	24419
040	−3.21888	19418	17009	14656	12357	10109	07911	05761	03655	01593
0.050	−2.99573	−2.97593	−2.95651	−2.93746	−2.91877	−2.90042	−2.88240	−2.86470	−2.84731	−2.83022
060	81341	79688	78062	76462	74887	73337	71810	70306	68825	67365
070	65926	64508	63109	61730	60369	59027	57702	56395	55105	53831
080	52573	51331	50104	48891	47694	46510	45341	44185	43042	41912
090	40795	39690	38597	37516	36446	35388	34341	33304	32279	31264
0.100	−2.30259	29263	28278	27303	26336	25379	24432	23493	22562	21641
110	20727	19823	18926	18037	17156	16282	15417	14558	13707	12863
120	12026	11196	10373	09557	08747	07944	07147	06357	05573	04794
130	04022	03256	02495	01741	00992	00248	−1.99510	−1.98777	−1.98050	−1.97328
140	−1.96611	95900	95193	94491	93794	93102	92415	91732	91054	90381
0.150	−1.89712	89048	88387	87732	87080	86433	85790	85151	84516	83885
160	83258	82635	82016	81401	80789	80181	79577	78976	78379	77786
170	77196	76609	76026	75446	74870	74297	73727	73161	72597	72037
180	71480	70926	70375	69827	69282	68740	68201	67665	67131	66601
190	66073	65548	65026	64507	63990	63476	62964	62455	61949	61445
0.200	−1.60944	60445	59949	59455	58964	58475	57988	57504	57022	56542
210	56065	55590	55117	54646	54178	53712	53248	52786	52326	51868
220	51413	50959	50508	50058	49611	49165	48722	48281	47841	47403
230	46968	46534	46102	45672	45243	44817	44392	43970	43548	43129
240	42712	42296	41882	41469	41059	40650	40242	39837	39433	39030
0.250	−1.38629	38230	37833	37437	37042	36649	36258	35868	35480	35093
260	34707	34323	33941	33560	33181	32803	32426	32051	31677	31304
270	30933	30564	30195	29828	29463	29098	28735	28374	28013	27654
280	27297	26940	26585	26231	25878	25527	25176	24827	24479	24133
290	23787	23443	23100	22758	22418	22078	21740	21402	21066	20731
0.300	−1.20397	20065	19733	19402	19073	18744	18417	18091	17766	17441
310	17118	16796	16475	16155	15836	15518	15201	14885	14570	14256
320	13943	13631	13320	13010	12701	12393	12086	11780	11474	11170
330	10866	10564	10262	09961	09661	09362	09064	08767	08471	08176
340	07881	07587	07294	07002	06711	06421	06132	05843	05555	05268
0.350	−1.04982	04697	04412	04129	03846	03564	03282	03002	02722	02443
360	02165	01888	01611	01335	01060	00786	00512	00239	−0.99967	−0.99696
370	−0.99425	99155	98886	98618	98350	98083	97817	97551	97286	97022
380	96758	96496	96233	95972	95711	95451	95192	94933	94675	94418
390	94161	93905	93649	93395	93140	92887	92634	92382	92130	91879
0.400	−0.91629	91379	91130	90882	90634	90387	90140	89894	89649	89404
410	89160	88916	88673	88431	88189	87948	87707	87467	87227	86988
420	86750	86512	86275	86038	85802	85567	85332	85097	84863	84630
430	84397	84165	83933	83702	83471	83241	83011	82782	82554	82326
440	82098	81871	81645	81419	81193	80968	80744	80520	80296	80073
0.450	−0.79851	79629	79407	79186	78966	78746	78526	78307	78089	77871
460	77653	77436	77219	77003	76787	76572	76357	76143	75929	75715
470	75502	75290	75078	74866	74655	74444	74234	74024	73814	73605
480	73397	73189	72981	72774	72567	72361	72155	71949	71744	71539
490	71335	71131	70928	70725	70522	70320	70118	69917	69716	69515

n	0	1	2	3	4	5	6	7	8	9
0.500	−0.69315	−0.69115	−0.68916	−0.68717	−0.68518	−0.68320	−0.68122	−0.67924	−0.67727	−0.67531
510	−0.67334	−0.67139	−0.66943	−0.66748	−0.66553	−0.66359	−0.66165	−0.65971	−0.65778	−0.65585
520	−0.65393	−0.65201	−0.65009	−0.64817	−0.64626	−0.64436	−0.64245	−0.64055	−0.63866	−0.63677
530	−0.63488	−0.63299	−0.63111	−0.62923	−0.62736	−0.62549	−0.62362	−0.62176	−0.61990	−0.61804
540	−0.61619	−0.61434	−0.61249	−0.61065	−0.60881	−0.60697	−0.60514	−0.60331	−0.60148	−0.59966
0.550	−0.59784	−0.59602	−0.59421	−0.59240	−0.59059	−0.58879	−0.58699	−0.58519	−0.58340	−0.58161
560	−0.57982	−0.57803	−0.57625	−0.57448	−0.57270	−0.57093	−0.56916	−0.56740	−0.56563	−0.56387
570	−0.56212	−0.56037	−0.55862	−0.55687	−0.55513	−0.55339	−0.55165	−0.54991	−0.54818	−0.54645
580	−0.54473	−0.54300	−0.54128	−0.53957	−0.53785	−0.53614	−0.53444	−0.53273	−0.53103	−0.52933
590	−0.52763	−0.52594	−0.52425	−0.52256	−0.52088	−0.51919	−0.51751	−0.51584	−0.51416	−0.51249
0.600	−0.51083	−0.50916	−0.50750	−0.50584	−0.50418	−0.50253	−0.50088	−0.49923	−0.49758	−0.49594
610	−0.49430	−0.49266	−0.49102	−0.48939	−0.48776	−0.48613	−0.48451	−0.48289	−0.48127	−0.47965
620	−0.47804	−0.47642	−0.47482	−0.47321	−0.47160	−0.47000	−0.46840	−0.46681	−0.46522	−0.46362
630	−0.46204	−0.46045	−0.45887	−0.45728	−0.45571	−0.45413	−0.45256	−0.45099	−0.44942	−0.44785
640	−0.44629	−0.44473	−0.44317	−0.44161	−0.44006	−0.43850	−0.43696	−0.43541	−0.43386	−0.43232
0.650	−0.43078	−0.42925	−0.42771	−0.42618	−0.42465	−0.42312	−0.42159	−0.42007	−0.41855	−0.41703
660	−0.41552	−0.41400	−0.41249	−0.41098	−0.40947	−0.40797	−0.40647	−0.40497	−0.40347	−0.40197
670	−0.40048	−0.39899	−0.39750	−0.39601	−0.39453	−0.39304	−0.39156	−0.39008	−0.38861	−0.38713
680	−0.38566	−0.38419	−0.38272	−0.38126	−0.37980	−0.37834	−0.37688	−0.37542	−0.37397	−0.37251
690	−0.37106	−0.36962	−0.36817	−0.36673	−0.36528	−0.36384	−0.36241	−0.36097	−0.35954	−0.35810
0.700	−0.35667	−0.35525	−0.35382	−0.35240	−0.35098	−0.34956	−0.34814	−0.34672	−0.34531	−0.34390
710	−0.34249	−0.34108	−0.33968	−0.33827	−0.33687	−0.33547	−0.33408	−0.33268	−0.33129	−0.32989
720	−0.32850	−0.32712	−0.32573	−0.32435	−0.32296	−0.32158	−0.32021	−0.31883	−0.31745	−0.31608
730	−0.31471	−0.31334	−0.31197	−0.31061	−0.30925	−0.30788	−0.30653	−0.30517	−0.30381	−0.30246
740	−0.30111	−0.29975	−0.29841	−0.29706	−0.29571	−0.29437	−0.29303	−0.29169	−0.29035	−0.28902
0.750	−0.28768	−0.28635	−0.28502	−0.28369	−0.28236	−0.28104	−0.27971	−0.27839	−0.27707	−0.27575
760	−0.27444	−0.27312	−0.27181	−0.27050	−0.26919	−0.26788	−0.26657	−0.26527	−0.26397	−0.26266
770	−0.26136	−0.26007	−0.25877	−0.25748	−0.25618	−0.25489	−0.25360	−0.25231	−0.25103	−0.24974
780	−0.24846	−0.24718	−0.24590	−0.24462	−0.24335	−0.24207	−0.24080	−0.23953	−0.23826	−0.23699
790	−0.23572	−0.23446	−0.23319	−0.23193	−0.23067	−0.22941	−0.22816	−0.22690	−0.22565	−0.22439
0.800	−0.22314	−0.22189	−0.22065	−0.21940	−0.21816	−0.21691	−0.21567	−0.21443	−0.21319	−0.21196
810	−0.21072	−0.20949	−0.20825	−0.20702	−0.20579	−0.20457	−0.20334	−0.20212	−0.20089	−0.19967
820	−0.19845	−0.19723	−0.19601	−0.19480	−0.19358	−0.19237	−0.19116	−0.18995	−0.18874	−0.18754
830	−0.18633	−0.18515	−0.18392	−0.18272	−0.18152	−0.18032	−0.17913	−0.17793	−0.17674	−0.17554
840	−0.17435	−0.17316	−0.17198	−0.17079	−0.16960	−0.16842	−0.16724	−0.16605	−0.16487	−0.16370
0.850	−0.16252	−0.16117	−0.16017	−0.15900	−0.15782	−0.15665	−0.15548	−0.15432	−0.15315	−0.15199
860	−0.15032	−0.14966	−0.14850	−0.14734	−0.14618	−0.14503	−0.14387	−0.14272	−0.14156	−0.14041
870	−0.13926	−0.13811	−0.13697	−0.13582	−0.13467	−0.13353	−0.13239	−0.13125	−0.13011	−0.12897
880	−0.12783	−0.12670	−0.12556	−0.12443	−0.12330	−0.12217	−0.12104	−0.11991	−0.11878	−0.11766
890	−0.11653	−0.11541	−0.11429	−0.11317	−0.11205	−0.11093	−0.10981	−0.10870	−0.10759	−0.10647
0.900	−0.10536	−0.10425	−0.10314	−0.10203	−0.10093	−0.09982	−0.09872	−0.09761	−0.09651	−0.09541
910	−0.09431	−0.09321	−0.09212	−0.09102	−0.08992	−0.08883	−0.08774	−0.08665	−0.08556	−0.08447
920	−0.08338	−0.08230	−0.08121	−0.08013	−0.07904	−0.07796	−0.07688	−0.07580	−0.07472	−0.07365
930	−0.07257	−0.07150	−0.07042	−0.06935	−0.06828	−0.06721	−0.06614	−0.06507	−0.06401	−0.06294
940	−0.06188	−0.06081	−0.05975	−0.05869	−0.05763	−0.05657	−0.05551	−0.05446	−0.05340	−0.05235
0.950	−0.05129	−0.05024	−0.04919	−0.04814	−0.04709	−0.04604	−0.04500	−0.04395	−0.04291	−0.04186
960	−0.04082	−0.03978	−0.03874	−0.03770	−0.03666	−0.03563	−0.03459	−0.03356	−0.03252	−0.03149
970	−0.03046	−0.02943	−0.02840	−0.02737	−0.02634	−0.02532	−0.02429	−0.02327	−0.02225	−0.02122
980	−0.02020	−0.01918	−0.01816	−0.01715	−0.01613	−0.01511	−0.01410	−0.01309	−0.01207	−0.01106
990	−0.01005	−0.00904	−0.00803	−0.00702	−0.00602	−0.00501	−0.00401	−0.00300	−0.00200	−0.00100

* To find the natural logarithm ($\log_e$) of a number which is a power of ten less or greater than a number given in the table: if the number concerned is *less*, e.g., $1/10$ (10^{-1}), $1/100$ (10^{-2}), $1/1000$ (10^{-3}), etc., *subtract* from the given logarithm $\log_e 10$, $2\log_e 10$, $3\log_e 10$, etc.; if the number concerned is *greater*, e.g., 10 times (10^1), 100 times (10^2), 1000 times (10^3), etc., *add* to the given logarithm $\log_e 10$, $2\log_e 10$, $3\log_e 10$, etc. Examples: $\log_e 0.02 = \log_e 2 - \log_e 10$; $\log_e 2000 = \log_e 200 + \log_e 10$.

Natural Logarithms

Natural Logarithms* 1.00—9.99

x	0.00	0.01	0.02	0.03	0.04	0.05	0.06	0.07	0.08	0.09
1.00	0.00000	0.00995	0.01980	0.02956	0.03922	0.04879	0.05827	0.06766	0.07696	0.08618
10	09531	10436	11333	12222	13103	13976	14842	15700	16551	17395
20	18232	19062	19885	20701	21511	22314	23111	23902	24686	25464
30	26236	27003	27763	28518	29267	30010	30748	31481	32208	32930
40	33647	34359	35066	35767	36464	37156	37844	38526	39204	39878
1.50	0.40547	0.41211	0.41871	0.42527	0.43178	0.43825	0.44469	0.45108	0.45742	0.46373
60	47000	47623	48243	48858	49470	50078	50682	51282	51879	52473
70	53063	53649	54232	54812	55389	55962	56531	57098	57661	58222
80	58779	59333	59884	60432	60977	61519	62058	62594	63127	63658
90	64185	64710	65233	65752	66269	66783	67294	67803	68310	68813
2.00	0.69315	0.69813	0.70310	0.70804	0.71295	0.71784	0.72271	0.72755	0.73237	0.73716
10	74194	74669	75142	75612	76081	76547	77011	77473	77932	78390
20	78846	79299	79751	80200	80648	81093	81536	81978	82418	82855
30	83291	83725	84157	84587	85015	85442	85866	86289	86710	87129
40	87547	87963	88377	88789	89200	89609	90016	90422	90826	91228
2.50	0.91629	0.92028	0.92426	0.92822	0.93216	0.93609	0.94001	0.94391	0.94779	0.95166
60	95551	95935	96317	96698	97078	97456	97833	98208	98582	98954
70	99325	99695	1.00063	1.00430	1.00796	1.01160	1.01523	1.01885	1.02245	1.02604
80	1.02962	1.03318	03674	04028	04380	04732	05082	05431	05779	06126
90	06471	06815	07158	07500	07841	08181	08519	08856	09192	09527
3.00	1.09861	1.10194	1.10526	1.10856	1.11186	1.11514	1.11841	1.12168	1.12493	1.12817
10	13140	13462	13783	14103	14422	14740	15057	15373	15688	16002
20	16315	16627	16938	17248	17557	17865	18173	18479	18784	19089
30	19392	19695	19996	20297	20597	20896	21194	21491	21788	22083
40	22378	22671	22964	23256	23547	23837	24127	24415	24703	24990
3.50	1.25276	1.25562	1.25846	1.26130	1.26413	1.26695	1.26976	1.27257	1.27536	1.27815
60	28093	28371	28647	28923	29198	29473	29746	30019	30291	30563
70	30833	31103	31372	31641	31909	32176	32442	32708	32972	33237
80	33500	33763	34025	34286	34547	34807	35067	35325	35584	35841
90	36098	36354	36609	36864	37118	37372	37624	37877	38128	38379
4.00	1.38629	1.38879	1.39128	1.39377	1.39624	1.39872	1.40118	1.40364	1.40610	1.40854
10	41099	41342	41585	41828	42070	42311	42552	42792	43031	43270
20	43508	43746	43984	44220	44456	44692	44927	45161	45395	45629
30	45862	46094	46326	46557	46787	47018	47247	47476	47705	47933
40	48160	48387	48614	48840	49065	49290	49515	49739	49962	50185
4.50	1.50408	1.50630	1.50851	1.51072	1.51293	1.51513	1.51732	1.51951	1.52170	1.52388
60	52606	52823	53039	53256	53471	53687	53902	54116	54330	54543
70	54756	54969	55181	55393	55604	55814	56025	56235	56444	56653
80	56862	57070	57277	57485	57691	57898	58104	58309	58515	58719
90	58924	59127	59331	59534	59737	59939	60141	60342	60543	60744
5.00	1.60944	1.61144	1.61343	1.61542	1.61741	1.61939	1.62137	1.62334	1.62531	1.62728
10	62924	63120	63315	63511	63705	63900	64094	64287	64481	64673
20	64866	65058	65250	65441	65632	65823	66013	66203	66393	66582
30	66771	66959	67147	67335	67523	67710	67896	68083	68269	68455
40	68640	68825	69010	69194	69378	69562	69745	69928	70111	70293

N	0	1	2	3	4	5	6	7	8	9
5.50	1.70475	1.70656	1.70838	1.71019	1.71199	1.71380	1.71560	1.71740	1.71919	1.72098
60	1.72277	1.72455	1.72633	1.72811	1.72988	1.73166	1.73342	1.73519	1.73695	1.73871
70	1.74047	1.74222	1.74397	1.74572	1.74746	1.74920	1.75094	1.75267	1.75440	1.75613
80	1.75786	1.75958	1.76130	1.76302	1.76473	1.76644	1.76815	1.76985	1.77156	1.77326
90	1.77495	1.77665	1.77834	1.78002	1.78171	1.78339	1.78507	1.78675	1.78842	1.79009
6.00	1.79176	1.79342	1.79509	1.79675	1.79840	1.80006	1.80171	1.80336	1.80500	1.80665
10	1.80829	1.80993	1.81156	1.81319	1.81482	1.81645	1.81808	1.81970	1.82132	1.82294
20	1.82455	1.82616	1.82777	1.82938	1.83098	1.83258	1.83418	1.83578	1.83737	1.83896
30	1.84055	1.84214	1.84372	1.84530	1.84688	1.84845	1.85003	1.85160	1.85317	1.85473
40	1.85630	1.85786	1.85942	1.86097	1.86253	1.86408	1.86563	1.86718	1.86872	1.87026
6.50	1.87180	1.87334	1.87487	1.87641	1.87794	1.87947	1.88099	1.88251	1.88403	1.88555
60	1.88707	1.88858	1.89010	1.89160	1.89311	1.89462	1.89612	1.89762	1.89912	1.90061
70	1.90211	1.90360	1.90509	1.90658	1.90806	1.90954	1.91102	1.91250	1.91398	1.91545
80	1.91692	1.91839	1.91986	1.92132	1.92279	1.92425	1.92571	1.92716	1.92862	1.93007
90	1.93152	1.93297	1.93442	1.93586	1.93730	1.93874	1.94018	1.94162	1.94305	1.94448
7.00	1.94591	1.94734	1.94876	1.95019	1.95161	1.95303	1.95445	1.95586	1.95727	1.95869
10	1.96009	1.96150	1.96291	1.96431	1.96571	1.96711	1.96851	1.96991	1.97130	1.97269
20	1.97408	1.97547	1.97685	1.97824	1.97962	1.98100	1.98238	1.98376	1.98513	1.98650
30	1.98787	1.98924	1.99061	1.99198	1.99334	1.99470	1.99606	1.99742	1.99877	2.00013
40	2.00148	2.00283	2.00418	2.00553	2.00687	2.00821	2.00956	2.01089	2.01223	2.01357
7.50	2.01490	2.01624	2.01757	2.01890	2.02022	2.02155	2.02287	2.02419	2.02551	2.02683
60	2.02815	2.02946	2.03078	2.03209	2.03340	2.03471	2.03601	2.03732	2.03862	2.03992
70	2.04122	2.04252	2.04381	2.04511	2.04640	2.04769	2.04898	2.05027	2.05156	2.05284
80	2.05412	2.05540	2.05668	2.05796	2.05924	2.06051	2.06179	2.06306	2.06433	2.06560
90	2.06686	2.06813	2.06939	2.07065	2.07191	2.07317	2.07443	2.07568	2.07694	2.07819
8.00	2.07944	2.08069	2.08194	2.08318	2.08443	2.08567	2.08691	2.08815	2.08939	2.09063
10	2.09186	2.09310	2.09433	2.09556	2.09679	2.09802	2.09924	2.10047	2.10169	2.10291
20	2.10413	2.10535	2.10657	2.10779	2.10900	2.11021	2.11142	2.11263	2.11384	2.11505
30	2.11626	2.11746	2.11866	2.11986	2.12106	2.12226	2.12346	2.12465	2.12585	2.12704
40	2.12823	2.12942	2.13061	2.13180	2.13298	2.13417	2.13535	2.13653	2.13771	2.13889
8.50	2.14007	2.14124	2.14242	2.14359	2.14476	2.14593	2.14710	2.14827	2.14943	2.15060
60	2.15176	2.15292	2.15409	2.15524	2.15640	2.15756	2.15871	2.15987	2.16102	2.16217
70	2.16332	2.16447	2.16562	2.16677	2.16791	2.16905	2.17020	2.17134	2.17248	2.17361
80	2.17475	2.17589	2.17702	2.17816	2.17929	2.18042	2.18155	2.18267	2.18380	2.18493
90	2.18605	2.18717	2.18830	2.18942	2.19054	2.19165	2.19277	2.19389	2.19500	2.19611
9.00	2.19722	2.19834	2.19944	2.20055	2.20167	2.20276	2.20387	2.20497	2.20607	2.20717
10	2.20827	2.20937	2.21047	2.21157	2.21266	2.21375	2.21485	2.21594	2.21703	2.21813
20	2.21920	2.22029	2.22138	2.22246	2.22354	2.22462	2.22570	2.22678	2.22786	2.22894
30	2.23001	2.23109	2.23216	2.23324	2.23431	2.23538	2.23645	2.23751	2.23858	2.23965
40	2.24071	2.24177	2.24284	2.24390	2.24496	2.24601	2.24707	2.24813	2.24918	2.25024
9.50	2.25129	2.25234	2.25339	2.25444	2.25549	2.25654	2.25759	2.25863	2.25968	2.26072
60	2.26176	2.26280	2.26384	2.26488	2.26592	2.26696	2.26799	2.26903	2.27006	2.27109
70	2.27213	2.27316	2.27419	2.27521	2.27624	2.27727	2.27829	2.27932	2.28034	2.28136
80	2.28238	2.28340	2.28442	2.28544	2.28646	2.28747	2.28849	2.28950	2.29051	2.29152
90	2.29253	2.29354	2.29455	2.29556	2.29657	2.29757	2.29858	2.29958	2.30058	2.30158

* To find the natural logarithm ($\log_e$) of a number which is a power of ten less or greater than a number given in the table: if the number concerned is *less*, e.g., $1/10$ (10^{-1}), $1/100$ (10^{-2}), $1/1000$ (10^{-3}), etc., *subtract* from the given logarithm $\log_e 10$, $2\log_e 10$, $3\log_e 10$, etc.; if the number concerned is *greater*, e.g., 10 times (10^1), 100 times (10^2), 1000 times (10^3), etc., *add* to the given logarithm $\log_e 10$, $2\log_e 10$, $3\log_e 10$, etc. Examples: $\log_e 0.02 = \log_e 0.2 - \log_e 10$; $\log_e 2000 = \log_e 200 + \log_e 10$.

Natural Logarithms* 10.0—99.9

x	0.0	0.1	0.2	0.3	0.4	0.5	0.6	0.7	0.8	0.9
10.0	2.30259	2.31254	2.32239	2.33214	2.34181	2.35138	2.36085	2.37024	2.37955	2.38876
11.0	39790	40695	41591	42480	43361	44235	45101	45959	46810	47654
12.0	48491	49321	50144	50960	51770	52573	53370	54160	54945	55723
13.0	56495	57261	58022	58776	59525	60269	61007	61740	62467	63189
14.0	63906	64617	65324	66026	66723	67415	68102	68785	69463	70136
15.0	2.70805	2.71469	2.72130	2.72785	2.73437	2.74084	2.74727	2.75366	2.76001	2.76632
16.0	77259	77882	78501	79117	79728	80336	80940	81541	82138	82731
17.0	83321	83908	84491	85071	85647	86220	86790	87356	87920	88480
18.0	89037	89591	90142	90690	91235	91777	92316	92852	93386	93916
19.0	94444	94969	95491	96011	96527	97041	97553	98062	98568	99072
20.0	2.99573	3.00072	3.00568	3.01062	3.01553	3.02042	3.02529	3.03013	3.03495	3.03975
21.0	3.04452	04927	05400	05871	06339	06805	07269	07731	08191	08649
22.0	09104	09558	10009	10459	10906	11352	11795	12236	12676	13114
23.0	13549	13983	14415	14845	15274	15700	16125	16548	16969	17388
24.0	17805	18221	18635	19048	19458	19867	20275	20680	21084	21487
25.0	3.21888	3.22287	3.22684	3.23080	3.23475	3.23868	3.24259	3.24649	3.25037	3.25424
26.0	25810	26194	26576	26957	27336	27714	28091	28466	28840	29213
27.0	29584	29953	30322	30689	31054	31419	31782	32143	32504	32863
28.0	33220	33577	33932	34286	34639	34990	35341	35690	36038	36384
29.0	36730	37074	37417	37759	38099	38439	38777	39115	39451	39786
30.0	3.40120	3.40453	3.40784	3.41115	3.41444	3.41773	3.42100	3.42426	3.42751	3.43076
31.0	43399	43721	44042	44362	44681	44999	45316	45632	45947	46261
32.0	46574	46886	47197	47507	47816	48124	48431	48736	49043	49347
33.0	49651	49953	50255	50556	50856	51155	51453	51750	52046	52342
34.0	52636	52930	53223	53515	53806	54096	54385	54674	54962	55249
35.0	3.55535	3.55820	3.56105	3.56388	3.56671	3.56953	3.57235	3.57515	3.57795	3.58074
36.0	58352	58629	58906	59182	59457	59731	60005	60278	60550	60821
37.0	61092	61362	61631	61899	62167	62434	62700	62966	63231	63495
38.0	63759	64021	64284	64545	64806	65066	65325	65584	65842	66099
39.0	66356	66612	66868	67122	67377	67630	67883	68135	68387	68638
40.0	3.68888	3.69138	3.69387	3.69635	3.69883	3.70130	3.70377	3.70623	3.70868	3.71113
41.0	71357	71601	71844	72086	72328	72569	72810	73050	73290	73529
42.0	73767	74005	74242	74479	74715	74950	75185	75420	75654	75887
43.0	76120	76352	76584	76815	77046	77276	77506	77735	77963	78191
44.0	78419	78646	78872	79098	79324	79549	79773	79997	80221	80444
45.0	3.80666	3.80888	3.81110	3.81331	3.81551	3.81771	3.81991	3.82210	3.82428	3.82647
46.0	82864	83081	83298	83514	83730	83945	84160	84374	84588	84802
47.0	85015	85227	85439	85651	85862	86073	86283	86493	86703	86912
48.0	87120	87328	87536	87743	87950	88156	88362	88568	88773	88978
49.0	89182	89386	89589	89792	89995	90197	90399	90600	90801	91002
50.0	3.91202	3.91402	3.91602	3.91801	3.91999	3.92197	3.92395	3.92593	3.92790	3.92986
51.0	93183	93378	93574	93769	93964	94158	94352	94546	94739	94932
52.0	95124	95316	95508	95700	95891	96081	96272	96462	96651	96840
53.0	97029	97218	97406	97594	97781	97968	98155	98341	98527	98713
54.0	98898	99083	99268	99452	99636	99820	4.00003	4.00186	4.00369	4.00551

	.0	.1	.2	.3	.4	.5	.6	.7	.8	.9
55.0	4.00733	4.00915	4.01096	4.01277	4.01458	4.01638	4.01818	4.01998	4.02177	4.02356
56.0	02535	02714	02892	03069	03247	03424	03601	03777	03954	04130
57.0	04305	04480	04655	04830	05004	05178	05352	05526	05699	05872
58.0	06044	06217	06389	06560	06732	06903	07073	07244	07414	07584
59.0	07754	07923	08092	08261	08429	08598	08766	08933	09101	09268
60.0	4.09434	4.09601	4.09767	4.09933	4.10099	4.10264	4.10429	4.10594	4.10759	4.10923
61.0	11087	11251	11415	11578	11741	11904	12066	12228	12390	12552
62.0	12713	12875	13036	13196	13357	13517	13677	13836	13996	14155
63.0	14313	14472	14630	14789	14946	15104	15261	15418	15575	15732
64.0	15888	16044	16200	16356	16511	16667	16821	16976	17131	17285
65.0	4.17439	4.17592	4.17746	4.17899	4.18052	4.18205	4.18358	4.18510	4.18662	4.18814
66.0	18965	19117	19268	19419	19570	19720	19870	20020	20170	20320
67.0	20469	20618	20767	20916	21065	21213	21361	21509	21656	21804
68.0	21951	22098	22244	22391	22537	22683	22829	22975	23120	23266
69.0	23411	23555	23700	23844	23989	24133	24276	24420	24563	24707
70.0	4.24850	4.24992	4.25135	4.25277	4.25419	4.25561	4.25703	4.25845	4.25986	4.26127
71.0	26268	26409	26549	26690	26830	26970	27110	27249	27388	27528
72.0	27667	27805	27944	28082	28221	28359	28496	28634	28772	28909
73.0	29046	29183	29320	29456	29592	29729	29865	30000	30136	30271
74.0	30407	30542	30676	30811	30946	31080	31214	31348	31482	31615
75.0	4.31749	4.31882	4.32015	4.32149	4.32281	4.32413	4.32546	4.32678	4.32810	4.32942
76.0	33073	33205	33336	33467	33598	33729	33860	33990	34120	34251
77.0	34381	34510	34640	34769	34899	35028	35157	35286	35414	35543
78.0	35671	35800	35927	36055	36182	36310	36437	36564	36691	36818
79.0	36945	37071	37198	37324	37450	37576	37701	37827	37952	38078
80.0	4.38203	4.38328	4.38452	4.38577	4.38701	4.38826	4.38950	4.39074	4.39198	4.39321
81.0	39445	39568	39692	39815	39938	40060	40183	40305	40428	40550
82.0	40672	40794	40916	41037	41159	41280	41401	41522	41643	41764
83.0	41884	42004	42125	42245	42365	42485	42604	42724	42843	42963
84.0	43082	43201	43319	43438	43557	43675	43793	43912	44030	44147
85.0	4.44265	4.44383	4.44500	4.44617	4.44735	4.44852	4.44969	4.45085	4.45202	4.45318
86.0	45435	45551	45667	45783	45899	46014	46130	46245	46361	46476
87.0	46591	46706	46820	46935	47050	47164	47278	47392	47506	47620
88.0	47734	47847	47961	48074	48187	48300	48413	48526	48639	48751
89.0	48864	48976	49088	49200	49312	49424	49536	49647	49758	49870
90.0	4.49981	4.50092	4.50203	4.50314	4.50424	4.50535	4.50645	4.50756	4.50866	4.50976
91.0	51086	51196	51305	51415	51525	51634	51743	51852	51961	52070
92.0	52179	52287	52396	52504	52613	52721	52829	52937	53045	53152
93.0	53260	53367	53475	53582	53689	53796	53903	54010	54116	54223
94.0	54329	54436	54542	54648	54754	54860	54966	55071	55177	55282
95.0	4.55388	4.55493	4.55598	4.55703	4.55808	4.55913	4.56017	4.56122	4.56226	4.56331
96.0	56435	56539	56643	56747	56851	56954	57058	57161	57265	57368
97.0	57471	57574	57677	57780	57883	57985	58088	58190	58292	58395
98.0	58497	58599	58701	58802	58904	59006	59107	59208	59310	59411
99.0	59512	59613	59714	59815	59915	60016	60116	60217	60317	60417

* To find the natural logarithm ($\log_e$) of a number which is a power of ten less or greater than a number given in the table: if the number concerned is *less*, e.g., $1/10$ (10^{-1}), $1/100$ (10^{-2}), $1/1000$ (10^{-3}), $1/10000$ (10^{-4}), etc., *subtract* from the given logarithm $\log_e 10$, $2 \log_e 10$, $3 \log_e 10$, etc.; if the number concerned is *greater*, e.g., 10 times (10^1), 100 times (10^2), 1000 times (10^3), etc., *add* to the given logarithm $\log_e 10$, $2 \log_e 10$, $3 \log_e 10$, etc. Examples: $\log_e 0.02 = \log_e 2 - \log_e 10$; $\log_e 2000 = \log_e 200 + \log_e 10$.

Natural Logarithms

Natural Logarithms* 0—999

x	0	1	2	3	4	5	6	7	8	9
00	∞	0.00000	0.69315	1.09861	1.38629	1.60944	1.79176	1.94591	2.07944	2.19722
10	2.30259	2.39790	2.48491	2.56495	2.63906	2.70805	2.77259	2.83321	2.89037	2.94444
20	2.99573	3.04452	3.09104	3.13549	3.17805	3.21888	3.25810	3.29584	3.33220	3.36730
30	3.40120	3.43399	3.46574	3.49651	3.52636	3.55535	3.58352	3.61092	3.63759	3.66356
40	3.68888	3.71357	3.73767	3.76120	3.78419	3.80666	3.82864	3.85015	3.87120	3.89182
50	3.91202	3.93183	3.95124	3.97029	3.98898	4.00733	4.02535	4.04305	4.06044	4.07754
60	4.09434	4.11087	4.12713	4.14313	4.15888	4.17439	4.18965	4.20469	4.21951	4.23411
70	4.24850	4.26268	4.27667	4.29046	4.30407	4.31749	4.33073	4.34381	4.35671	4.36945
80	4.38203	4.39445	4.40672	4.41884	4.43082	4.44265	4.45435	4.46591	4.47734	4.48864
90	4.49981	4.51086	4.52179	4.53260	4.54329	4.55388	4.56435	4.57471	4.58497	4.59512
100	4.60517	4.61512	4.62497	4.63473	4.64439	4.65396	4.66344	4.67283	4.68213	4.69135
110	4.70048	4.70953	4.71850	4.72739	4.73620	4.74493	4.75359	4.76217	4.77068	4.77912
120	4.78749	4.79579	4.80402	4.81218	4.82028	4.82831	4.83628	4.84419	4.85203	4.85981
130	4.86753	4.87520	4.88280	4.89035	4.89784	4.90527	4.91265	4.91998	4.92725	4.93447
140	4.94164	4.94876	4.95583	4.96284	4.96981	4.97673	4.98361	4.99043	4.99721	5.00395
150	5.01064	5.01728	5.02388	5.03044	5.03695	5.04343	5.04986	5.05625	5.06260	5.06890
160	5.07517	5.08140	5.08760	5.09375	5.09987	5.10595	5.11199	5.11799	5.12396	5.12990
170	5.13580	5.14166	5.14749	5.15329	5.15906	5.16479	5.17048	5.17615	5.18178	5.18739
180	5.19296	5.19850	5.20401	5.20949	5.21494	5.22036	5.22575	5.23111	5.23644	5.24175
190	5.24702	5.25227	5.25750	5.26269	5.26786	5.27300	5.27811	5.28320	5.28827	5.29330
200	5.29832	5.30330	5.30827	5.31321	5.31812	5.32301	5.32788	5.33272	5.33754	5.34233
210	5.34711	5.35186	5.35659	5.36129	5.36598	5.37064	5.37528	5.37990	5.38450	5.38907
220	5.39363	5.39816	5.40268	5.40717	5.41165	5.41610	5.42053	5.42495	5.42935	5.43372
230	5.43808	5.44242	5.44674	5.45104	5.45532	5.45959	5.46383	5.46806	5.47227	5.47646
240	5.48064	5.48480	5.48894	5.49306	5.49717	5.50126	5.50533	5.50939	5.51343	5.51745
250	5.52146	5.52545	5.52943	5.53339	5.53733	5.54126	5.54518	5.54908	5.55296	5.55683
260	5.56068	5.56452	5.56834	5.57215	5.57595	5.57973	5.58350	5.58725	5.59099	5.59471
270	5.59842	5.60212	5.60580	5.60947	5.61313	5.61677	5.62040	5.62402	5.62762	5.63121
280	5.63479	5.63835	5.64191	5.64545	5.64897	5.65249	5.65599	5.65948	5.66296	5.66643
290	5.66988	5.67332	5.67675	5.68017	5.68358	5.68698	5.69036	5.69373	5.69709	5.70044
300	5.70378	5.70711	5.71043	5.71373	5.71703	5.72031	5.72359	5.72685	5.73010	5.73334
310	5.73657	5.73979	5.74300	5.74620	5.74939	5.75257	5.75574	5.75890	5.76205	5.76519
320	5.76832	5.77144	5.77455	5.77765	5.78074	5.78383	5.78690	5.78996	5.79301	5.79606
330	5.79909	5.80212	5.80513	5.80814	5.81114	5.81413	5.81711	5.82008	5.82305	5.82600
340	5.82895	5.83188	5.83481	5.83773	5.84064	5.84354	5.84644	5.84932	5.85220	5.85507
350	5.85793	5.86079	5.86363	5.86647	5.86930	5.87212	5.87493	5.87774	5.88053	5.88332
360	5.88610	5.88888	5.89164	5.89440	5.89715	5.89990	5.90263	5.90536	5.90808	5.91080
370	5.91350	5.91620	5.91889	5.92158	5.92426	5.92693	5.92959	5.93225	5.93489	5.93754
380	5.94017	5.94290	5.94542	5.94803	5.95064	5.95324	5.95584	5.95842	5.96101	5.96358
390	5.96615	5.96871	5.97126	5.97381	5.97635	5.97889	5.98141	5.98394	5.98645	5.98896
400	5.99146	5.99396	5.99645	5.99894	6.00141	6.00389	6.00635	6.00881	6.01127	6.01372
410	6.01616	6.01859	6.02102	6.02345	6.02587	6.02828	6.03069	6.03309	6.03548	6.03787
420	6.04025	6.04263	6.04501	6.04737	6.04973	6.05209	6.05444	6.05678	6.05912	6.06146
430	6.06379	6.06611	6.06843	6.07074	6.07304	6.07535	6.07764	6.07993	6.08222	6.08450
440	6.08677	6.08904	6.09131	6.09357	6.09582	6.09807	6.10032	6.10256	6.10479	6.10702
450	6.10925	6.11147	6.11368	6.11589	6.11810	6.12030	6.12249	6.12468	6.12687	6.12905
460	6.13123	6.13340	6.13556	6.13773	6.13988	6.14204	6.14419	6.14633	6.14847	6.15060
470	6.15273	6.15486	6.15698	6.15910	6.16121	6.16331	6.16542	6.16752	6.16961	6.17170
480	6.17379	6.17587	6.17794	6.18002	6.18208	6.18415	6.18621	6.18826	6.19032	6.19236
490	6.19441	6.19644	6.19848	6.20051	6.20254	6.20456	6.20658	6.20859	6.21060	6.21261

	0	1	2	3	4	5	6	7	8	9
500	6.21461	6.21661	6.21860	6.22059	6.22258	6.22456	6.22654	6.22851	6.23048	6.23245
510	23441	23637	23832	24028	24222	24417	24611	24804	24998	25190
520	25383	25575	25767	25958	26149	26340	26530	26720	26910	27099
530	27288	27476	27664	27852	28040	28227	28413	28600	28786	28972
540	29157	29342	29527	29711	29895	30079	30262	30445	30628	30810
550	6.30992	6.31173	6.31355	6.31536	6.31716	6.31897	6.32077	6.32257	6.32436	6.32615
560	32794	32972	33150	33328	33505	33683	33859	34036	34212	34388
570	34564	34739	34914	35089	35263	35437	35611	35784	35957	36130
580	36303	36475	36647	36819	36990	37161	37332	37502	37673	37843
590	38012	38182	38351	38519	38688	38856	39024	39192	39359	39526
600	6.39693	6.39859	6.40026	6.40192	6.40357	6.40523	6.40688	6.40853	6.41017	6.41182
610	41346	41510	41673	41836	41999	42162	42325	42487	42649	42811
620	42972	43133	43294	43455	43615	43775	43935	44095	44254	44413
630	44572	44731	44889	45047	45205	45362	45520	45677	45834	45990
640	46147	46303	46459	46614	46770	46925	47080	47235	47389	47543
650	6.47697	6.47851	6.48004	6.48158	6.48311	6.48464	6.48616	6.48768	6.48920	6.49072
660	49224	49375	49527	49677	49828	49979	50129	50279	50429	50578
670	50728	50877	51026	51175	51323	51471	51619	51767	51915	52062
680	52209	52356	52503	52649	52796	52942	53088	53233	53379	53524
690	53669	53814	53959	54103	54247	54391	54535	54679	54822	54965
700	6.55108	6.55251	6.55393	6.55536	6.55678	6.55820	6.55962	6.56103	6.56244	6.56386
710	56526	56667	56808	56948	57088	57228	57368	57508	57647	57786
720	57925	58064	58203	58341	58479	58617	58755	58893	59030	59167
730	59304	59441	59578	59715	59851	59987	60123	60259	60394	60530
740	60665	60800	60935	61070	61204	61338	61473	61607	61740	61874
750	6.62007	6.62141	6.62274	6.62407	6.62539	6.62672	6.62804	6.62936	6.63068	6.63200
760	63332	63463	63595	63726	63857	63988	64118	64249	64379	64509
770	64639	64769	64898	65028	65157	65286	65415	65544	65673	65801
780	65929	66058	66185	66313	66441	66568	66696	66823	66950	67077
790	67203	67330	67456	67582	67708	67834	67960	68085	68211	68336
800	6.68461	6.68586	6.68711	6.68835	6.68960	6.69084	6.69208	6.69332	6.69456	6.69580
810	69703	69827	69950	70073	70196	70319	70441	70564	70686	70808
820	70930	71052	71174	71296	71417	71538	71659	71780	71901	72022
830	72143	72263	72383	72503	72623	72743	72863	72982	73102	73221
840	73340	73459	73578	73697	73815	73934	74052	74170	74288	74406
850	6.74524	6.74641	6.74759	6.74876	6.74993	6.75110	6.75227	6.75344	6.75460	6.75577
860	75693	75809	75926	76041	76157	76273	76388	76504	76619	76734
870	76849	76964	77079	77194	77308	77422	77537	77651	77765	77878
880	77992	78106	78219	78333	78446	78559	78672	78784	78897	79010
890	79122	79234	79347	79459	79571	79682	79794	79906	80017	80128
900	6.80239	6.80351	6.80461	6.80572	6.80683	6.80793	6.80904	6.81014	6.81124	6.81235
910	81344	81454	81564	81674	81783	81892	82002	82111	82220	82329
920	82437	82546	82655	82763	82871	82979	83087	83195	83303	83411
930	83518	83626	83733	83841	83948	84055	84162	84268	84375	84482
940	84588	84694	84801	84907	85013	85118	85224	85330	85435	85541
950	6.85646	6.85751	6.85857	6.85961	6.86066	6.86171	6.86276	6.86380	6.86485	6.86589
960	86693	86797	86901	87005	87109	87213	87316	87420	87523	87626
970	87730	87833	87936	88038	88141	88244	88346	88449	88551	88653
980	88755	88857	88959	89061	89163	89264	89366	89467	89568	89669
990	89770	89871	89972	90073	90174	90274	90375	90475	90575	90675

* To find the natural logarithm ($\log_e$) of a number which is a power of ten less or greater than a number given in the table: if the number concerned is *less*, e.g., $1/10$ (10^{-1}), $1/100$ (10^{-2}), $1/1000$ (10^{-3}), etc., *subtract* from the given logarithm $\log_e 10$, $2 \log_e 10$, $3 \log_e 10$, etc.; if the number concerned is *greater*, e.g., 10 times (10^{1}), 100 times (10^{2}), 1000 times (10^{3}), etc., *add* to the given logarithm $\log_e 10$, $2 \log_e 10$, $3 \log_e 10$, etc. Examples: $\log_e 0.02 = \log_e 2 - \log_e 10$; $\log_e 2000 = \log_e 200 + \log_e 10$.

Author Index

Numbers in brackets are reference numbers and indicate that an author's work is referred to although his name is not cited in the text. Underlined numbers give the page on which the complete reference is listed.

A

Abbott, F.S., 300[13], 334.
Abraham, E. P., 223[8], 245[8], 250[8], 279.
Abrutyn, E., 241[55], 281.
Abruzzo, C.W., 28[11], 43.
Actor, P., 251[79], 252[79], 283.
Adir, J., 149[40], 171, 234[15], 280, 297[9], 333.
Aguiar, A.J., 147[38], 171.
Alegnani, W.C., 147[38], 148[38b], 171.
Alexander, K., 28[11], 43.
Allen, E.S., 239[40], 280.
Allen, J.P., 313[34], 314[34], 335.
Altemeier, W.A., 145[36], 146[36], 171, 235, 280.
Altman, M., 326[60], 329[60], 336.
Alway, C.D., 193[7], 211.
Anagnostakos, N., 145[35], 171.
Andersgaard, H.A., 147[39], 171.
Anderson, E.T., 317[37], 335.
Anderson, R.C., 132[11], 169, 264 [152], 287.

Anderson, S.M., 262[125,129], 285, 286.
Archer, G.L., 251[84], 283.
Aronson, J.K., 332, 333[74], 337.
Atalus, E., 271[172], 288.
Atkinson, A.J., 310[28], 311[28], 334.
Atkinson, A.W., 260[102], 284.
Axelson, J.E., 300[13], 334.

B

Baars, R.E., 310[32], 335.
Baggot, J.D., 28, 43.
Baker, N.A., 235[29], 280.
Balant, L., 206[16], 211.
Ball, A.P., 270[170], 271[170], 288.
Barr, W.H., 148, 171, 234[25], 280, 297[9], 333.
Barrett, J.E., 235[31], 236[31], 237 [31], 280.
Barza, M., 235[26], 240[44], 241 [44], 246[64], 251[83], 280, 281, 282, 283.

365

Batterman, R.C., 238[36], 257[36], 280.
Baughman, K.L., 241[59], 282.
Baylis, E.M., 298[11], 334.
Beall, D., 139[17], 170.
Bear, D.M., 271[172], 288.
Beckett, A.H., 262[130, 131, 132, 133, 134, 135], 286, 301[15], 334.
Beckett, L., 263[145], 287.
Bell, H., 147[39], 171.
Bell, M.E., 238[36], 257[36], 280.
Bellward, G.D., 300[13], 334.
Benet, L.Z., 33[20], 43, 54, 56, 103, 104, 209[22], 212, 235[30], 241[57], 244[57], 247[57], 251 [88], 280, 281, 283, 308[25], 318[39], 334, 335.
Bennett, J.V., 231[14], 279.
Bennett, W.M., 206[17], 211.
Benowitz, N.L., 322[51], 336.
Bensley, J.G., 262[127], 286.
Benson, J., 297[10], 333.
Benson, S.W., 14[3], 43.
Bentley, D.L., 263[145], 287.
Bergan, T., 270[168,169], 288.
Berger, S., 251[83], 283.
Bielski, B.H.J., 73[22], 90[22], 105.
Bighley, L., 325[56], 336.
Bird, A.E., 262[123], 285.
Bischoff, K.B., 33[13, 25, 15], 43.
Black, H.R., 144[28,32], 170, 171.
Blackstone, M.O., 330[67], 337.
Blank, H., 139, 170.
Bloch, R., 251[82], 283.
Bodey, G.P., 247[67], 282.
Bodin, N-O., 269[162], 288.
Bonacci, A.C., 235[28], 280.
Borgmann, A.R., 140[20], 170.
Boxenbaum, H.G., 332[73], 333[73], 337.
Boyes, R.N., 260[103], 262[130], 284, 286.

Boyle, C., 302[17], 334.
Bran, J.L., 251[79], 252[79], 283.
Brater, D.C., 209[22], 212.
Breimer, D.D., 119, 169, 302[18], 303[18], 334.
Brodie, B.B., 120[2,3], 133[12], 169, 257[99], 284.
Brodie, J. L., 228[13], 229[13], 231[13, 14], 235[31], 236[31], 237[31], 279, 280.
Brown, A.D., 240[46,48], 281.
Brown, N.K., 271[172], 288.
Brown, P.M., 235[29], 280.
Brown, R.B., 235[26], 246[64], 280, 282.
Bryan, C., 321, 335.
Bryant, R.E., 251[89], 283.
Buch, J., 330[65], 336.
Bucht, H., 257[96], 284.
Buckwalter, F.H., 141[23], 170, 226, 279.
Buell, J., 330[62], 336.
Bundgaard, H., 268[158], 288.
Bunger, P., 174[3], 211.
Burkman, A.M., 218[1], 278.
Burris, B.C., 260[102], 284.
Butler, K., 271[171], 288.
Butler, V.P., 330[67], 337.
Byron, P.R., 191[5,6], 199[5], 211, 275[175], 277[176, 177], 289, 293[1], 333.

C

Cabana, B.E., 251[76], 252[76], 283.
Canafax, D., 310[32], 335.
Capellos, C., 73[22], 90[22], 105.
Carmichael, J., 325[56], 336.
Carpenter, O.S., 193[7], 211.
Carson, G., 1[1], 4.
Chapron, D.J., 297[10], 333.

Chatton, M.J., 256[93], <u>284</u>.
Cheney, L.C., 223[9], <u>279</u>.
Chiu, P.J.S., 240[46, 48], <u>281</u>.
Cho, M.J., 264[150], <u>287</u>.
Chulski, T., 133[12], 170.
Cipolle, R.J., 319[40], 320[40], 321 [40], <u>335</u>.
Clark, H., 271[172], <u>288</u>.
Clark, J.H., 326[59], <u>336</u>.
Clarke, J.T., 233[22], 246[63], <u>279</u>, <u>282</u>.
Clayton, J.M., 263[148], <u>287</u>.
Clayton, J.P., 269[163, 164], <u>288</u>.
Cobb, T.C., 332[73], 333[73], <u>337</u>.
Coggins, C.H., 206[17], <u>211</u>.
Colaizzi, J.L., 261[114], <u>285</u>, 300 [12], <u>334</u>.
Cole, M., 269[163, 164], <u>288</u>.
Conine, J.W., 144[27], <u>170</u>.
Conklin, J.D., 140[21], <u>170</u>.
Conn, H.F., 332[69], <u>337</u>.
Constantine, G.H., 250[74], <u>282</u>.
Corbett, J.C., 145[35], <u>171</u>.
Cotter, S., 28[11], <u>43</u>.
Craig, W.A., 237[32], 239[41], <u>280</u>, <u>281</u>.
Crooks, J., 308[22], <u>334</u>.
Crounse, R.G., 139, <u>170</u>.
Crouthamel, W.G., 261[110], <u>285</u>.
Crowley, J.M., 298[11], <u>334</u>.
Cucinell, S.A., 79[28], <u>105</u>.
Cumbo, T.J., 240[50], 241[50, 55], 242[50], 245[50], 247[50], <u>281</u>.
Curie, D.J., 262[126], <u>285</u>.
Cutler, R.E., 246[65], <u>282</u>, 317[36], <u>335</u>.

D

Dahlgren, J.G., 317[37], <u>335</u>.
Dam, M., 309[27], 311[27], <u>334</u>.

Dasta, J., 326[60], 329[60], <u>336</u>.
Davis, N.E., 144[30], <u>171</u>, 272[174], 273[173], <u>288</u>, <u>289</u>.
Davis, S.S., 263[146], <u>287</u>.
Dayton, P.G., 79[28], <u>105</u>.
Dedrick, R.L., 33[13, 14, 15, 16], <u>43</u>.
deMaine, J.B., 251[87], <u>283</u>.
DeMenezes, J.P., 251[80], 252[80], <u>283</u>.
Dennis, M., 91, <u>105</u>.
Denten, C., 139[16], <u>170</u>.
Dettli, L., 174[3], 208, 210[18, 19], <u>211</u>, <u>212</u>, 241[57], 244[57], 247 [57], <u>281</u>, 318[39], <u>335</u>.
DeYoung, J.L., 94[38], 98[38], <u>106</u>.
DiSanto, A.R., 261[113], <u>285</u>.
Dittert, L.W., 93[37], <u>105</u>, 231[15], 238[15], 239[42], 246[66], 251 [76], 252[76], 261[110], <u>279</u>, <u>281</u>, <u>282</u>, <u>283</u>, <u>285</u>.
Doerschuk, A. P., 145[35], <u>171</u>.
Doherty, J.E., 33[23], <u>44</u>.
Doluisio, J.T., 93[37], <u>105</u>, 231[15], 238[15], 239[42], 246[66], 251 [76], 252[76], 261[110,115], <u>279</u>, <u>281</u>, <u>282</u>, <u>283</u>, <u>285</u>.
Dominguez, R., 56[6], 91[34], <u>104</u>, <u>105</u>.
Dourne, D.W.A., 251[76], 252[76], <u>283</u>.
Dubuc, J., 139[17], <u>170</u>.
Duce, B.R., 260[105], <u>284</u>.
Dugal, R., 240[51], 247[51], <u>281</u>.
Dunn, W.J., 262[119], <u>285</u>.
Dvoracek, K., 226, 227[12], 231[12], 267[12], <u>279</u>.

E

Eadie, M.J., 309[26], 310[26], <u>334</u>.

Edwards, C.Q., 241, 282.
Ekstrom, B., 269[162], 288.
Elson, S.W., 269[163, 164], 288.
Elvin, A.T., 260[105], 284.
Elwood, C.M., 332[71], 333[71], 337.
Engelking, E.R., 251[90], 284.
English, A.R., 271[171], 288.
Ernst, E.C., 251[83], 283.
Evans, D.A.P., 68[21], 104.

F

Fabre, J., 206[16], 211, 223[7], 238[7], 239, 258[7], 279.
Faymond, F., 260[102], 284.
Feld, S.L., 300[12], 334.
Ferres, H., 269[163, 164], 288.
Field, J.B., 302[17], 334.
Fillastre, J.P., 247[68], 282.
Finland, M., 261[116], 285.
Flanigan, W.J., 33[23], 44.
Fletcher, H.P., 264[151], 287.
Flynn, E.H. 245[73], 282.
Flynn, G.L., 262[122], 263[144], 285, 287.
Folkers, K., 223[10], 279.
Follath, F., 241[57], 244[57], 247[57], 281, 318[39], 335.
Foltz, E.L., 267[155], 269[155], 287.
Fong, I.W., 251[90], 284.
Forester, W.F., Jr., 332[73], 333[73], 337.
Forrey, A., 317[36], 335.
Forsgren, U., 269[162], 288.
Fox, C.L., 256[95], 284.
Franklin, B.A., 326[58], 336.
Freyhof, J.N., 137[15], 170.
Frost, A.A., 14[4], 43.

Fu, K.P., 240[52], 241[52], 246[52], 247[52], 281.
Fuchs, T., 240[47], 281.
Fujita, T., 262[118, 128], 285, 286.
Fusari, S., 147[38], 171.
Fuss, R.J., 252[81], 283.

G

Gal, P., 326[58], 336.
Gambertoglio, J.G., 209[22], 212.
Gamble, C., 235[26], 280.
Gardner, M., 326[59], 336.
Garrett, E.R., 28[9], 33[9], 43.
Garrettson, L., 148[40], 171, 234[25], 280, 297[9], 333.
Gaudrey, R., 139[17], 170.
Gerding, D.N., 320[43], 321[43], 335.
Gibaldi, M., 20[5], 34[24], 43, 44, 53[2], 56[10], 57[2], 59[11, 12, 13], 101[10], 102[39], 103, 104, 106, 180[4], 193[8, 9], 211, 239[43], 246[64], 281, 282, 301[16], 334.
Gilette, J.R., 295[3], 333.
Gilman, A., 145[34], 171.
Ginchansky, E., 326[57], 327[57], 329[57], 336.
Glascock, H.W., 140[22], 170.
Glazko, A.J., 147[38], 148[38b], 171.
Godman, M.J., 260[103], 284.
Godtfredsen, W.O., 269[166], 288.
Goodhart, G., 247[69], 282.
Goodman, E.L., 317, 335.
Goodman, L.S., 145[34], 171.
Gourevitch, A., 223[9], 279.
Goyan, J.E., 235[30], 280.
Grahame-Smith, D.G., 332, 333[74], 337.

Gravenkemper, C.F., 231[14], <u>279.</u>
Greenblatt, D.J., 330[68], 331[68], 332[72], <u>337.</u>
Greene, D.S., 250[75], 251[75], 252 [75], 253[75], <u>282.</u>
Gretch, M., 237[34], <u>280,</u> 304[19], <u>334.</u>
Griffin, W.O., 231[15], 238[15],251 [76], 252[76], <u>279, 283.</u>
Griffith, R.S., 144[28, 32], <u>170, 171.</u>
Gronroos, J.A., 145[33], <u>171.</u>
Grundhofer, B., 301[16], <u>334.</u>
Guerrant, R.L., 321, <u>335.</u>
Guttman, D.E., 238[38], <u>280.</u>
Gyselynck, A.M., 317[36], <u>335.</u>

H

Hailey, F.J., 140[21, 22], <u>170.</u>
Haleblian, J., 137[14], 138[14], <u>170.</u>
Halkin, H., 260[101], <u>284.</u>
Hamlin, W.E., 133[12, 13], <u>170.</u>
Hanano, M., 263[142, 143], <u>287.</u>
Hansch, C., 262[118, 119, 120, 121, 124, 125, 128, 129), 263[145, 148], <u>285, 286, 287.</u>
Hansen, J. M., 269[160], <u>288.</u>
Hanson, J.C., 269[164], <u>288.</u>
Harris, P.N., 132[11], <u>169,</u> 264 [152], <u>287.</u>
Hartstein, A.I., 251[89], <u>283.</u>
Hayes, K. J., 140[20], <u>170.</u>
Hendeles, L., 324[54], 325[54, 56], 326[54], 327, 328[54], <u>336.</u>
Henderson, F.G., 132[11], <u>169,</u> 264 [152], <u>287.</u>
Hepler, C.D., 325[56], <u>336.</u>
Hewitt, W.L., 317[37], <u>335.</u>

Higuchi, T., 263[146], <u>287.</u>
Higuchi, W.I., 261[106], 263[106, 138, 139, 140, 141], <u>284, 286.</u>
Hirschman, S.Z., 242[60], 247[70, 72], 251[91], <u>282, 284.</u>
Hitzenberger, G., 223, <u>278.</u>
Ho, N.F.H., 261[106], 263[106, 138, 139, 140, 141), <u>284, 286.</u>
Hoehn, M.M., 272[174], 273[173], <u>288, 289.</u>
Hoffman, S.F., 313[34], 314[34], <u>335.</u>
Hogben, C.A.M., 120[2], 133[12], <u>169.</u>
Hollister, L.E., 61[14], 62[14], <u>104,</u> 130[9], 164[9], 165[9], 166[46], <u>169, 172,</u> 259, <u>284.</u>
Hollum, E., 147[39], <u>171.</u>
Hollunger, G., 260[104], <u>284.</u>
Holmes, E.L., 147[38], 148[38b], <u>171.</u>
Holmes, H. L., 262[126], <u>285.</u>
Holmes, R., 317[38], <u>335.</u>
Horiguchi, H., 269[167], <u>288.</u>
Hottendorf, G.H., 251[76], 252[76], <u>283.</u>
Hou, J.P., 141[24], <u>170,</u> 223[6], 245[6], <u>279.</u>
Housholder, G.E., 33[19], 34[19], <u>43.</u>
Howald, W., 300[13], <u>334.</u>
Huang, M-Y., 191[6], <u>211,</u> 277[176, 177], <u>289,</u> 293[1], <u>333.</u>
Hughes, W.H., 256[97], <u>284.</u>
Hull, A.R., 317[38], <u>335.</u>
Hull, J.H., 321, <u>335, 336.</u>
Humbert, G., 247[68], <u>282</u>
Hvidberg, E.F., 309[27], 311[27], <u>334</u>

I

Ikeda, K., 264[153], 287.
Isaka, I., 269[167], 288.
Itatani, Y., 268[159], 288.
Iwasa, J., 262[118, 128], 285, 286.

J

Jackson, A., 251[80], 252[80], 283.
Jaffe, J.M., 300[12], 334.
Jahre, J.A., 240[52], 241[52], 246 [52], 247[52], 281.
Jalar, L-P., 269[162], 288.
Jebson, P.J., 260[103], 284.
Jeffrey, J.J., 35[29], 44.
Jelliffe, R.W., 329[61], 330[62], 336.
Jencks, W.P., 14[1], 42.
Johansen, H., 147[39], 171.
Johnson, G., 324[54], 325[54], 326 [54], 327[54], 328[54], 336.
Jones, P.M., 133[12], 170.
Jones, S.R., 251[89], 283.
Jonsson, S., 241[56,58], 281.
Jordan, M.C., 149[43], 150[43], 172, 231[16], 279.
Julian, D.G., 260[103], 284.
Juncher, H., 132[11], 169.
Jusko, W.J., 232[19], 237[34], 240 [49, 50], 241[49, 50, 55], 242 [49, 50], 244[49], 245[49, 50], 246[49], 247[50], 267[19, 154, 157], 269[19, 154, 157], 269, 279, 280, 281, 287, 304[19], 326[58, 59], 330[64], 332[71, 72], 333[71], 334, 335, 337.

K

Kaczka, E., 223[10], 279.

Kahlmeter, G., 241[53, 56, 58], 281.
Kalaba, R., 330[62], 336.
Kalfopoulos, P., 223[7], 238[7], 239 [7], 258[7], 279.
Kallings, L.O., 257[96], 284.
Kalliomaki, J.L., 145[33], 171.
Kamme, C., 241[53, 56, 58], 281.
Kampmann, J.P., 269[160], 288.
Kangis, L.A., 239[40], 280.
Kaplan, S.A., 28, 43.
Karger, S., 146[37], 171.
Kashiwagi, T., 269[167], 288.
Kaye, D., 247[69], 282.
Kelly, R.G., 239[40], 280.
Kemmerich, B., 242[61], 246[61], 247[61], 282.
Kenny, D., 144[29], 170.
Kern, J.W., 325[55], 329[55a], 336.
Kezdy, F.J., 264[150], 287.
Kind, A.C., 228[13], 229[13], 231 [13], 279.
King, J.C., 166[48], 172.
Kinkel, A.W., 147[38], 148[38b], 171.
Kirby, W.M.M., 149[43], 150[43], 172, 228[13], 229[13], 231[13, 14, 16], 233[22], 235[31], 236[31], 237[31], 251[87, 90], 279, 280, 283, 284.
Kirby, W.W., 246[63], 282.
Klastersky, J., 246[62], 247[71], 269[161], 270[161], 282, 288.
Kline Bolton, W., 252[77], 283.
Klink, P.R., 261[114], 285.
Knirsch, A.K., 271[171], 288.
Knoechel, E.L., 133[13], 170.
Koch, P.A., 237[32], 280.
Koch-Weser, J., 237[35], 280, 304 [20], 330[68], 331[68], 332[72], 334, 337.
Koda, A., 269[167], 288.

Koeppe, P., 242[61], 246[61], 247 [61], 282.
Kohli, R.K., 331[71], 333[71], 337.
Korst, J.J., 271[171], 288.
Korzeniowski, O.M., 251[78], 252 [78], 283.
Kostenbauder, H.B., 67[15], 104, 301[14], 334.
Koup, J.R., 331[71, 72], 333[71], 337.
Kramer, P.A., 297[10], 333.
Kramer, W.G., 332[73], 333[73], 337.
Kraml, M., 139, 170.
Kristensen, M.B., 295[4], 302[4], 303[4], 333.
Krueger, J.E., 234[24], 280.
Kruger-Theimer, E., 174, 199, 211.
Krupp, M.A., 256[93], 284.
Kunin, C.M., 223[4], 237[33], 238 [37], 256[98], 261[116], 278, 280, 284, 285, 293[2], 333.
Kurono, Y., 264[153], 287.
Kwan, K.C., 267[155], 269[155], 287.

L

Laidler, K.J., 14[2], 42.
Lalka, D., 260[105], 284, 313[34], 314[34], 335.
Landau, B.R., 35[26], 44.
Langenberg, G., 241[54], 281.
LaPiana, J.C., 93[37], 105, 231[15], 238[15], 246[66], 279, 282.
Lasezkay, G., 240[50], 241[50], 242 [50], 245[50], 247[50], 281.
Law, C.C., 237[32], 280.
Lee, C.C., 132[11], 169, 264[152], 287.
Lee, C.S., 209[22], 212.

Leeson, L.J., 234[24], 280.
Leonards, J.R., 129[8], 130[8], 169.
Leroy, A., 247[68], 282.
Levine, R.R., 261[109, 111], 262 [117], 285.
Levy, G., 33[21], 34[21, 24], 44, 53[2], 57[2], 61[14], 62[14], 77, 78, 79[25, 26, 27, 29, 30], 101 [27], 103, 104, 105, 163[45], 172, 301[16], 305[21], 308[24], 324[52], 325[52], 326[52], 334, 336, 343.
Levy, J., 246[62], 282.
Lewis, G.P., 232[19], 267[19, 154, 157], 268[19, 154, 157], 269, 279, 287.
Lewis, R.P., 332[73], 333[73], 337.
Libke, R.D., 233[22], 246[63], 279, 282.
Lien, E.J., 262[124], 263[149], 285, 287.
Lietman, P.S., 241[59], 282.
Lindahl, F., 269[160], 288.
Lindberg, A.A., 257[96], 284.
Lindenbaum, J., 330, 337.
Lipman, A.G., 325[55], 329[55a], 336.
Lode, H., 242[61], 246[61], 247 [61], 282.
Long, J.F., 240[46, 48], 281.
Long, S., 143[25], 170.
Longstreth, J.A., 33[14], 43.
Loo, J.C.K., 20[8], 43, 56[9], 91, 94, 101[9], 102[40], 104, 105, 106, 267[155], 269[155], 287.
Loo, T.L., 33[19], 34[19], 43.
Lough, C.E., 262[126], 285.
Lower, R., 251[84], 283.
Lucas, S.B., 313[35], 335.
Lucyszyn, G., 251[79], 252[79], 283.
Ludden, T.M., 313[34], 314, 335.

Luft, F.C., 240[45], 251[82], 281, 283.
Lund, B., 269[160], 288.
Lund, L., 310[29], 311, 334.
Lunde, P.K.M., 147[39], 171.
Luthy, R.P., 233[22], 279.
Lyon, J.A., 322[49], 336.

M

McCrone, W., 137[14], 138[14], 170.
MacDonald, H., 239[40], 280.
McFarland, J.W., 263[147], 287.
MacLeod, C., 232[20], 267[20], 279.
McNay, J.L., 313[34], 314[34], 335.
Madsen, P.O., 251[85], 283.
Magni, L., 269[162], 270[168], 288.
Malitt, G.E., 144[31], 171.
Mao, J.C.H., 144[29], 170.
Marcus, F.I., 330[63], 331[63], 336.
Marks, V., 298[11], 334.
Marshall, A.C., 262[123], 285.
Martin, E., 310[30], 314, 315[30], 316[30], 317[30], 335.
Martin, G.J., 161[44], 172.
Marvel, J.R., 139[16], 170.
Matin, S.B., 295[5], 305[5], 333.
Matkovic, C.S., 322[49], 336.
Matsui, H., 269[167], 288.
Mattie, H., 230, 279.
Mawer, G.E., 313, 335.
Mayersohn, M., 20[5], 43.
Mayfield, D.E., 260[102], 284.
Meffin, P., 260[101], 284.
Meister, W., 322[51], 336.
Melethil, S., 251[83], 283.
Melikian, A.P., 310[31], 335.
Mellin, H-E., 251[85], 283.
Mellow, M.H., 330[67], 337.
Melmon, K., 260[101], 284.

Mercik, S.A., 297[10], 333.
Merier, G., 223[7], 238[7], 239[7], 258[7], 279.
Meunier-Carpentier, F., 247[71], 282.
Meyer, M.B., 260[105], 284.
Meyer, M.C., 238[38], 280, 310[31], 335.
Meyers, B.R., 242[60], 247[70, 72], 251[91], 282, 284.
Midtvedt, T., 147[39], 171.
Milek, E., 223[7], 238[7], 239[7], 258[7], 279.
Miller, E., 262[120], 285.
Miller, G.H., 240[46, 48], 281.
Miller, M.J., 251[89], 283.
Mirtallo, J.M., 326[60], 329[60], 336.
Mitchard, M., 270[170], 271[170], 288.
Mitscher, L.A., 235[28], 280.
Mizen, L.W., 269[164], 288.
Modr, Z., 226, 227[12], 231[12], 267[12], 279.
Moffat, A.C., 262[132, 133, 134, 135), 286.
Morgan, A.M., 130[10], 169.
Morozowich, W., 133[12], 170, 261[106], 263[106], 264[150], 284, 287.
Mullen, P.W., 313[35], 335.
Murakami, M., 269[167], 288.
Murphy, H.W., 144[27], 170.
Murray, H.M., 264[151], 287.

N

Nagashima, R., 33[21], 34[21], 44, 53[2], 57[2], 79[27,30], 101[27], 103, 105, 343.
Nakano, K., 269[167], 288.

Nappi, J.M., 313[34], 314[34], 335.
Nash, R.A., 234[24], 280.
Nation, R.L., 308[23], 334.
Nauta, E.H., 230, 279.
Nayler, J.H.C., 231[17], 279.
Nedden, R., 240[47], 281.
Nelson, E., 91[35], 97, 105, 132[11], 133[12, 13], 169, 170.
Neu, H.C., 240[52], 241[52], 246[52], 247[52], 281.
Niebergall, P.J., 202[4], 211.
Nightingale, C.H., 250[75], 251[75], 252[75], 253[75], 282.
Nimmo, W.S., 296, 333.
Noble, J.F., 239[40], 280.
Nogami, H., 263[142, 143], 286, 287.
Northram, J.I., 56[7], 104, 133[12], 170, 193[7], 211.
Notari, R.E., 94[38], 98[38], 106, 191[5, 6], 199[5], 211, 218[1], 275[175], 277[176, 177], 278, 289, 293[1], 332[70], 333, 337.
Nyberg, L., 330[66], 331[66], 337.

O

Ogilvie, R.I., 232[20], 267[20], 279, 324[53], 325[53], 326[52], 327, 328[53], 336.
Ohta, M., 302[17], 334.
Oksenhendler, G., 247[68], 282.
O'Malley, K., 308[22], 334.
O'Reilly, R.A., 33[21], 34[21], 44, 79[27], 101[27], 105, 305[21], 334, 343.
Orme, B.M., 246[65], 282.
Overton, E., 121[5], 169.
Owen, G., 138[15], 170.

P

Pagliaro, L.A., 54, 103, 251[88], 283.
Pang, S., 295[3], 333.
Park, J.Y., 261[106], 263[106], 284.
Parsons, J., 247[69], 282.
Parsons, R.L., 296, 333.
Pasculle, A.W., 322[49], 336.
Patrick, K.E., 251[89], 283.
Paul, H.E., 140[20], 170.
Paul, M.F., 140[20], 170.
Pazin, G.J., 322[49], 336.
Pearson, R.G., 14[4], 43.
Pechere, J-C., 240[51], 247[51], 281.
Pechere, M-M., 240[51], 247[51], 281.
Pelikan, E.W., 261[109, 111], 285.
Penniston, J.T., 263[145], 287.
Perel, J.M., 79[28], 105.
Perkins, W.H., 33[23], 44.
Perrier, D., 59[11, 12], 104, 180[4], 193[9], 211.
Pfeffer, M., 251[80], 252[80], 283.
Philipson, A., 233[21], 279.
Pitkin, D.H., 251[79], 252[79], 283.
Plaut, M.E., 240[50], 241[50, 55], 242[50], 245[50], 247[50], 281.
Polk, R.E., 251[84], 283.
Pomerene, E., 91[34], 105.
Poole, J.W., 138, 141[24], 170, 223[6], 245[6], 279.
Portman, G.A., 33[18], 35[18], 43.
Portnoff, J.B., 67[15], 104, 301[14], 334.
Poust, R.I., 300[12], 334.
Pratt, R., 223, 278.
Preece, J.M., 298[11], 334.
Price, K.E., 223[9], 279.

Prior, R.B., 252[81], 283.
Pugh, C.T., 144[30], 171, 272[174], 273[173], 288, 289.
Purcell, W.P., 262[127], 286.
Purmalis, A., 133[12], 170.

Q

Quintana, R.P., 262[127], 286.
Quintiliani, R., 250[75], 251[75], 252[75], 253[75], 282.

R

Raaschov, F., 132[11], 169.
Raichlen, J.S., 321[48], 336.
Ralph, E.D., 233[22], 251[90], 279, 284.
Ralston, S., 272[174], 273[173], 288, 289.
Ramsay, C-H., 269[162], 288.
Rapp, R.P., 310[32], 335.
Rattie, E.S., 251[86], 283.
Ravin, L.J., 251[86], 283.
Regamey, C., 246[63], 282.
Remers, A., 302[17], 334.
Remmer, H., 68[17], 104.
Remmers, R.G., 145[35], 171.
Rescigno, A., 20[6], 33[6], 43.
Reudy, J., 232[20], 267[20], 279.
Reuning, R.H., 68, 94[38], 98[38], 104, 106, 261[112], 285, 332[70, 73], 333[73], 337.
Ribner, B., 247[72], 251[91], 282, 284.
Richardson, R.H., 325[56], 336.
Richter, E., 302[18], 303[18], 334.
Riegelman, S., 20[8], 43, 56[9], 91, 94, 101[9], 102[40], 104, 105, 106, 310[30], 314[30], 315[30], 316[30], 317[30], 335.

Riggs, D.S., 56[8], 104, 344, 345.
Ritschel, W.A., 35[32], 44.
Robins, A.J., 313[35], 335.
Robinson, J.R., 169, 172.
Rodgers, M., 313[35], 335.
Rogers, J.F., 241[59], 282.
Roholt, K., 233[23], 269[166], 270[23], 280, 288.
Ronfeld, R.A., 56, 104.
Rose, H.M., 256[95], 284.
Rosenberg, T., 35[25], 44.
Rosenblatt, J.E., 228[13], 229, 231[13], 235, 236, 237[31], 279, 280.
Rosenman, S.B., 138[15], 170.
Rosner, B., 233[21], 279.
Ross, B.L., 261[112], 285.
Rowland, M., 20[8], 43, 56[9], 101[9], 104, 260[101], 284, 295[5], 301[15], 305[5], 322[50], 323, 333, 334, 336.
Rozencweig, M., 269[161], 270[161], 288.

S

Saarimaa, H.A., 145[33], 171.
Sabath, L.D., 233[21], 279.
Sado, T., 269[165], 288.
Sakmar, E., 333[75], 337.
Sams, R.A., 332[70], 337.
Sande, M.A., 251[78], 252[77, 78], 283.
Sanford, J.P., 317[38], 335.
Santoro, J., 245[69], 282.
Sarcione, E.J., 79[30], 105.
Sarubbi, F.A., 321, 335, 336.
Sasaki, H., 269[165], 288.
Sawchuk, R., 319[40, 42], 320[40, 42, 43], 321[43], 335.
Schach von Wittenau, M., 239[39], 280.

Schaldemose, I., 91[35], 105.
Schanker, L.S., 35[27, 28, 29], 44, 68[19], 104, 120[3], 121, 169, 261[107, 108], 284, 285.
Scheife, R.T., 240[44], 241[44], 281.
Scheiner, J., 145[36], 146[36], 171, 235, 280.
Scheld, W.M., 251[78], 252[78], 283.
Scheline, R.R., 68[20], 104.
Schentag, J.J., 240[49, 50], 241[49, 50, 55], 242 [49, 50], 244[49], 245[49, 50], 246[49], 247[50], 281, 326[59], 336.
Schichting, D.A., 139[16], 170.
Schmitt, G.W., 267[154], 268[154], 287.
Schnaare, R.L., 202[14], 211.
Schroder, K., 240[47], 281.
Schumacher, G.E., 196, 211, 319[41], 335.
Schwartz, M., 59[13], 104.
Schwartz, M.A., 141[23], 170, 226, 279.
Schwartz, S.N., 322[49], 336.
Scott, D.B., 260[103], 284.
Sedman, H.J., 149[41], 171.
Segre, G., 20[6], 33[6], 43.
Sellers, E.M., 237[35], 280, 304[20], 334.
Seydel, J.K., 48[1], 103, 255[92], 256[94], 284.
Shainfeld, F.J., 231[15], 238[15], 279.
Shanks, C., 235[26], 280.
Shaw, W.R., 239[41], 281.
Sheiner, L.B., 310[30], 314[30], 315[30], 316[30], 317[30], 335.
Shen, D., 246[64], 282.
Shepard, B.J., 33[19], 34[19], 43.
Shiobara, Y., 269[165], 288.
Shoemaker, B.J., 261[112], 285.

Shore, P.A., 120[2], 169.
Siegel, D., 247[70], 282.
Sieger, G.M., 145[35], 171.
Silver, R.F., 262[126], 285.
Silverio, J., 138[15], 170.
Singer, I., 206[17], 211.
Singer, J.A., 262[127], 286.
Sinholt, P., 147[39], 171.
Sjoberg, B., 269[162], 288.
Sjovall, J., 270[168], 288.
Sloan, R.S., 251[82], 283.
Slywka, G.W.A., 310[31], 335.
Smith, C.R., 241[59], 282.
Smith, R.L., 68[18], 104.
Smith, T.W., 330[68], 331[68], 332[72], 337.
Sokoloski, T.D., 129[7], 130[7], 169, 235[28], 280.
Sparks, M.C., 272[174], 273[173], 288, 289.
Spitzy, K.H., 223, 278.
Spring, P., 174[3], 211, 241[57], 244[57], 247[57], 281, 318[39], 335
Spyker, D.A., 252[77], 283, 321, 335.
Standiford, H.C., 149, 150[43], 172, 231[16], 279.
Staquet, M., 247[71], 269[161], 270[161], 282, 288.
Stehle, R.G., 263[137], 286.
Stein, W.D., 35[31], 44.
Stephens, V.C., 144[27], 170, 272[174], 273[173], 288, 289.
Stevenson, I.H., 308[22], 334.
Stewart, D., 247[67], 282.
Stewart, H.C., 256[97], 284.
Stoll, R.G., 149[41], 171, 333[75], 337.
Strate, R.G., 319[40], 320[40, 43], 321[40, 43], 335.
Straughn, A.B., 310[31], 335.

Strong, J.M., 260[102], 284.
Sugita, E.T., 202[14], 211.
Sutherland, R., 269[164], 288.
Suzuki, A., 263[140, 141], 286.
Swahn, A., 267[156], 269[156], 287.
Swintosky, J.V., 67[15], 104, 261 [115], 285, 301[14], 334.
Sylvester, P.E., 298[11], 334.
Szwed, J.J., 251[82], 283.

T

Tachibana, A., 269[165], 288.
Takahashi, K., 269[167], 288.
Tamblyn, D., 232[20], 267[20], 279.
Tan, G.H., 261[110], 285.
Tanner, B.B., 33[19], 34[19], 43.
Taraszka, M.J., 262[136], 286.
Tardrew, P.H., 144[29], 170.
Tauber, L.F., 238[36], 257[36], 280.
Teorell, T., 35[33], 44.
Thomas, B.L., 252[77], 283.
Thompkins, L., 272[174], 273[173], 288, 289.
Tocco, D.J., 35[27, 28], 44, 120[3], 169.
Tozer, T.N., 310[30], 314[30], 315 [30], 316[30], 317[30], 335.
Travell, J., 121, 169.
Trestman, I., 247[69], 282.
Triggs, E.J., 262[130, 131], 286, 308 [23], 334.
Truitt, E.B., 130[10], 169.
Tse, F.L.S., 239[41], 281.
Tsuji, A., 268[159], 288.
Tukamoto, T., 264[153], 287.
Turck, M., 271[172], 288.
Twomey, T.M., 239[39], 280.
Tybring, L., 269[166], 288.

U

Uman, S.J., 239[41], 281.

V

Vance, J.W., 241[55], 281.
VanGelder, J., 317[38], 335.
Van Harken, D.R., 251[76], 252[76], 283.
Van Rossum, J.M., 200[12], 211.
Van Tyle, W.K., 218[1], 278.
Vatutsky, W.A., 313[34], 314[34], 335.
Vaughan, D.P., 91, 105.
Veldkamp. W., 143[25], 170.
Vicuna, A.V., 313[34], 314[34], 335.
Visconti, J.A., 332[73], 333[73], 337.
Viswan, A.K., 270[170], 271[170], 288.
von Daehne, W., 269[166], 288.
von Kobyletzki, D., 241[54], 281.
Vora, K.R.M., 263[139], 286.

W

Wagner, J.G., 20[7], 33[12], 39[34], 43, 44, 54, 56[7], 88, 91, 97, 104, 105, 133[12, 13], 143[25, 26], 146[37], 149, 170, 171, 193[7], 200[13], 211, 261[113], 285, 333 [75], 337.
Wahlig, H., 241[54], 281.
Waldorff, S., 330[65], 336.
Wallace, J.E., 313[34], 314[34], 335.
Wallace, J.F., 271[172], 288.
Wallick, H., 267[155], 269[155], 287.
Wanke, L.A., 332[73], 333[73], 337.

Wargin, W.A., 319[40], 320[40], 321[40], 335.
Warren, G.H., 223[5], 237[5], 238 [5], 278.
Warren, P.M., 300[13], 334.
Wartz, J.A., 240[48], 281.
Watanabe, T., 269[165], 288.
Watson, S.S., 261[112], 285.
Webster, L.T., 260[102], 284.
Weddon, T.E., 264[151], 287.
Weinberger, M., 324[54], 325[54, 55], 326[54, 57], 327[54, 57], 328[54], 329[55b, 57], 336.
Weinfeld, R.E., 28[11], 43.
Weinstein, L., 235[26], 246[64], 280, 282.
Weintraub, H., 193[8], 211, 239[43], 281.
Weisbach, J.A., 251[79], 252[79], 283.
Weiss, M., 79[28], 105.
Welling, P.G., 237[32], 239[41], 251 [85], 280, 281, 283, 296, 333.
Wempe, E., 174[3], 211.
Wenk, M., 241[57], 244[57], 247 [57], 281, 318[39], 335.
Wheeler, L.M., 147[38], 171.
Whyatt, P.L., 310[31], 335.
Wick, W.E., 144[31], 171.
Wilbrandt, W., 35[25, 30], 44.
Wilkinson, P.K., 149[41], 171.

Willis, P.W., 333[75], 337.
Wilson, T.H., 35[26], 44.
Winek, C.L., 202, 203, 211.
Wingard, L.B., Jr., 305[21], 334.
Wise, R., 270[170], 271[170], 288.
Wormser, G., 247[70], 282.
Worth, H.M., 132[11], 169, 264 [152], 287.
Wundt, W., 240[47], 281.

Y

Yalkowsky, S.H., 263[144], 287.
Yamada, H., 263[142, 143], 287.
Yamana, T., 268[159], 288.
Yancovitz, S., 247[72], 251[91], 282, 284.
Yap, B-S., 247[67], 282.
Yates, J.D., 333[75], 337.
Young, B., 310[32], 335.
Yurchak, A.M., 326[58, 59], 336.

Z

Zaharko, D.S., 33[13, 14, 17], 43.
Zarowny, D., 232[20], 267[20], 279.
Zaske, D.W., 319[40, 42], 320[40, 42, 43], 321[40, 42, 43], 335.
Zelmer, J.E., 147[38], 171.
Zimenes, J., 251[80], 252[80], 283

Subject Index

A

Absorption
  buccal membrane, 262
  fraction, 228
  gastrointestinal, 119, 123
    factors decreasing, 140
  HCl salts, 133
  instability (stomach), 143
  ionized species, 261
  loss from sites, 141, 296
  oral, 260, 295
  prodrugs, 265
  rate constants, 90
  solid-dosage forms, 126
    controlling rate from, 127
  solutions, 123
  tetracyclines, 234
  weak acids, 130
  weak bases, 130, 133
Accumulation, 190
  repetitive dosing, 176, 190
Active transport, 35, 38, 123
  characteristics, 36
"All or none effect," 143
Alpha
  calculations of, 21
  phase, 20, 28, 32, 53

Aminoglycosides
  biological half-lives
    (table) 246, 247
  ideal properties, 240
  pharmacokinetics
    literature inconsistencies, 244
  pharmacokinetics, 241
    table, 246-247
Amoxicillin
  bioavailability, 231-233, 267
  comparison to ampicillin, 231-233,
    268
  structure, 268
Ampicillin, 232, 267-269
  anhydrous, 138
  bioavailability, 267, 269
  half-life, 151
  prodrugs, 268
  renal clearance, 151
  trihydrate, 138
  volume of distribution, 150-151
Anhydrous form; see Ampicillin
Antibiotics
  ideal properties, 223, 256
  protein binding, 237
  site of action, 223
  systemic, 223
  urinary tract, 256

Anticonvulsants
  therapeutic range, 309
Antimicrobial agents, 223
  urinary tract, 256
Apomorphines, 219
  potency, 220
Arabinosycytosine (Ara-C), 33
Areas under curves (AUC), 113
  determination of, 87, 175, 177,
    231, 232, 318, 346
  equations, 346
  one-compartment open model equa-
    tions, 346
  oral equation, 232
  relationship to dose, 84, 232
  two-compartment open model
    equations, 347
Aspirin, 62, 129, 134, 138, 259
  buffered, 129, 130, 134
  volume of distribution, 62
AUC; see Areas under curves

                        B

Bicampicillin, 268-270
Barbital, 261
Barbiturates, 132
Beta
  calculations of, 23
  infusion, 101
  phase, 19, 28, 32, 53
Binding
  displacement from, 304
  effect on distribution, 237, 257
  effect on elimination, 237, 257
  plasma protein, 17, 304
Bioavailability, 113, 228, 292
  absolute, 225, 86, 228, 233
  aminosalicylic acid, 149
  chloramphenicol, 149

definition, 3
  formulation, 146
  relative, 86, 88, 111-112
Bioavailable dose, 113, 292
  definition, 3
Bioequivalency, 292
  definition, 3
Biological response, 114
Biopharmaceutics
  definition, 3
  description, 109
Bishydroxycoumarin, 33
Blood level curves, 83
  area under, 84
  comparing, 119
  different drugs, 112
  effect of
    absorption, 86
    distribution, 113
    dose, 88
    elimination rate constant, 113
Body water
  compartments, 55-56
BSP; see Sulfobromophthalein

                        C

Carbenicillin, 224, 230
  half-life, 150-151, 230
  prodrug, 271
  renal clearance, 150-151, 231
  volume of distribution, 150-151, 231
Carbenicillin indanyl sodium, 271
Cefaclor, 248, 251
Cefadroxil, 248, 251
Cefamandole, 248, 251
Cefatrizine, 248, 251
Cefazolin, 248, 251
Cefoxitin, 248, 251
Central compartment, 18

Cephalexin, 59, 248
Cephaloglycin, 248
Cephaloridine, 248
Cephalosporins, 245
  clinical use, 252
  ideal properties, 250
  in renal failure, 210, 252
  new, 253
  oral absorption, 252
  pharmacokinetics, 250, 251
  structure-activity, 245
  structures, 248, 249
Cephalothin, 248
Cephapirin, 248, 251
Cephradine, 248, 251
Chloramphenicol, 147, 148
Chloramphenicol palmitate, 138
Chloromycetin, 148
Clearance
  creatinine, 65
  definition, 62
  Diodrast, 66
  nonrenal, 68
  para-aminohippurate (PAH), 66-68
  renal, 64, 299-302
    calculation, 64
  urea, 65
  values, 65
Cloxacillin, 224, 228, 230
  half-life, 150-151, 230
  renal clearance, 150-151, 231
  steady-state levels, 228, 230
  volume of distribution, 150-151, 229
Creatinine clearance, 204
Co-administration of drugs, 110
Colistimethate, 59
Compartment
  definition, 47
Compartmental
  analysis, 46
  schemes, 20, 47, 76, 98, 111, 154
    definition of, 47

Competition, 79
Complexation, 145
  effect on absorption, 145
Cortisone acetate, 132
Coumarin, 61

D

Deaggregation, 147
Declomycin, 146, 235-239
Deconvolution, 91
Demethylchlortetracycline, 146,
  235-239
  half-life, 239
Dicloxacillin, 150, 226-230
  half-life, 150-151, 226-230
  nonlinear kinetics, 230
  renal clearance, 150-151, 231
  volume of distribution, 150-151,
    229, 231
Diffusion, 132
  coefficient, 128
  constant (equation), 338
  layer, 132
Digoxin, 33, 329
  bioavailability, 330
  blood levels
    therapeutic, 330
  dosage adjustment, 331
    clearance, 332
    homogram, 333
Diodrast (TM), 66
Dissolution rate, 128, 131, 147
Distribution; see also Volume of
  distribution,
  effect of binding, 237, 257
  phase, 20
  tetracycline, 234
Donnatal extentab, 156
Dosage
  adjustment, 202-210

[Dosage]
  bibliography, 206
  amount absorbed, 118
  form, 110
  interval, 176
  of sulfonamides, 254
  maximum safe concentrations, 117
  minimum effective concentrations,
    117, 194, 293
  multiple, 174
  regimens, 174-175
Dose-response, 117
Drug
  concentrations
    minimum effective, 117, 194, 293
    therapeutic, 203
      anticonvulsants, 309
    toxic, 203
  urinary, 257
  interactions, 67-68, 79, 110-111,
    123, 129, 145-147, 165-166,
    294-307
Drug-receptor interaction, 216
Doxycycline, 234-239
  half-life, 239
Duration, 118, 274
  optimum, 276-278

E

Elimination, 70, 298
  capacity-limited, 77, 302, 311-314
  change in fraction metabolized, 79
  effect of binding, 237
  phase, 20
  rate constants, 70
Equations
  Hansch, 262
  Henderson-Hasselbach, 16, 125
  Loo-Riegelman, 94
  Michaelis-Menten, 39
  Noyes-Whitney, 127

[Equations]
  Wagner-Nelson, 94
Equilibrium, 13-14, 36
  constant, 14
  one-compartment model, 25
Erosion core, 157
Erythromycin, 61, 143, 144, 271-273
  estolate, 144, 273
  pK$_a$ of, 143
Excretion
  biliary, 68
  one-compartment model, 72
  two-compartment model, 76
Extended action, 152

F

Feathering, 23, 93, 182, 185
Fick's Law, 7
  equations, 338-340
First-order
  absorption, 82-83
  plot, 10, 12
  rate, 8-9
    constant, 9
First-pass metabolism, 258

G

Garamycin, 65
Gastrointestinal tract
  drug stability, 140, 226, 250, 296
  ion content (table), 161
  pH of, 123
    adjustment, 130, 297
Gentamicin, 240-245, 246, 257, 317
  blood levels
    factors affecting, 321
    monitoring, 319
    therapeutic range, 317
  pharmacokinetics, 241, 246, 318

Gradumets, 159-160
Griseofulvin, 139

H

Half-life
  biological, 48-55
    aminoglycosides, 246-247
    apparent, 191
    cephalosporins, 251
    determination, 52
    effect of
      binding, 199
      urinary pH, 67, 300
    factors affecting, 210, 300, 303, 304
    pH effect, 257, 299-302
    penicillins, 150, 229, 230, 231
    salicylic acid, 67
    sulfonamides, 255
    tetracyclines, 239
  equations, 49, 50
  first-order, 48
  hydrolysis of penicillins, 142
  zero-order, 50
Hansch equation, 262
Henderson-Hasselbach equation, 16
Hetacillin, 268-270
Hydrolysis, 141
  half-life, 142
Hydrocortisone, 138

I

Ideal drug properties
  antibiotics, 223
  defined, 217
  urinary tract, 256

Infusion
  intravenous, 98, 149
  volume of distribution equations, 58, 101, 344
Insulin, 59
Intestinal tract
  area of, 125
  pH of, 123

K

Kanamycin, 246
Kidney function, 65-67, 299-302
  glomerular filtration, 65, 66
  tubular resorption, 65, 67
  tubular secretion, 65, 67
Kinetics
  dose-dependent, 77, 79
  first-order, 9
  Michaelis-Menten, 39, 311
  mixed, 37
  nonlinear, 40, 79
    dicloxacillin, 230
    phenytoin, 310
    theophylline, 326
  zero-order, 37

L

Laminated tablet, 150
Lidocaine, 260, 322
  blood levels
    therapeutic, 322
  dosage adjustment, 323
Linomycin, 59
Loading dose, 151, 154, 199
  calculation, 199
Long-acting dosage forms, 152

[Long-acting dosage forms]
  table of, 158-159
Loo-Riegelman equations, 94

                          M

Macrocrystalline, 139
Macrodantin, 140
Maximum safe dose, 118, 202
Measurin, 165
M.E.C.; see Minimum effective
Macillinam, 233, 270
Metabolism, 39, 75-82, 302
  one-compartment model, 75
  two-compartment model, 76
Metastable, 138
  polymorph, 138
Methacycline, 239
Methanamine, 145, 306
  mandelate, 145, 306
  prodrug, 306
Methicillin, 59, 215
Methotrexate, 33
Methylprednisolone, 138
M.I.C.; see Minimum inhibitory
  concentration
Microcrystalline, 134, 139
Michaelis-Menten, 39
Minimum effective
  concentration (M.E.C.), 117, 194,
    203, 293, 309, 311, 317, 322,
    325, 330
  dose, 117
Minimum inhibitory concentration,
  198, 238, 252
  penicillins, 238
Multicompartment models, 33-35
Multiple Dose Regimens
  individualization, 206

[Multiple Dose Regimens]
  approximation method (Dettli),
    208
  steady state
  average, 192
  maximum, 179, 186
  minimum, 179, 186, 194, 196

                          N

Nafcillin
  half-life, 150
  renal clearance, 150
  volume of distribution, 150
Nitrofurantoin, 140
Nomogram
  construction, 314
Novobiocin, 138
Noyes-Whitney law, 127

                          O

One-compartment model
  area equation, 346
  definition, 25
  equations, 25-28, 341, 342, 346
  test for, 28
Onset, 118, 151, 199
Order, 9
  defined, 8-9
  first, 9
  zero, 37
Ouabain, 68
Oxacillin, 188, 190
  half-life, 150-151
  renal clearance, 150-151
  steady state, 228, 230
  volume of distribution, 150-151

P

PAH; *see* Para-aminohippurate
Para-aminohippurate (PAH), 66, 68, 69
Parallel drug loss, 70
P-aminosalicylic acid (PAS), 67
Particle size, 128, 139
Partition coefficient, 121, 122, 261, 262, 263
  effect on absorption, 263
PAS; *see* P-aminosalicylic acid
Passive transport, 35
  characteristics, 36
  definition, 7
Peak height, 86
Penicillins, 132, 223-233
  biological half-lives, 150, 229-231
  blood levels, 67
  C_R, 150, 231
  hydrolysis half-lives, 142
  M.I.C., 238, 252
  prodrugs, 267-271
  P_{ss}, 228-230
  structure, 224-225, 268
    activity, 223
  volume of distribution, 150, 231
Penicillin G, 135, 224
  half-life, 150-151
  renal clearance, 150-151
  volume of distribution, 150-151, 229, 231
Pharmacokinetic analysis, 24
Pharmacokinetics
  aminoglycosides, 241,
    (table), 246-247
  clinical, 308
    digoxin, 329
    gentamicin, 317
    lidocaine, 322
    phenytoin, 309

[Pharmacokinetics].
  theophylline, 324
  definition, 3
  drug interactions, 294-307
pH
  adjustment-urine, 145, 256, 301, 306
  intestinal, 124
  microenvironment, 130
  partition
    hypothesis, 120-123, 261
    theory, 120
  stomach, 124, 128, 296
  urine, 300
Phenosulfonphthalein (PSP), 67
Phenylbutazone, 305
Phenytoin, 309
  bioavailability, 310
  compliance, 311
  dosage adjustment, 311
    nomogram, 316
  pharmacokinetics, 310
π-additivity principle, 262
Pivampicillin, 268-270
Placebo, 164
Planimeter, 86
Plasma levels
  average, 192
  maximum, 179, 186, 190
  minimum, 194-198
  repetitive dose, 176-192
Polymorphism, 137
Potency
  comparison, 218
    apomorphines, 220
Prednisolone, 138
Presystemic Metabolism, 258
Probenicid, 67, 302
Prodrugs, 264-278
  absorption, 265
  ampicillin, 267-269
  assay specificity, 267

[Prodrugs]
  blood level curves, 266, 269, 272,
    273
  carbenicillin, 271
  erythromycin, 271
  long acting, 274
    optimum, 276
  methenamine, 307
  rate-determining step, 275
  reasons for, 265
  schemes, 265, 266, 273, 274, 275
Prolonged action, 152, 276
Protein binding, 61
PSP; *see* Phenosulfonphthalein

[Renal]
  dosage adjustment, 202-210
  drug interactions, 299-302
  tests, 65-66, 68
  glomerular filtration, 65, 299
    dosage adjustment, 204
  insufficiency, 206-210
    elimination rate constants
      (table), 210
  tubular
    resorption, 65, 299
    secretion, 66, 299, 302
Repeat action
  definition, 152, 204
Reserpine, 163

                        R

Rate
  constant
    absorption, 90, 94, 98
    first-order, 9
      calculation, 10
      determination in two-
        compartment model, 19-20
    two-compartment, 20
    zero-order, 38
  -determining step, 91, 123, 126, 274
  -limiting step, 155
  process
    capacity-limited, 77
    first-order, 8
    forward, 14
    reversible, 14, 339
    zero-order, 37, 50
Renal
  clearance
    penicillins, 150, 231
  failure
    dosage adjustment, 202-210
  function, 202

                        S

Salicylates, 61, 129, 182
Salicylic acid
  excretion, 67
Saturation, 66, 79
SETD; *see* Sulfaethylthiadiazole
Serum levels; *see* Plasma levels
Solubility
  aqueous, 129
  dissolution rate, 127, 131
  intrinsic, 129
  total, 129, 132
  weak acids, 130
  weak bases, 130
Steady-state plasma levels, 91-93,
  100, 149, 179-184, 228-230
  average, 192
  any route and model, 192-193
  one-compartment model, 193
  time to achieve, 99, 199-202
  two-compartment model, 193
Stevens-Johnson syndrome, 254
Stomach buffering, 178

Sulfobromophthalein, 67
Sulfonamides, 132, 254
  dose interval, 255
  half-life (table), 255
  structures, 255
Sulfonylureas, 61
Supply constants, 82, 265, 276
Sustained release, 152
  calculations, 154
  definition, 152
  design, 154
  evaluation, 162-163
  products (table), 158-159
  theory, 153
  use of products, 166
Symbols
  defined, 351-353
Talampicillin, 268-270
Tetracyclines, 145, 233
  absorption, 234
  binding
    dairy products, 145, 235-237
    divalent cations, 145, 235-237
    trivalent cations, 145, 235-237
  distribution, 237
  dosage interval, 196-197, 239
  half-life (table), 239
  sodium bicarbonate
    effect on absorption 297
  structures, 234
Theophylline, 324
  blood levels
    therapeutic, 325
  dosage
    adjustment, 326
    forms, 329
    loading, 327
    maintenance, 328
    oral, 328
  pharmacokinetics, 325

Three-compartment open model, 33
Thymine, 35
Ticarcillin, 233
Tissue compartment, 20
Tocainide, 260
Tolbutamide, 133
  sodium 133
Transferable species, 14
Trapezoidal rule, 86-87
Trihydrate; see Ampicillin
Tubocurarine, 33
Two-compartment model
  closed, 6-18
  open, 18
    area (equations), 347
    description, 18
    equations, 20-24, 342
    rate constants, 20-24
    schemes, 19, 76-78, 83, 98, 99,
      145

U

Uracil, 35, 123
  5 bromouracil, 35, 123
  5 flurouracil, 35, 123
Urea, 65
Urine
  acidification, 70-71, 301
  alkalization, 70-71, 301
  antimicrobial agents, 255-258
    properties of, 256
  concentration in, 257
  effect of pH (anti-infective agents),
    257
  pH
    antacids, 301
    half-life, 67, 300

V

Volume
  body water compartments, 55
  of distribution
    aspirin, 62
    calculations, 56, 57-59
      area method, 57, 342-343
      equations, 55-58, 101, 341
      one-compartment, 56, 341
      two-compartment, 56, 342
    definition, 55
  extrapolation, 57
    equations, 57, 342

[Volume]
  factors effecting, 61, 304
  infusion, 58, 100, 149, 344
  penicillins (table), 150
  protein binding effect, 61
  sodium salicylate, 61
  variation in estimates, 58

W

Wagner-Nelson equation, 97
Warfarin, 305
Water content of body; *see* Volume